PRACTICAL DESIGN
OF POWER SUPPLIES

Books of Related Interest from IEEE Press . . .

POWER ELECTRONICS AND VARIABLE FREQUENCY DRIVES: Technologies and Applications
Bimal K. Bose
1997   Hardcover   668 pp   IEEE Order No. PC4382   ISBN 0-7803-1084-5

POWER ELECTRONICS: Converters, Applications, and Design
Ned Mohan, Tore M. Undeland, and William P. Robbins
1995   Hardcover   826 pp   IEEE Order No. PC5640   ISBN 0-471-14208-5

PRACTICAL DESIGN
OF POWER SUPPLIES

Ron Lenk

Fairchild Semiconductor, Inc.,
Mountain View, California

IEEE Power Electronics Society, *Sponsor*

McGRAW-HILL

New York   San Francisco   Washington, D.C.   Auckland   Bogotá
Caracas   Lisbon   London   Madrid   Mexico City   Milan
Montreal   New Delhi   San Juan   Singapore
Sydney   Tokyo   Toronto

The Institute of Electrical
and Electronics Engineers, Inc.,
New York

This book and other books may be purchased at a discount
from the publisher when ordered in bulk quantities. Contact:

IEEE Press Marketing
Attn: Special Sales
Piscataway, NJ 08855-1331
Fax: (732) 981-9334

For more information about IEEE PRESS products,
visit the IEEE Home Page: http://www.ieee.org/

Printed in the United States of America

10   9   8   7   6   5   4   3   2   1

ISBN 0-7803-3458-2
IEEE Order Number PC5715

McGraw-Hill ISBN 0-07-134324-5

Library of Congress Cataloging-in-Publication Data

Lenk, Ron, 1958–
    Practical design of power supplies / Ron Lenk.
      p.   cm.
    Includes bibliographical references and index.
    ISBN 0-7803-3458-2 (alk. paper)
    1. Electric power.   I. Title.
  TK1001.L46   1998
  621.3—dc21   98-6459
                                            CIP

To My Parents,
My Sister and Brother-in-Law,
and My Wife:
Thank You!

Contents

PREFACE xv

LIST OF TABLES xvii

CHAPTER 1 **Introduction** 1

Sources 2
Lab Supplies 2
AC Mains 3
Batteries 4
Solar Cells 6

Loads 7
High Speed Requirements 7
Low Noise Requirements 8
Batteries, Again 10
Telephones 11
Fluorescent Tubes 12
Other Converters 13

Safety 13

CHAPTER 2 **Practical Selection of Topology** 17

Introduction: There Are Hundreds of Topologies! 17

General Considerations 18
Step-Up or Step-Down 18
Practical Limits on Duty Cycle 18
How Many Outputs? 19
Isolation 19

EMI 19
Bipolar versus MOSFET versus ? 20
Continuous and Discontinuous 20
Synchronous Rectification 21
Voltage Mode versus Current Mode 22
Conclusions 22

The Buck Topology 22
Limitations 23
Gate Drive Difficulties 23

The Flyback 25
Two Kinds 25
Name Confusion with Boost 26
Continuous versus Discontinuous 27
Capacitor Limitations 27
Power Limits 27
Practical Limits on Number of Outputs 28

The Buck–Boost 28
Limitations of the Buck-Boost 29

The Forward 29
Minimum Load 30
Leakage Inductance 30
Summary 31

The Push–Pull 31
Voltage-Fed 31
Current-Fed 32
Transformer Utilization 33

Resonant Converters and Soft-Switching Converters 33
The Difference between Resonant and Soft-Switching Converters 33
Why You Should Not Use Resonant Converters 34
Why You Should Use Soft-Switching Converters 34

Compound Converters 35
When to Use Them 36

References 36

CHAPTER 3   Practical Selection of Components   37

Introduction 37

Resistors 38
Values 38
Types of Resistor 38
Tolerance 39
Selecting Ratios 39
Maximum Voltage 39
Temperature Coefficient 39
Power Rating 39
Pulse Power 40
Rheostats: A What? 40

Noninductive Wirewound Resistors 42
Shunts 42
Using a Trace as a Resistor 43

Capacitors and their Usage 43

Types of Capacitors 43
Standard Values 44
Tolerance 44
ESR and Power Dissipation 44
Aging 45
dV/dt 45
Putting Caps in Series 46

Schottky Diodes 46

Rectifier Diodes 47

Reverse Recovery 47
Is Faster Better? 48

Transistors: BJTs 48

Pulse Current 48
How Much Beta Can I Get? 49
Don't Forget Collector Leakage Current 49
Emitter–Base Zenering—Is It Bad? 49
Fast Turnoff 49

Transistors: MOSFETs 50

Don't Confuse JFETs and MOSFETs 50
p-Channel and n-Channel 50
Bidirectional Conduction 50
Calculating Losses: Conduction Loss 51
Calculating Losses: Gate Charge Loss 51
Calculating Losses: Switching Loss 51
The Need for Gate Resistors 52
Maximum Gate Voltage 52

Op Amps 53

Offsets: Input Offset Voltage 53
Offsets: Input Offset Current 53
Offsets: Input Bias Current 54
What to Do About Offsets 54
Limits on Large Resistances 54
Gain Bandwidth 56
Phase Shift 56
Slew Rate 56

Comparators 57

Hysteresis 57
Output Saturation Voltage 58

References 58

CHAPTER 4   Practical Guide to Instrumentation   59

Introduction 59
Calculators and Calculations 59

How Many Digits? 59
Do I Care? 60
A Closely Related Problem 60
One More Problem to Avoid 61

DVMs and Other Meters 61

Accuracy versus Precision 61
Averaging 61
How to Filter a DVM 62
Measuring RMS and DVM Bandwidth 62
Measuring Efficiency: Cross-Calibration 63
Where to Put the Probes 63
Measuring Very Low Resistances 64
Using a Shunt for $I > 10A$ 64
How to Use a DVM to Measure a MOSFET 65

Electronic Loads 65

Why Is My Stable Converter Oscillating? 65
Minimum Input Voltage 66

Oscilloscopes 66

Aliasing 66

Network Analyzer 67

Step-by-Step Instructions 67
Nyquist Plots 69

CHAPTER 5   Practical Design of Magnetics   71

Fundamentals of Magnetics 71

Introductory Comments 71
Ampere's Law 72
Faraday's Law 72
About Inductance 73
Units Confusion 74
Weird Words: The Three R's 75

The Ideal Transformer 76

What About a Flyback "Transformer"? 77

Real Transformers 78

Core Materials 80
Saturation 80
Other Core Limitations 82
Optimum Design 83

Practical Design of a DC Inductor 83

Core Selection 84
First Try 84
Second Try 88
Selecting the Wire 89
Calculating the Resistance 90
Power Loss 92
Temperature Dependence 94
Conclusion 95

Practical Design of a Flyback Transformer 95

Equations Governing the Flyback 95
Selecting a Core Material Type 97
Core Selection 98
Selecting Core Material 98
Selecting the Gap 98
Core Loss 104
How Did He Read That Little Graph? 104
Can I Get Lower Core Losses by Lowering the Switching Frequency? 106
Winding Losses 107
Do I Need to Worry About Skin Effect? 108
Copper Loss and Total Transformer Loss 109

Flux Density: Two Formulas? 110

Practical Design of a Forward Transformer 110

Practical Design of a Current Transformer 113

Tips for Designing Manufacturable Magnetics 115

Wire Gauge 115
Wire Gauge Ratio 116
Toroid Winding Limits 116
Tape versus Wire Insulation 116
Layering 117
Number of Windings 117
Potting 117
Specs 118

Concluding Comments 118

References 119

CHAPTER 6   Practical Feedback Design   121

Introduction 121

Refresher 121

Logarithms and dB 121
Complex Numbers 122
Complex Functions 123
What Is a Transform? 124
Two Transforms 124
What's the Difference? 125
Transform of C and L 125

Transfer Functions 126

What Is a Transfer Function and Who Cares? 126
Composition Law for Transfer Functions 126
There's No Such Thing as a (Useful) Transform of a Nonlinear System! 128

Basic Control Theory 128

Bode Plots 129
Requirement for Stability 130
How Much Phase Margin Is Enough? 132
Gain Margin? 133

About Conditional Stability 134
Small- versus Large-Signal Stability 134

How to Stabilize a Voltage Mode Buck Converter 135

How to Measure Open Loop Response 136
Venable's *K*-Factor Paper 138
Practical Considerations 142
Other Comments 142
How to Measure Closed Loop Response 143
How to Measure It: Transformer Method 144
How to Measure It: The Mixer Method 144
Converter Closed Loop 145
How NOT to Measure a Loop 146
A Better Method of Measuring the Open Loop 147
What If the Noninverting Pin of the Error Amp Isn't Available? 149

Current Mode Control 149

Theory 149
A Limitation of Current Mode Control 150
Slope Compensation 150
How to Compensate a Current Mode Controller 152
Can I Measure the Current Loop? 152
Average Current Mode Control 152

Non-Minimum-Phase Systems 153

Nyquist Plots 154

Some Concepts of System Stability 155

Input and Output Impedance 155
Converter Output Impedance 158
Two Stable Converters Can Make an Unstable System! 159
Example of an Unstable System 161

Some Thoughts on the Role of Simulations 161

References 163

CHAPTER 7   Practical Design of Control and Monitoring Circuitry   165

Control Circuitry 165

Start-Up 165
Soft Start 167
Sequencing 168
Feedback 168
Current Limiting 170
Switching Frequency 171
Synchronization 171

Monitoring Circuitry 172

How to Monitor Voltage 172
Voltage References 173
How to Monitor a Negative Supply Without a Negative Rail 173
Why You Should Always Use Hysteresis on Comparators 174
Resistors and Shunts 175
Differential Amplifiers 175

Compensating Shunt Inductance 177
Fail Should Be Low 178
Driving That Red LED 178

CHAPTER 8   Practical Efficiency and Thermal Management   179

Efficiency 179

Definition 179
Why Is Efficiency Important? 179
Modules 180
90% Is Doing Great! 180
Example Calculation 1 181
Example Calculation 2 188
Improving Efficiency 189

Thermal Management 190

Component Life versus Temperature 190
Modules 191
MIL-HDBK-217 192
MIL-HDBK-217: Example 192
MIL-HDBK-217: Discussion 194
Temperature Calculation 195
Heat Sinks, etc. 196
FEA 197

References 197

CHAPTER 9   Practical EMI Control   199

An Overview 199

Radiated and Conducted 200
What to Do About Radiated Noise 200
What Kind of Box Material? 201
Common Mode versus Normal Mode 201
Return versus Ground 202
Military versus Commercial Measurements 203

How Can I Separate CM from NM? 203

Where Does the Noise Come From? 204

Switching Waveforms 205
Capacitive Coupling 205

Concepts of Layout 207

Signal Ground versus Power Ground 207
Grounding a High Current Driver; Ground Islands 209
What If the Device Has a Signal Input But No Signal Ground? 210
Where to Put the Current Transformer 210
Feedback Lines 211
Further Layout Tips 212

Low Frequency Filtering 212

The Basics 212
Normal Mode Filters 213

Commercial versus Military 213
Selecting the Values 214
Common Mode Filters 214
Selecting the Values 215
Caps and Inductors and Their Limits 216
MOVs Have Capacitance 216
Two for the Price of One 216
You Can't Get 100dB Attenuation! 217

High Frequency Filtering 217
Where Should I Use Beads? 217
Feedthroughs 218

Some Other Topics 218
Noise Estimation 218
Optimal Filtering 219

Optimal Military EMI-Filter Design 219
Converter Stability versus EMI Filtering 222

References 223

CHAPTER 10 Practical Worst-Case Analysis   225

Introduction 225
The Purpose of Worst-Case Analysis 225
How Do You Do WCA? 225
The Purpose of Stress Analysis 226
RMS versus Worst Case 227
Mathematics versus Simulation 227
Monte Carlo? Sensitivity Analysis? 228

An Exhausting Example 228
The Circuit 229
Properties to be Analyzed 229
Table Evaluation Techniques 230
Worst-Case Analysis: Comparator Trip Levels 233
Worst-Case Analysis: The BJT Is Normally Off 234
Worst-Case Analysis: How Long Until the PWM Is Turned Off? 235
Stress Analysis 236
Conclusions 238

Some Concluding Thoughts   238

APPENDIX 1   List of Acronyms Used in the Book and Some Symbols   239

APPENDIX 2   Data Sheets for Worst-Case Analysis   241

INDEX 259

ABOUT THE AUTHOR 267

Preface

This book is written for a variety of people involved in one way or another with power supplies and power systems. The primary audience consists of practicing power supply designers, people who have been in the field between 2 and 20 years: for them, *Practical Design of Power Supplies* is just that, a compendium of important knowledge needed on a daily basis. Too often, practicing engineers spend their days rushing about putting out fires (sometimes literally!), and don't have the time to dig through obscure manuals and references to obtain the information that would make life easier. For them, this book sets out exactly what they need to know to make a good power supply, with very detailed examples making it almost easy to do.

Practical Design of Power Supplies should also benefit skilled technicians in the field, those who have observed that doing <u>this</u> fixes <u>that</u>, but without knowing just why. I have tried to set everything out clearly, both the why and the how—even those with dozens of years of experience will find things of interest. In particular, I have tried to encapsulate items of immediate practical use in a series of boxed **Practical Notes** and **Safety Tips** throughout the book; these features tell you things that will immediately make your work easier. There is also an appendix that defines every acronym used in the book, and a few of the symbols.

I have avoided making this a cookbook, since there are so many ways of making a workable design, and there are so many different circumstances: there are clear explanations of why things work, which enable you to make the right choices based on your own particular circumstances. Neither is this book full of long mathematical derivations, except in the part of Chapter 6 on closing the loop, where some mathematics is essential. My goal throughout has been to concentrate on the *practical* aspects of design, how to really do things that work and how to make practical measurements.

The book's examples all come from the field of low to medium power supplies (say 1W to 10kW), since that is where my experience lies. However, much of the material is applicable to higher power systems, and I hope will benefit practitioners there, too. Finally, I have intentionally avoided the subject of computer simulations (except for a brief example in Chapter 6), feeling that this subject, treated properly, would require its own book.

I have greatly benefited over the years from the wise advice and unshakable good humor of my friend Stan Canter, one of the unsung heroes of the field. I wish to thank Anatoly Shteynberg and Ericsson EUS for providing the opportunity to present some of this material in an earlier form as a series of lectures, to Steve Cartier for explaining the mysteries of the telephone to me, and Chae Lee and Siliconix for patience during the writing process.

Ron Lenk

List of Tables

2.1 Topology Selection Checklist 22

3.1 Brief Resistor Selection Guide 38

3.2 Brief Capacitor Selection Guide 43

4.1 Sample Averaging Data 61

5.1 MKS and CGS Units Often Used in Magnetics 74

5.2 Some MKS-to-CGS Conversions 74

5.3 Core Materials: Pros, Cons, and Usage 81

5.4 As Flux Increases, Permeability Drops: 3F3 Material 82

5.5 Calculating Flux Densities of Pregapped Cores 104

8.1 Losses for Example 1 Converter 188

8.2 Losses for Example 2 Converter 189

8.3 Correspondence Between Thermal and Electrical Characteristics 195

10.1 Listing of Worst-Case Values for Example Circuit 231

10.2 Example Stress Analysis Table 237

1

Introduction

This book is targeted at designers of power supplies in the low to medium power range, roughly defined as 0W to 10kW. If you are in this group, you probably already have some experience with converters, at least to the extent of realizing that there are many different kinds. (Chapter 2 on topology talks about the various types.) There is an excellent reason for having many different kinds, rather than having all power supplies be mere variations of parameter values on a single type. This reason is twofold: the wide variety of sources from which converters are expected to run, and the similarly wide variety of loads converters are expected to provide power to. Unless you have spent many years designing converters, you probably don't realize how truly diverse these two groups are—this is one of the things that makes power supply engineering far more challenging than, say, digital design. To start off this book, then, examples of sources and loads, both common and less so, are presented in some detail, to give you a feel for the sorts of thing you may encounter. The samples here are of course not exhaustive, but rather represent some of the (occasionally not so nice) experiences of the author in the power range under consideration; you can start your own collection. Don't take these discussions to be comprehensive, as some of the sources and loads have a large literature attached to them; rather, this material is intended to give the flavor of the sorts of environment in which power supplies often need to operate.

This introductory chapter also makes a few comments on lab safety. This is a subject that seems to be always ignored, both in the lab and in texts, or at least pushed to the side when time becomes short; and yet it is of critical importance both to you and the people who work for you, and for visitors to areas in which your lab work is taking place. Make sure to take the time to read it!

SOURCES

Lab Supplies

Everybody uses lab supplies to begin development work on a new converter. Still, there are a few surprises to be had, even with these supposedly ideal sources.

The most obvious difference between lab supply types is between old lab supplies and new: you can easily tell which is which because the old ones seem to weigh a million pounds. The reason for their great weight is that there is a big hunk of steel inside, acting as a 60Hz (or 50Hz) transformer. The old lab supplies then act by linear-regulating the voltage down, and end up with a really big capacitor [10s of millifarads (sic) and more]. The rest of the volume of the supply houses a fan to keep the linear regulator from burning up. This reliance on steel guarantees that some supplies that are old now will still be around when you're ready to retire! They just never seem to break; the author is personally aware of labs with quite a few old lab supplies dating from WW II.

New supplies are (almost) invariably based on switching regulators. (The caveat is for the arena of lab supplies that are required to be *extremely* free of electrical noise—these still tend to be linears, but usually only low power ones.) The switching regulator design makes them of course vastly lighter than their older counterparts, but does leave them prone to the ills that afflict switchers, a subject that will be recurring throughout this book. For one thing, although they also usually sport large output capacitors, any switching regulator can be made to oscillate if you attach enough capacitance to its output. The manufacturer's intent, of course, is to have the output capacitance of the lab supply dominate anything you may reasonably hang on the lab supply's output, and the internal control loop is compensated to provide stability with this capacitance; but if you put *enough* extra capacitance there, eventually the loop will break up and the supply will oscillate. The 60Hz transformer style supplies seem to be immune to oscillations in practice, although it ought to be possible to make a linear regulator oscillate too; maybe it's just really difficult to hang *that* much capacitance there.

Another problem for lab supplies is 60Hz (line) feedthrough. Here, switchers are much better, because they have gain at 60Hz, which radically reduces the amount of 60Hz signal that appears on their outputs. Also, newer switchers are better than older ones, as some of the older ones were actually thyristors whose control was based on line phase angle; these tend to have much more 60Hz noise than modern switchers using MOSFETs with high bandwidth control loops. The old linear supplies relied on their gigantic output caps to filter the ripple, but it could still be quite a nuisance.

One other area where sometimes the old linears are better exemplified is when you need to parallel two or more supplies to get up to the current level your application requires. (This of course requires remote sense to work at all, regardless of the type of converter.) With the old converters, the noise is all at 60Hz, and each converter produces the noise in phase with all the others, since it's just feedthrough from the line. Though additive, the noise at least has a well-defined spectrum. With switchers, there never seems to be a synchronization pin when you need it, so that each switcher runs at its own frequency. If you're unlucky, these frequencies may be fairly close together, and then you may get beats between the frequencies of the various paralleled converters at a low frequency. This is definitely undesirable for attempting to debug a new converter design.

AC Mains

When you plug the toaster in, the bread gets brown. If only it were so simple for electronics! The AC mains is actually a wide assortment of power types, with numerous types of problems. Being able to really guarantee that a power supply is going to work successfully and have a long life running off the mains requires a lot of work, and lots of research into relevant (national and international) standards. Perhaps this shouldn't be too surprising, when you remember that there are engineers who spend their entire lives working on it!

The most obvious difference between various AC mains is the different frequencies. In the United States the line is at 60Hz; in Europe it's 50Hz. Actually there's also a tolerance to these numbers, so if you're designing a supply for international use, it needs to work down to 47Hz, and in the United States up to 63Hz. This tolerance is necessary because the electric companies won't guarantee that their big turbines will always run at exactly the same speed. The requirement to work at 50Hz (really 47Hz) translates into considerably bigger capacitors than would be needed if the design only has to work at 60Hz.

There are *lots* of different mains voltages around. In this country, 110VAC (sometimes 120VAC) is the usual for wall outlets, but there's also 208VAC (for your washer), 480VAC three-phase (for industrial sites), and 277VAC (for fluorescent lighting, though it also runs off 120VAC, depending on the building). Then in Europe there's 230VAC . . . and in Australia it's 240VAC! Let's not forget the cable TV coax, which distributes what's *called* 60VAC but is really a quasi–square wave of pretty high impedance, with a peak-to-peak value of about 120V.

These are just the *nominal* values; each mains has all sorts of tolerances as well. Taking the 110VAC as an example, anything from 95V to 135VAC may be considered to be within normal range for a power supply to operate in without degradation of performance. Then there are sags and brownouts—basically the power supply has to be able to avoid damaging itself for any voltage from 0V up to nominal (use an undervoltage lockout to accomplish this). Also, it may be required to provide uninterrupted power even when its input disappears for several line cycles of 60Hz. (The only way to do this is with lots of capacitance or a battery; if the supply is power factor corrected, the capacitance has to be on the output, making it even bigger.)

Then there are overvoltage conditions. There are lightning strikes, which may be 6000V at an impedance of 2Ω, both line to line and common mode (see Chapter 9 on EMI for these concepts). The types of lightning come in two flavors, a short one (1.2µs rise time and 50µs decay time), and a much higher energy one that decays in 1ms. There are also transients: the line can go to $750V_{pk}$ for a half-line cycle! (This is a requirement for certain telecommunications supplies; the regulatory agency is anticipating that a high voltage wire will fall across the mains during a storm, and it will take some time for the circuit breaker to act.)

This short account doesn't even scratch the surface of the numerous problems a power supply faces when attached to the line. Altogether, the AC mains is an extremely nasty environment, and it can easily happen that as much time is required to make a supply robust and able to pass all the national safety requirements (and which of course are different in each country) as is needed to design the whole rest of the supply.

Batteries

Batteries represent something utterly outside the ken of most power engineers, since they involve chemical reactions and metallurgy. Indeed, when you talk with experts in electrochemistry, it turns out there's plenty *they* don't understand either. Compared with batteries, the AC mains is understandable, if nasty. Let's try to collect some of the basics here, to let you know some of the questions to ask when faced with designing a supply that will run off a battery.

First off, the author's pet peeve: batteries are NOT gigantic capacitors. Although you can put energy into a battery and get it back out, application of a sine wave will reveal that there is no phase shift between voltage and current. Batteries also are not much good as filters, as we'll discuss in a moment. So let's talk about what batteries are, at least as sources; what they look like when sinking current is discussed below in the section on loads.

A battery consists of a number of cells, usually, though not always, connected in series. It's useful to bear in mind the terminology: a cell is the basic unit of the battery, while a battery consists of one or more cells connected together.

> **Warning!** Don't attempt to hook up cells in parallel to form your own battery, as this can be dangerous. Have the battery manufacturer configure the cells into the battery voltage and capacity you need. This caution is unnecessary if you have ORing diodes, and for series cell connections.

A single cell is basically a chemical reactor of sorts. It typically consists of two metallic plates, with some sort of conductive path between them, which can be either liquid or solid depending on the particular chemistry used. The key aspect of this arrangement is that it has a reversible chemical reaction dependent on electricity (for rechargeable, or "secondary" cells; the nonrechargeable ones are called "primary"). When you put electricity in by attaching a source to the two metal plates (which are the cathode and anode), there is a chemical reaction that causes some of the material to change chemical state; this stores energy. When you attach a load, the chemical reaction goes backward toward its original state, releasing electricity again.

What batteries look like as sources depends on what frequency is being considered. Let's start with the highest frequencies and work our way down. At typical converter switching frequencies, 20kHz or more, batteries look like open circuits, because they have some small amount of inductance associated with their terminals, internal plates, and so on; also, chemical reactions take a finite amount of time to occur, and so present the equivalent of some impedance. For example, a NiH (nickel–hydrogen) cell may have something like 200nH inductance; a battery of five of these cells in series (to get the voltage up to 6V) would have about 1μH. At a switching frequency of 200kHz, this is about 1Ω. Thus, you can't assume that a battery is going to sop up all the switching ripple your converter is generating; it is actually usually necessary to put some capacitors in parallel with the battery!

Looking now at lower frequencies, say 1kHz down to a few hertz, there are a lot of nonlinearities due to the chemical processes. As you draw increasing current out of the battery, the voltage drops (the relationship is approximately a hyperbolic sine). Figure 1.1 shows a nominal current–voltage curve of a 12V NiH battery. Nominal voltage is 12V, and

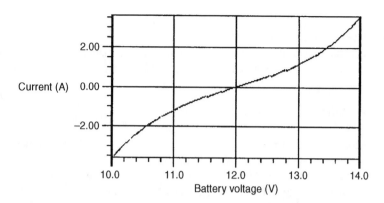

Figure 1.1 Typical *I-V* characteristics of a 12V battery.

current coming out of the battery is defined to be negative. At small currents drawn from the battery, there is a voltage drop at the battery's terminals that is approximately like a resistor: doubling the current doubles the voltage drop. At higher currents, the voltage drop becomes relatively less, until (not shown in the figure) you can pull quite gigantic currents out of the battery before the terminal voltage reaches 0V. (DON'T TRY THIS—if you short a battery, it may explode!) The author saw test results on a NiH cell that produced 1500A short circuit!

The relationship between current pulled from the battery and output voltage is dependent on temperature, and also on how much charge the battery has left. And you can damage a battery if you try to pull too <u>much</u> current out of it. You can damage almost any battery if you try to pull current out of it below its rated operating temperature; for example, sealed lead–acid batteries don't work very well much below −10°C, which is why your car doesn't want to start when it's cold.

Continuing down in frequency, on the time scale of minutes to hours, the capacity of a battery is measured by manufacturers by how many "amp-hours" of charge it has (current × time = charge). Confusingly for power supply designers, this has no simple relationship to how much energy you can get out, which is *not* equal to the capacity times the output voltage; unfortunately the output voltage depends on the current being pulled! The behaviour of every one of these parameters is described in curves from the manufacturer, but the curves never seem to cover the operating point at which you're actually operating. Lots of interpolation and hope are required; it's almost always impractical to do your own tests on batteries. And it should be borne in mind that each manufacturer makes batteries a bit differently, so you can't assume that just because two batteries have the same chemistry and amp-hour rating, they're going to have the same run time in the field.

Another phenomenon in this approximate frequency range is self-discharge. If you leave a charged battery sitting around, it will gradually lose its energy all by itself, without any load attached. The time required to lose a substantial portion of the stored energy varies widely depending on chemistry, from 24 hours for NiH to years for some lithium batteries.

Finally, on a scale of years, after many charge/discharge cycles, the battery will no longer store its rated capacity. This time, which may be considered end of life for the battery, depends on how it is operated: how many charge/discharge cycles it's undergone, how deep the discharges were, and so on. Even a battery used only for backup, and so being "float-charged" (always held fully charged) will need to be replaced in 5–10 years.

Every type of battery chemistry—lead–acid, NiCd (nickel–cadmium), zinc–air, whatever—has its own set of characteristics. So you get the idea: you could spend a lifetime studying batteries. The best plan is to find a manufacturer who is willing to work closely with you and lean heavily on that person's technical expertise.

Solar Cells

Yet another entertaining power source is solar cells. A solar cell is a diode that produces a current when exposed to visible light. Actually all ICs respond to light (this is why an EEPROM can be erased by UV), but solar cells are optimized for producing a maximum output of electricity per unit light exposure. The current is produced at a voltage with characteristics pretty much like that of a regular rectifier, if you imagine it putting out energy rather than dissipating it. It thus has an *I-V* curve that is logarithmic in current, as idealized in a typical curve shown as Figure 1.2. Note that contrary to the way you at first expect, this curve shows current versus voltage, not the other way around. This is standard for solar cells. If you use this curve to determine power output as a function of current (power = current × voltage), you find (see Figure 1.3) that there is some curent at which output power is maximum; of course it is not at open circuit, because then current is zero, nor at short circuit, since then voltage is zero. A converter always needs to operate on the

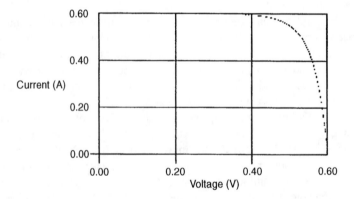

Figure 1.2   Typical *I-V* curve of a solar cell.

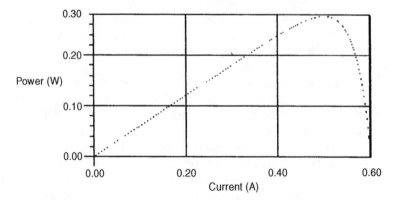

Figure 1.3   There is a peak in the delivered power from the solar cell.

left side of this peak power point, so that pulling increasing current will produce increased power. If you ever go beyond the peak power point (to the right), the system becomes unstable: if the converter wants to pull more power, it pulls more current, which <u>reduces</u> delivered power, causing it to pull more current, etc. That is to say, it falls down the curve. Finding the peak power point and ensuring that the system doesn't go past it is always a major challenge for designs utilizing solar cells.

Some types of converter utilizing solar cells act as a flyback; that is, the current is shorted to ground for some duty cycle and then released to power an inductor during the remainder of the period. This brings in another difficult aspect of solar cells: being semiconductors, they have a voltage- and temperature-dependent capacitance. This capacitance produces a momentary surge of current into the shunting device until it is discharged. Then, of course, the voltage doesn't come right back up, it ramps up while recharging the capacitance! This time to recharge is typically a few microseconds, and so sets a maximum switching frequency for the attached flyback converter.

LOADS

High Speed Requirements

Many people have by now heard about requirements on power supplies for microprocessors running at 3.3V: the data sheets are calling out a load step of up to 30A/µs. So referring to Figure 1.4, let's suppose the load changes from no load to 7A: this takes less than 1µs. If your switching supply has a bandwidth of 20kHz (no mean feat), it still takes something like $1/20kHz = 50µs$ to change to the new load level, and so you have a deficit of approximately $(7A/2)50µs = 175µC$ to support. If you need 2% tolerance on the 3.3V line, which is 66mV, you need $175µC/66mV = 3mF$ (sic) of capacitance to hold up the output during the transient!

It is worth observing that you can't just stick a 3300µF capacitor in this job either, you have to parallel multiple smaller caps. This is because the initial voltage drop on the bus (see Figure 1.5) is going to be due to ESR of the caps, not bandwidth limitations of the converter: you need $66mV/7A = 9mΩ$ of ESR maximum. If each cap has about 100mΩ ESR, you need at least 11 caps in parallel to achieve this, so maybe 330µF tantalum chip caps would be a good choice here. Of course, this calculation assumes that the connection from the output of the converter to the load has no resistance and no inductance—if there's any trace length, you need even better power supply performance!

Another assumption in this calculation is that the large-signal response of the converter is adequate, also. This is discussed in detail in Chapter 6 on stability, but basically you have to make sure that the error amplifier has a slew rate adequate to track the small-signal response of the converter; this may not always be true. The large-signal bandwidth of the converter can't be greater than the small-signal bandwidth, and if there is inadequate slew rate, it may be considerably smaller.

This sample calculation makes it clear that having wider bandwidth converters and higher speed amplifiers is essential to keeping converter size down. In industry today, this is the dominant reason for continuing to push to higher switching frequency converters (since bandwidth can't exceed roughly half the switching frequency). Certain actually working converters now switch at 2MHz, and have bandwidth of over 100kHz.

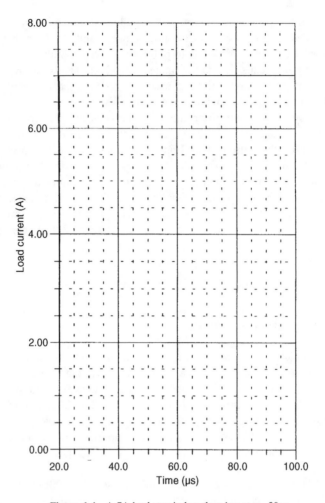

Figure 1.4   A 7A load step in less than 1μs at $t = 20$μs.

Low Noise Requirements

A load that again requires some thought is the low noise load. The power supply engineer should not be surprised to see a requirement for an output that requires, say, 1mV_{pp} ripple noise. (This is in addition to the transient response mentioned in the preceding section).

> **Practical Note** Somehow these ultralow noise requirements often seem to be on one of the outputs of the same converter that is also expected to provide 10A at 5VDC to a tankful of TTL ICs. Before spending weeks in the lab working on complex filters, it's a good idea to go talk with the users and make sure they really *need* that low noise: maybe they just didn't want to bother thinking about it and hadn't realized that their casual spec would make you go prematurely gray.

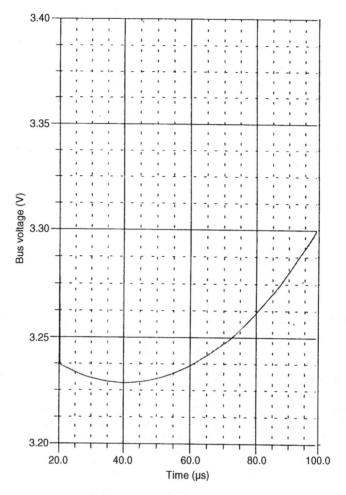

Figure 1.5 Response of bus voltage.

A common load that *does* require low noise is an rf (radio frequency) power amplifier—for example, as used in a cellular phone. The converter provides both gate and drain voltage to the amplifier (the amplifier is basically a FET). If there is ripple on these voltages at the switching frequency of the converter, the output of the amplifier will also have ripple, since the output power is determined by the gate and drain voltage—indeed, changing these voltages is the usual method of *controlling* the power level. Since the output of the amplifier is rf, the ripple shows up as sidebands on the carrier frequency. It's easy to see that you don't want any ripple (or harmonics), since this would create sidebands that would be demodulated as a signal by the receiver.

Both the ripple, which is due to the peak-to-peak inductor current times the ESR of the output caps, as well as the switching noise, which is due to transition times of diodes and transistors, have to be considered to meet low noise requirements. At these levels, it is no longer practical to try to get a big enough inductor and enough output caps in parallel: the only choices turn out to be a linear post-regulator or extra filter poles following the main converter.

The linear postregulator is never very desirable because it is inefficient. The extra filter poles mean specifically an extra L and C following the main output filter as shown in Figure 1.6. The only tricky part is deciding what to do with the feedback loop to the converter. The simplest solution is to continue to use feedback from the main converter output cap; the converter then sees only two poles and is easily stabilizable regardless of how large the additional filter is. However, the response of the additional filter is now uncontrolled, and it will probably ring when excited by a step load, defeating its purpose.

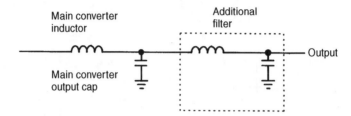

Figure 1.6   Low noise output can be achieved with an additional LC filter.

A better choice is to get the converter feedback at the output of the additional filter. This introduces two extra poles, making the converter unstabilizable if the poles are too low in frequency.

Practical Note A good choice is to make the resonant frequency of the additional filter approximately 10 times higher than the bandwidth of the converter. This then gives little phase shift for the compensation to deal with (see Chapter 6), and may still give adequate attenuation at the switching frequency. Generally, the inductance should be made small and the capacitance large, to decrease the converter's output impedance.

Practical Note You usually end up with quite small inductance required for this type of post-filtering, perhaps some hundreds of nanohenrys to a few microhenrys. Instead of trying to use a ferrite bead, which has trouble supporting DC current, try using one of the small MPP toroids as a bead, making it a single turn by just passing the output bus through it.

The worst load will occur when you need fast transient response and low noise together; then you will have to combine techniques from both these sections, and can expect to spend a lot of sweat on it.

Batteries, Again

Batteries were unpleasant sources, so, just as you would expect, they are unpleasant loads, too. The first thing about them is pretty obvious: when you need to charge a battery you can't just apply a voltage to it, because the amount of current the battery takes is exponential in the voltage. You need to have a way of controlling the current.

The way charging current is measured in databooks (discharge current is measured this way, too) is in terms of "C." This is best elucidated with an example: a 20A-h capacity battery is said to be being charged at $C/5$ (no one says $0.2C$ for some reason) if the current into it is 4A ($20/5 = 4$). That is, the $1C$ rate is a current that would nominally recharge the battery in 1 hour ($20A \times 1h = 20A$-h). Notice that "C" is a current, measured in amps; the capacity of the battery is measured in amp-hours, making its units charge.

To get a battery fully recharged, (don't ever discharge a primary battery to zero, it damages the battery), you need to first recharge it at a relatively high rate. (How high? The higher the charge rate, the more inefficient the recharging will be, because the battery will actually warm up. If you don't expect to use the battery soon in the system—for example, if it's used in a standby application—$C/20$ is a good choice.) After recharging to maybe 80–90% of capacity, you can taper the current off, that is, reduce the charge rate, to get back to a fully charged state. You usually don't want to continue charging at the high rate for this last portion of charge because this can cause the battery to heat. Keeping up the high charge also makes it difficult to know the actual state of the battery, since the "resistance" of the battery means that the terminal voltage will be higher when a lot of current is being pumped in. Some types of battery can be severely damaged by being overcharged. Because of the inefficiency of the chemical reactions inside the battery, you typically have to put 5–10% extra charge in beyond what you took out. Actually, the battery self-discharges, so you have to keep on putting a little bit of current in forever, even when you don't use the battery.

This last state, called trickle charge (or float charge), is usually done with a voltage rather than a current, because the amount of current required can be so small as to be hard to measure. A typical float-charge regime for a 12V, sealed lead–acid battery might be $13.6V + 30mV$ $(T - 25°C) \pm 0.2V$; in a fully charged battery, this may correspond to a rate of $C/1000$, a few milliamps.

So handling a battery properly requires fairly good measurement of current (down to milliamps and up to several amps), and voltage ($200mV/13.6V = 1.5\%$), and long integration times (keeping track of current for a 20-hour recharge). This application cries out for a microcontroller in your converter. Are you ready for this?

Telephones

Telephones, which have been around for 100 years, were designed with large pieces of steel and copper in mind, not semiconductors. They are powered by the phone line, not by the local mains, which is why your phone continues working when the lights go out. They are thus typically located hundreds of meters away from their power supply, which introduces substantial resistance and inductance between the supply and the phone.

A telephone can be modeled as having three different states: either it is not in use, or it is ringing, or else it is off-hook and in use. These three states have different characteristics, and the characteristics of each are (naturally) different in each country.

To appreciate how hard it is to drive a telephone in the ringing state, consider some sample numbers. In the ringing state, a phone looks like a resistor in series with a capacitance, and it has to be driven by a low frequency sine wave. This sine wave has to have a minimum voltage at the phone of $40V_{rms}$ (in the U.S.) or $35V_{rms}$ (in Germany); in reality, the voltages required from the supply are considerably higher because the output of the supply is divided down by the various line impedances before it reaches the phone. U.S. phones are approximately 7kΩ in series with 8μF, and are driven with a 20Hz sine wave. German phones look like 3.4kΩ in series with 850nF and are driven with 25Hz. Phones in France are required to be more than 2kΩ and less than 2.2μF, and can be driven at either 25 or 50Hz, depending on whether the driver is differential ("balanced") or not. Electronic phones can be almost any load whatsoever, from 6kΩ to 60kΩ or more! And yet the power supply has no way of knowing which of these telephones it will be powering, unless it is tailored for each country individually; indeed a supply running five phones needs to be able to power both conventional and electronic types simultaneously.

A quick calculation $[\chi_C = 1/(2\pi \times 20\text{Hz} \times 8\mu\text{F}) = 1\text{k}\Omega < 7\text{k}\Omega]$ shows that U.S. phones, because of their large capacitance, are dominantly resistive, whereas German phones $[\chi_C = 1/(2\pi \times 25\text{Hz} \times 850\text{nF}) = 7.5\text{k}\Omega > 3.4\text{k}\Omega]$ are dominantly capacitive. French phones $[\chi_C = 1/(2\pi \times 25\text{Hz} \times 2.2\mu\text{F}) = 2.9\text{k}\Omega > 2\text{k}\Omega$, while $\chi_C = 1/(2\pi \times 50\text{Hz} \times 2.2\mu\text{F}) = 1.45\text{k}\Omega < 2\text{k}\Omega]$ can be either resistive or capacitive! Thus the power supply has to be able to produce this high voltage sine wave into a load that may have either 0° or 90° of phase shift. When you add in cabling inductance, it turns out the load could even be inductive and have a −90° phase!

As if this weren't nasty enough, when you are talking on the phone, it looks like a pure 200Ω resistance. So here you are driving a 120V_{pp} sine wave into a reactive load, and when the user picks it up, suddenly it becomes a 200Ω resistor! Of course, the supply must quickly change its drive—otherwise it would be supplying huge power (a single supply should be able to power five phones). But because of the differences in phones of different types, the same measurement technique can't be used even to determine when the phone has been picked up. In the United States, for example, they look for a certain level of current (since it is mostly resistive), but in Germany, with the big capacitor, there is no substantial change in current (although there is in power), so they look for a phase change.

Fluorescent Tubes

Fluorescent tubes are another unusual type of load, driven by a special type of power supply called a ballast. Tubes come in quite a variety of types, the ubiquitous 4-foot-long ones you never pay attention to overhead, 8-foot-long ones you see in supermarkets, circular ones, cold-cathode types you use on your desk, sodium lamps in parking lots, etc., etc. They all have different characteristics to contend with, but the fundamental distinction among them is whether or not they have heated filaments. Those that don't have heated filaments require only a single pair of wires; those that do work basically the same, but require in addition extra pairs of wires for the filaments. Since the two types are otherwise similar, this section concentrates on tubes with heated filaments.

A fluorescent tube can be thought of as similar to a vacuum tube, except it's not a very good vacuum. The glass tube has some gases in it (such as argon), and a drop of mercury liquid, which vaporizes when the tube is working. The glass in turn has some phosphors coating its inside (similar to a television tube). The tube works when a voltage is applied across the gas from one end to the other. (There is actually a cathode and an anode, but since fluorescent tubes are usually operated with AC, this is an unimportant distinction. AC is used rather than DC so that both ends have a chance to be the anode, reducing wear on the electrode.) The voltage is enough to cause the gas to ionize, which is to say, it forms a plasma. Getting a headache yet? The plasma gives off UV light, which the phosphor coating on the glass changes into visible light. Altogether, this is not a real efficient electrical process, but it is substantially more efficient than what normal incandescent bulbs do, which is to make a piece of metal so hot that it glows.

Safety Tip Since fluorescent tubes contain mercury, which is highly dangerous, don't go smashing fluorescent tubes! Leave them intact to be handled by those who know where to dispose of them without contaminating either people or the environment.

When a fluorescent tube has been off for a while, it requires a high voltage to get it started (because the mercury is liquid). In this state the tube is a high impedance. Cold cathode types (i.e., those without heated filaments) just require this high voltage to be applied for a certain length of time, after which they turn on. Those with a filament require their filaments to be heated, preferably for several hundred milliseconds prior to application of the high voltage; failure to preheat seriously degrades the life of the tube. The whole electronic ballast industry got off to a bad start because early electronic ballast designers overlooked this fact.

After the filaments have been heated and the high voltage has been applied, the tube turns on. In this state, it is approximately like a zener: passing double the current through the tube changes the end-to-end voltage perhaps 10%. Of course, passing double the current the tube is rated for almost doubles the light output, but it also degrades the life of the tube.

In this on state, the filaments still have to be heated, but with considerably less power than during preheat. Since the filaments are basically just pieces of resistive wire, this can be accomplished by reducing the filament voltage.

Other Converters

The most common type of load for your converter is another switching converter. The troubles potentially associated with having two converters in series are discussed in some depth in Chapter 6 on stability. Here it is sufficient to state that two converters, each of which is individually stable, can both oscillate if attached in series! The reason has to do with the negative input impedance of a switching converter, that is, increasing the input voltage causes the input current to <u>decrease</u>, because the converter is a constant power load. It is well known that negative impedance loads are used in oscillators of many types (intentional or unintentional).

SAFETY

Power supplies often generate high voltages, or work off an AC mains. The author feels very strongly that he would be remiss not to at least touch on a subject that is often ignored in labs under the pressure of schedules: personal safety.

To start off with a true horror story, the author was once in a lab working on 277VAC when one of the engineers accidentally touched this voltage inside a circuit he was probing. The engineer fell backward over the chair he was sitting on, crashed to the ground, and lay there twitching uncontrollably for a minute or more. Falling over probably saved his life, since it disconnected his hands from the line.

The important thing to know is that (aphoristically) current is what kills, not voltage. If more than a few milliamps passes through your heart, it can fibrillate (stop beating).

How much current is required depends on all sorts of factors (How humid is it? Are your palms sweaty?), but here is the practical safety tip:

> **Safety Tip** If you're working on anything higher than 5VDC, keep one hand behind your back (e.g., hold onto your belt). This prevents current from flowing into one hand, through your heart, and to the other hand to complete the circuit.

All the time people tell me that this rule is too conservative: It's only 12V! It's only 60V! It's only 120VAC!—(Someone actually told me this last one.) But you can actually get a nasty jolt from a *1.5V D-cell*, if you go about it right. It's better to be safe.

For the same reason, you don't want to have a good conducting path to ground:

> **Safety Tip** Wear shoes with rubber soles in the lab. This prevents current from flowing into your hand, through your heart, and down your leg to ground, completing the circuit.

Did you know that the metallic case of an oscilloscope is attached to the ground of the BNC inputs? In many labs people look at signals that are not ground-referenced by floating the oscilloscope, that is, defeating the three-wire connection on the oscilloscope's power cord by using a "cheater" to convert it to a two-wire connection. Unfortunately, the oscilloscope's case thus sits at the potential at which the probe ground is attached, just waiting for someone to come along and get a shock by touching it. (The $10\text{M}\Omega$ impedance of the probe is in the *signal* path; the *ground* connection is a short.) There's a good *reason* that the plug is three wire, and as power engineers you should be the most familiar with it.

> **Safety Tip** Buy an isolator for the oscilloscope, and throw away all cheaters. The isolator allows each probe's ground to be at any potential. If you are trying to use cheaters because of perceived noise in the system, you'd better look at system grounding rather than covering it up. (Try connecting all the ground posts of the different instruments together, and attaching them to the converter's return at only a single point. Also try attaching all instruments' power cords to the same power strip.) You can now get isolators with bandwidths up to 50MHz, and isolation of 1500V, more than enough for most power work.

Buying isolators for each oscilloscope in the lab may seem expensive at first, but management will become very receptive to the idea as soon as they hear the words "wrongful death lawsuit".

Another practice to be careful about is leaving a power supply running while you go out of the room to do something else. It is a particularly bad idea to leave a power supply running overnight, as in a burn-in test. There's always a VP walking through at such a time who feels obliged to stick a finger in; or else, have you thought about the janitorial staff sweeping the floor and snagging a dangling line?

Safety Tip If you're not present, the power supplies you work with should either be off, inaccessible, or surrounded by a barrier. A plastic link chain would be good. Or how about a piece of magnet wire strung in front across two chairs? A warning sign would be a nice addition (*not* replacement), and maybe you can make it multilingual and graphically enhanced (with a skull and crossbones).

2

Practical Selection
of Topology

INTRODUCTION: THERE ARE HUNDREDS OF TOPOLOGIES!

Before you can begin any sort of design work on a converter, you have to select a topology. This is a really important task, as all other design selections depend on it: component selection, magnetics design, loop compensation, and so on; if the topology changes, these must change as well. So before getting started, it's always a good idea to spend some time carefully looking at the power supply's requirements and specifications to ensure that a proper topology is selected.

But how to choose? Some books on power supplies are nothing but compendiums of dozens of topologies, each with a few paragraphs describing the general idea of how the topology works, but little or nothing about the pros and cons of each, and certainly without guidance as to how to select one out of the many. Indeed, it has been shown in recent classification papers (see, e.g., Ref. 1) that resonant topologies alone number in the hundreds!

In this chapter, we're going to do it more practically. We're going to mention only the half-dozen or so topologies that are most commonly used in the low to medium power range, and clearly spell out their pros and cons. This book can't give absolute guidelines about which topology to use, because in fact you can make almost any of them work for a given application; but it will give strong opinions about which topologies not to use when, and the reasons why. In the first section on general considerations, we list the various criteria you need to consider when selecting a topology. The remainder of the chapter discusses the common topologies and some of their aspects vis-à-vis the criteria.

GENERAL CONSIDERATIONS

Step-Up or Step-Down

One of the very first things you need to think about to select a topology is whether the output voltage or voltages is (are) higher or lower than the input voltage, and whether this is true over the whole range of input voltages. For example, the buck converter can only step down the voltage; so the output voltage <u>has</u> to be less than the input at all times. (Details about the various types of converter mentioned in this section can be found in the sections of the chapter below.) If you have a 24V input that you want to step down to 15V, that's fine for a buck; but if the 24V actually has a range from 8V to 80V (as in MIL-STD-704A) then you can't use a buck, because you can't have 8V in and 15V out.

Practical Limits on Duty Cycle

Furthermore, there is a practical limit to how large or small a conversion ratio (output voltage divided by input voltage) can be achieved with a switching converter. First, the achievable duty cycle (definition: duty cycle = on time/switching period of a switch) for a converter has both a maximum and a minimum limit. In some topologies, you can't go above 50% duty cycle. In any case, commonly available PWM ICs often don't guarantee that they can reach duty cycles above about 85%. And in any case, many of them also don't function properly below about 5% duty cycle; which at reasonable switching frequencies is just as well, for you can't drive the gates of MOSFETs fast enough to get reasonable losses.

EXAMPLE

If your switching frequency is 250kHz, the period is 4μs. At a duty cycle of 10%, the on-time of the MOSFET is only 400ns, and if it takes 100ns to turn on the MOSFET and another 100ns to turn it off, almost all the period is eaten up in transitions, making for a lossy converter.

> **Practical Note** Don't plan on running duty cycles outside the limits of approximately 10% minimum or 80% maximum (45% maximum for converters with a theoretical maximum of 50%), without taking special precautions (type of IC used, high current gate drives, etc.).

There is a way around the limitation in duty cycle just illustrated: by using a topology that has a transformer, you can achieve a greater conversion ratio by a factor of the turns ratio. However, there are limits even to this. If the turns ratio becomes extremely large, the gross mismatch in wire gauge between the primary and secondary makes the transformer difficult to wind.

> **Practical Note** In general, transformers should have a maximum primary to secondary turns ratio of 10 : 1 or a minimum of 1 : 10. If you need to get really high voltages from a low voltage, or vice versa, you should think about either a two-stage converter or a voltage multiplier on the secondary.

How Many Outputs?

Closely connected with the question of duty cycle is the need to determine how many output voltages are to be generated. For example, if the answer is anything other than "one," a buck isn't suitable. Other practical limitations with some types of converter (concerning how many outputs should be planned on) are discussed below.

In the general sort of case, you may find that there are ways around such limits. For example, it may be possible to postregulate an output to generate another voltage. A common example might be a buck converter which produces a $+5$V output, and then uses a linear regulator (or even another switcher) with the $+5$V as input to generate $+3.3$V. The losses associated with this may be justifiable due, for example, to transient or noise requirements on the additional line.

In the worst case, it may make sense to design two separate converters, rather than trying to design and produce extremely complex magnetic pieces with large numbers of windings. Indeed, some of the worst converters the author has ever had to deal with (from the standpoint of producability and maintenance) have been multiwinding units, whose designer thought a few pennies could be saved by using a single PWM IC instead of two, and instead ended up spending dollars trying to make a very complicated transformer. The cost of magnetics should be considered up front, before any design is done, to avoid getting trapped with this problem.

Isolation

Another question that should be asked up front is whether primary to secondary isolation is required. There are all sorts of safety rules in the commercial world (as well as EMI questions, considered below) that may make isolation necessary. A typical example might be that the input has 500VAC applied to it relative to the output. But as soon as you know you need isolation, a number of topologies are immediately ruled out, that is, anything without a transformer (buck, nonisolated flyback, etc.).

EMI

Hopefully you've been lectured often enough, "Think about EMI from the start of the design, don't wait till the converter's already designed to start looking for Bandaids." Topology can have a lot to do with success in EMI. To start with the most basic aspect, if you have a nonisolated system, you have no common mode noise, since there is no third wire involved in the system! (EMI has a special chapter, Chapter 9, that explains these concepts in detail.) This makes filtering easier on you, the designer, if not easier overall.

Furthermore, some topologies are inherently more noisy than others. A distinction is to be made between topologies that disconnect the input from the converter during some portion of the period (and thus necessarily have discontinuous input current), and those that don't; the latter are easier to filter because the current has "less sharp edges." Among the latter, we distinguish those that operate in discontinuous mode from those that operate in continuous mode (this concept is discussed below), since the discontinuous operation also results in some portion of the period when the input current goes to zero; by the same reasoning, continuous mode will be easier to filter.

An example of a converter that disconnects the input is a buck, since when the switch is open, input current is zero. A nonisolated flyback always has the inductor connected to the input, but whether the input current is continuous depends on whether the flyback is being operated in continuous or discontinuous mode.

I recommend against using any of the topologies that claim they have no input ripple. Experience shows that they generally have very expensive magnetics.

Bipolar versus MOSFET versus ?

This question of what switch to use isn't directly related to topology selection, but should be considered up front also. The reason is that different types of devices have very different types of drive requirement; driving a bipolar transistor can be so hard that you will want to limit yourself to a single-switch topology. As of the date of writing, in the low to medium power range covered by this book, MOSFETs are used at least 90% of the time, both in commercial and military work. Indeed, except for special reasons, you should simply plan on using MOSFETs.

One of the special reasons is cost. For really high production quantities, a bipolar may still at times be cheaper than a MOSFET. However, a bipolar usually means a lower switching frequency than a MOSFET, and so the magnetics will be larger. Where does the cost advantage lie? You will have to do a detailed cost study to find this out.

You may also weigh the possibilities of a bipolar design for high input voltages, such as in 277V off-line conversion, or in a converter such as a push–pull, where you get double the input voltage, plus transients. You can get a 1500V bipolar, but the maximum MOSFET voltage is 1000V. Of course, for this you might consider an IGBT, which is industry standard for off-line these days. Unfortunately, although these transistors are driven like a MOSFET, you are then back to bipolar switching speeds again.

Continuous and Discontinuous

Continuous or discontinuous refers to the current in the inductor: in a discontinuous mode converter, the inductor current goes to zero at some time during the period. Stated differently, the difference between continuous and discontinuous mode is that to have continuous mode, you have to have enough inductance that at minimum load (including any preloading) there is still inductor current flowing at all times. In equations:

$$I_{\text{load,min}} \geqslant \frac{V_{\text{out}} T (1 - D)}{L}$$

where T is the period and D the duty cycle, and we have assumed that the forward voltage drop of the rectifier is small compared with the output voltage. Of course, if minimum load current is zero, you necessarily have discontinuous mode (except see below).

> **Practical Note** The key thing is to choose <u>either</u> continuous or discontinuous; don't allow the converter to be sometimes one and sometimes the other depending on the load. This can make it difficult to stabilize the loop.

An exception to this general rule occurs with synchronous rectification. A converter using synchronous rectification is <u>always</u> in continuous mode. Thus, no minimum inductance is required.

Synchronous Rectification

In many applications nowadays, converter efficiency is (almost!) more important than cost. Indeed, looked at from the consumer's viewpoint, a more efficient but more expensive up-front converter actually is cheaper, because the cost of downtime can be so high: an extra half-hour of compute time on a laptop computer, for example, would certainly be worth an extra dollar in the power supply.

When efficiency is important, it certainly pays to consider the use of a synchronous rectifier, that is, a system in which the function of the output rectifier is accomplished by a switch, invariably a MOSFET. Many ICs available today will drive both a main switching FET and a synchronous rectifier as well, so this can be far less painful than it was just a few years ago, when a second drive had to be developed using discrete components.

A further reason to consider using synchronous rectification is that as noted above, it converts a (potentially) discontinuous mode operation converter into a continuous mode operation. This is because even at no load, the current can flow in either direction in the inductor (because an "on" MOSFET can conduct in both directions). Using a synchronous rectifier, then, relieves you of having to worry about changing modes (which can be bad for converter stability, see Chapter 6), or about minimum inductance to ensure continuous operation.

One small downside to synchronous rectification deserves mention here. The main switching MOSFET has to be off before the synchronous rectifier is turned on, and vice versa. If this detail is neglected, there will be shoot-through: the input (or output) voltage will have a direct path to ground, engendering very high losses and potential failure. During the interval of time when both MOSFETs are off, the current in the inductor has to flow *somewhere*. Generally, the body diode of the MOSFET should not be used to carry this current, because this diode has a very long reverse recovery time. Suppose the body diode is intended carry the current while the MOSFETs are off. While the body diode is recovering, it acts like a short, so there is once again a path from input (or output) to ground, giving rise to shoot-through. To get an idea of the potential for trouble here, consider Figure 2.1*B*.

The bottom line is that it is necessary to have a schottky diode in parallel with the MOSFET's body diode, to carry the current during the time when both FETs are off. (The schottky has a much lower V_f than the body diode, and so carries essentially all the current; the reverse recovery time of the body diode depends on its previous forward conduction current, which is therefore negligible.)

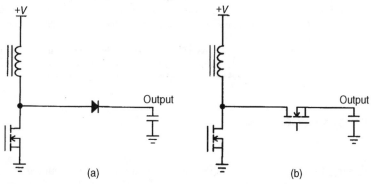

Figure 2.1   (a) Nonsynchronous converter uses a diode, whereas (b) a synchronous converter uses a MOSFET.

Voltage Mode versus Current Mode

You might observe that the distinction between current mode control and voltage mode control has not been mentioned in this list of things to consider up front. This is because this is really a control issue; most every topology can have either type of control. There is one point, though, on which there can be significant effects of selecting one or the other: if currents are high, current mode is going to require sensing the current with either a resistor (which will dissipate a lot of power) or a current transformer (which costs money). As a mitigating factor, though, this sensing makes overcurrent limiting straightforward. So for higher power outputs, it's worth thinking about this choice as well.

Conclusions

The more you know about the system in which your power supply is going to be operating, the better you can make design choices up front. And making proper choices at the beginning is vastly less costly and time-consuming than trying to make fixes later.

> **Practical Note** Make yourself a checklist from the specification sheet for the converter, and go through each of the items above. You'll often find that you come down to only one or two possibilites for a topology based on these constraints, and then topology selection may be easy, based on cost or size. For convenience, Table 2.1 summarizes the various choices talked about in this section.

TABLE 2.1   Topology Selection Checklist

1. *Step-up or step-down.* Is the input voltage always higher or always lower than the output? If not, you can't use a buck or non-isolated flyback.
2. *Duty cycle.* Is the output voltage different by more than a factor of 5 from the input voltage? If so, you probably will need a transformer. Calculate duty cycle to ensure that it doesn't have to get too small or too large.
3. *How many output voltages are required?* If more than one, a transformer may be required, unless you can postregulate. Large numbers of outputs suggest more than one converter may be a good choice.
4. *Is isolation required?* How much voltage? Isolation necessitates a transformer.
5. *What are the EMI requirements?* Tight requirements suggest staying away from topologies with discontinuous input current, such as a buck, and choosing continuous mode operation.
6. *Is cost so paramount that a BJT might be a choice?* Or if off-line, an IGBT? Otherwise, plan on MOSFETs.
7. *Is the supply required to operate with no load?* If so, choose discontinuous mode—unless the answer to question 8 is yes:
8. *Can synchronous rectification be afforded?* This makes the converter continuous regardless of load.
9. *Is the output current very high?* Then it might be good to use voltage mode rather than current mode.

THE BUCK TOPOLOGY

Turning from generalities to specific converters now, it is assumed that you know what a buck converter looks like. A sample is shown later (Figure 6.17). Instead of being yet another compendium of topologies, this section, and those following it on the other topologies, concentrates on practical difficulties with each topology, and some possibilities for circumventing them. Concentrating on the problems up front will enable you to make a better selection of topology, by highlighting areas that will consume much of your time in the design and debugging phases.

Limitations

As mentioned under General Considerations, there are a number of limitations to the buck topology that need to be addressed at the start.

1. Although a buck converter is conceptually clean in having only an inductor and no transformer, this means in turn that it's not possible to have input-to-output isolation.
2. The buck can <u>only</u> step down the input voltage: if the input is ever less than the desired output, the converter won't work. (However, see the section below on the buck-boost.) You <u>can</u> use a buck to generate a negative voltage. Figure 2.2 shows such a configuration. When the transistor turns on, current in the inductor ramps up. When the transistor turns off, the inductor current is pulled from the output capacitor, pulling it negative.

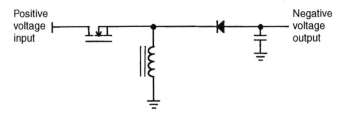

Figure 2.2   Using a buck to convert a positive input voltage to a negative output voltage.

3. The buck only has one output. This is fine if you're looking for a 5V-to-3.3V converter, but unless you're willing to contemplate a second stage of regulation, such as a linear postregulator, the many applications in which you're looking for multiple outputs are ruled out.
4. Although the buck can be either continuous or discontinuous, its input current is always discontinuous, meaning that during the portion of the cycle when the transistor is off, the input current goes to zero. This makes the EMI filter larger than it might need to be with other topologies.

Gate Drive Difficulties

Driving the gate of a buck can get to be quite a nuisance, not to say a problem. The trouble is that to turn on an n-channel MOSFET, the gate voltage has to be at least 5V and more likely 10V above the input voltage (respectively 1V and 5V for logic-level FETs). But how do you generate a voltage higher than the input? The easiest way around this problem is no doubt to use a p-channel FET, so it can be turned on just by pulling the gate to ground. Unfortunately, p-channel FETs usually have substantially higher $R_{DS,on}$ than n-channels do, and cost rather more. Besides, the input voltage would have to be less than 20V to avoid blowing out the gate, ruling it out in a number of applications. The reality of using p-channel MOSFETs is this: with a pull-down resistor, you usually can't get enough switching speed on the gate for the efficiency you want, and you end up going back to an n-channel after a few frustrating days of lab work.

Practical Note Except for very low input voltage converters, build your buck converter with an n-channel MOSFET.

One common way to drive the gate is to use a gate drive transformer that isolates the driver from the gate (Figure 2.3).

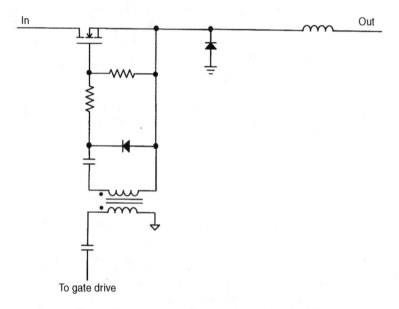

Figure 2.3 Use of a transformer to drive a buck transistor.

The capacitor on the drive side of the isolation transformer prevents DC current from flowing through the primary while the gate drive output is high. The capacitor and diode on the other side restore the voltage to unidirectionality—otherwise a 12V drive on the primary becomes a ±6V drive on the secondary. The gate resistor is always necessary (see the discussion in Chapter 3 on components), and finally, the gate–source resistor is just a bleed: if the gate drive stops switching for some reason, the gate eventually turns off.

Practical Note Choose the two capacitors in this gate drive circuit to be at least 10 times bigger than the gate capacitance—remember that they form a divider with this capacitance, and so this way you'll get at least 90% of the drive voltage on the gate.

Although this system is relatively cheap and works well, it is limited in maximum duty cycle because the transformer has to have time to reset.

A method that allows extremely fast gate drives utilizes a separate push–pull housekeeping converter to generate a DC secondary voltage referenced to the source of the MOSFET (*F* ground in Figure 2.4). It's not necessary for this second converter to be in a closed loop; if it comes from a regulated source, a fixed duty cycle converter works well. You can then have a gate driver IC referenced to the source, and really drive the MOSFET fast. Although I have used this circuit many times, it is somewhat expensive because of all the extra parts needed. (You could use a 555 timer for generating the 50% duty cycle.)

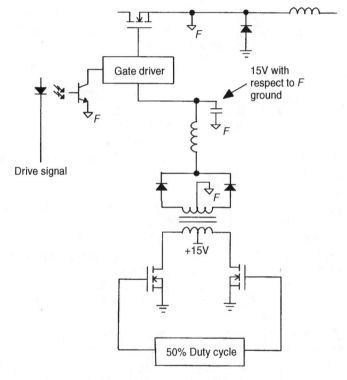

Figure 2.4   Generating a floating supply to drive a buck transistor.

You also need a way of signaling the floating system to control the gate driver. The signal of course can't tolerate excessive propagation delay, ruling out slow optocouplers such as the 4N48. To avoid having yet another transformer, I have found the HCPL2601 family of optocouplers to be excellent even for very high input voltages, because of their excellent dV/dt rating.

THE FLYBACK

Two Kinds

There are two kinds of flyback, the nonisolated flyback (Figure 2.5) and the isolated flyback (Figure 2.6),

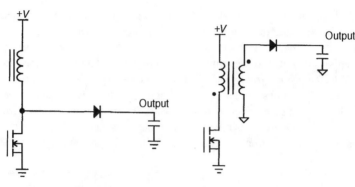

Figure 2.5 Basic nonisolated flyback topology.

Figure 2.6 Basic isolated flyback topology.

which we explicitly show to avoid name confusion (see below). To be absolutely sure, let's briefly describe their operation.

The nonisolated flyback turns on its switch for a fraction D of the switching period, which, since it produces a voltage across the inductor, causes current to ramp up, storing energy in the inductance. (More explicit details are given in Chapter 5 on magnetics design.) When the switch turns off, the inductor current goes through the diode and into the output capacitor and load.

The isolated flyback works entirely analogously. During the on-time of the switch, energy is stored in the inductance of the primary. Looking at the dots on the transformer, we see that when the switch turns off, the drain voltage rises above the input voltage, which causes the secondary voltage to rise above ground; this turns on the diode, again providing output current to the capacitor and load.

The nonisolated flyback has a single output (there's no way to make more than one). That output is not isolated from the input, and the output can't be made less than the input voltage—even if you turn the transistor completely off, the output will equal the input (minus a diode drop). On the other hand, if all you're looking for is a single nonisolated output, this flyback has only a single-winding inductor to deal with.

The isolated flyback can have multiple outputs if multiple secondaries are put on the transformer, and all those outputs can be isolated from the primary, and potentially from each other. Further, the outputs can be made to have any value whatsoever, simply by adjusting the primary to secondary turns ratio. The downside is that the magnetics is now a multiwinding transformer (see below).

Name Confusion with Boost

Frequently people call the nonisolated flyback a "boost" converter. The term "boost" does not appear again in this book. The terms "nonisolated flyback" and "isolated flyback" are consistently used to refer to the topologies shown in Figures 2.5 and 2.6. As discussed in Chapter 6, the distinguishing feature of a flyback topology is that the magnetic structure stores energy during a portion of the switching cycle; this is why we use the same name for these two topologies.

> **Practical Note** Whenever you're reading something that refers to a "flyback" or "boost," look carefully at the schematic to see what topology is actually being talked about. The literature is inconsistent, resulting in endless confusion.

Continuous versus Discontinuous

Both types of flyback can be run in either continuous or discontinuous mode. In a general sort of way, though, a flyback is usually used to enable the converter to go to no-load current without needing any preload. (At no load, the switch is simply turned off until the charge on the output capacitor bleeds off, and then turns on again for a single pulse. This is known variously as "pulse-skipping mode" and other similar terms.) For this no-load operation to work, you need to operate in discontinuous mode, and as indicated before, it's best not to change modes because of difficulties in controlling the converter's loop. The most common operation of a flyback is thus in discontinuous mode.

Capacitor Limitations

When the flyback transistor turns off (see the discussion in the magnetics chapter, Chapter 5, for more on this), the energy stored in the primary inductance comes out on the secondary winding(s). Since there is no inductor on the secondary, the full peak current goes straight into the capacitor. At higher power levels, it can become quite hard to find a capacitor with sufficient ripple current rating to handle this: remember that you have to calculate the RMS current to know whether the capacitor can handle it. Suppose for example that we are running a 5V output at 10A (this is about the limit for a flyback, see below), and the duty cycle is 50% at this power level. The transformer has to deliver the 50W for the full period in just half the period (since the duty cycle is 50%), so the current it delivers during the conduction time of the diode is double, 20A. So the RMS current is

$$I_{\text{RMS}} = \sqrt{\tfrac{1}{2}(20\text{A})^2} = 14\text{A}$$

This extremely high current will require paralleling many aluminum or tantalum capacitors, or else the use of a high-priced MLC cap. Failure to get adequate capacitance on the output of a flyback is a major cause of capacitor failure.

Power Limits

There is a maximum power that can usefully be used with a flyback, on the order of 50W for low voltage inputs. (You sometimes hear stories from people who say they built one at 500W, but they don't tell you that it could never be made to work on the production line.) In any event the power output is inversely proportional to the inductance; to get a large power requires a tiny inductance (the math is detailed in the chapter on magnetics). By the time you get up to 50W at a reasonable switching frequency, the inductance is very small (the same order of magnitude as strays); this makes the design almost impossible to produce consistently in production. For example, a slight change in the lay of the wires by the magnetics vendor will affect the inductance enough to prevent you from getting maximum power out.

> **Tip** For low voltage inputs, limit flybacks to designs requiring less than 50W, somewhat more for high voltage inputs.

Practical Limits on Number of Outputs

Of course, for all converters, the transformer becomes more difficult to wind as you add more windings to it. For an isolated flyback, however, this difficulty is crucial. The regulation of each output depends on the leakage inductance of the winding, because the leakage inductance subtracts from the voltage delivered to the output. So to get good tolerance on the outputs, the leakages must be either negligibly small (almost impossible) or the same from unit to unit, so that they can be compensated for. If you have multiple windings, however, controlling (and even measuring and specifying) the leakage on each winding is almost impossible. The author once saw an isolated flyback design with (believe it or not!) 13 outputs. According to the designer, a flyback "was cheaper than a forward because it didn't need an inductor." Unfortunately, after this was in production, the vendor's winding person (there was only one vendor, no one else wanted to touch it) left the magnetics company, and thereafter no one else was ever able to wind the transformer in a way that made the circuit work!

> **Practical Note** If you need more than three or four outputs, don't use a flyback. It will be cheaper in the long run to go to a forward.

THE BUCK-BOOST

"Buck-boost" is the standard name for what might be better called, in line with the terminology used in this book, a "buck-flyback." It's not a very common topology yet, but it has some advantages that suggest it will become increasingly used.

The buck-boost converter, as its name suggests, works as either a buck or a flyback, depending on whether the input voltage is, respectively, higher or lower than the output voltage. The great thing about this topology (Figure 2.7) is that this transition is accomplished automatically, there are no discrete changes involved.

In the buck-boost, both switches are on at the same time, and both are off at the same time. Consider first the case of the input voltage higher than the output. The top transistor

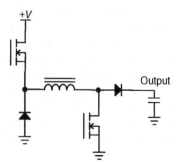

Figure 2.7 A nonisolated buck-boost.

(see Figure 2.7) acts as a buck switch, with the grounded-anode diode as the freewheeling rectifier. Since the bottom switch is on at the same time as the top switch, the full input voltage is applied across the inductor, ramping up the current. When both switches turn off, the grounded-anode diode carries the current, and the other diode simply forward conducts. This is thus a buck converter.

Next, suppose the input voltage is lower than the output. The ground-referenced transistor now acts as a flyback switch, and the second diode acts as the freewheeling rectifier. Once again, since both switches are on at the same time, the full voltage is applied across the inductor during the on-time.

Observe what the description has said: in both cases, whether acting as a buck or acting as a flyback, the full input voltage is applied across the inductor. But this means that *the same control circuit works for both "modes"* and consequently the converter does *not* switch between modes; therefore, stabilization of the loop is straightforward!

Limitations of the Buck-Boost

As we would expect, the problems with the buck-boost are a combination of the problems with the buck and the flyback. Acting as a buck converter, it has no input–output isolation, and there is only a single output. Acting as a (nonisolated) flyback, there's a maximum practical output power. And finally, unless you can replace the (schottky) diodes with two more MOSFETs to make the converter synchronous, there can be relatively poor efficiency; but a driver with four outputs (perhaps a full-bridge PWM IC?) would be required to achieve synchronous rectification. Still, the ability to work over a large range of input voltages, and the appearance of ICs for controlling this topology, may make the buck-boost an attractive choice.

THE FORWARD

Again, to avoid confusion with the term "boost," when this book refers to a forward converter, the topology illustrated in Figure 2.8 is always meant.

The forward works entirely differently from the similar appearing flyback. The key point is noticing that the dots on the transformer now mean that the output diode is forward-biased when the voltage across the primary is positive, that is, when the transistor is *on*; a flyback's diode is on when the switching transistor is off. Energy is thus not (intentionally) stored in the primary inductance, as it was for the flyback; the transformer

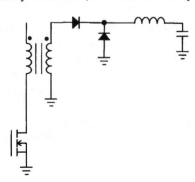

Figure 2.8 Basic forward topology.

acts strictly as a transformer. When the transistor is turned off, the only energy stored is that in the leakage inductance of the transformer; this is what causes the drain voltage to rise above the input voltage, resetting the core.

Minimum Load

The forward is one of those converters mentioned at the beginning of the chapter that requires a minimum load. The inductor has to be big enough to ensure that its peak ripple current is less than the minimum load current. Otherwise it will go discontinuous, and the output voltage will rise, peak detecting. This means that a forward converter cannot operate with no load, because you cannot have an infinite inductance.

> **Practical Note** A swinging choke, such as that produced with an MPP core, is an excellent choice here. A swinging choke is one whose inductance decreases gradually as the current through it increases. At minimum load, you get a lot of inductance, keeping the core continuous, and at maximum load you still have some inductance, but not as much; you allow the ripple to increase as the load current increases, so that the inductor doesn't have to be designed as physically big as would be needed to maintain the full inductance at maximum load.

One commonly used way around a minimum load is to attach a small load resistor (a "preload") permanently at the output terminals, as a part of the converter itself. Then, even when the external load is zero, the converter can remain continuous because it is still supplying some minimum power to this resistor. Of course this eats up a certain amount of power when the external load is above minimum.

> **Practical Note** Schemes abound for turning off this preload as external load increases. Very frequently, the result is oscillations: the preload turns off, then the converter goes discontinuous, which causes the preload to turn on, and the converter is continuous, causing the preload to turn off, etc. Just bite the bullet and accept the small efficiency hit compared with the cost (and efficiency hit) of a much larger inductor.

Leakage Inductance

Unlike the flyback, which uses its primary inductance to store energy, the forward really has parasitic leakage inductance. When current is flowing through the primary, there is energy stored in the leakage inductance, $\frac{1}{2}L_{leakage}\,I^2$. This energy has to go someplace. In the simplest case, you just throw it away, either into an RC snubber, or into the transistor itself, letting it avalanche. More sophisticated schemes recover more or less of the energy, using an additional winding on the transformer (though this doesn't work perfectly either because of leakage!) or some form of switched reactance, often using another FET. Regardless of what is done with the energy, it is a nuisance and to some degree an efficiency hit; the best approach is to wind the magnetics in a way that minimizes the leakage inductance.

Summary

Because the forward doesn't store energy in the transformer, it doesn't have the limitation that hinders the flyback in terms of power level; it also has an inductor, which smoothes the current seen by the output capacitors. Forwards can be straightforwardly constructed at a level of 500W or more. The main limitation of the topology eventually comes about, rather, from the available size of MOSFETs. Increased power translates into increased currents, and eventually losses in the MOSFETs become unacceptable. When this is the case, a topology with more than one transistor to share the burden is desirable.

THE PUSH–PULL

There are two basic styles of push–pull converter, current-fed and voltage-fed. The difference between them boils down to much nicer waveforms and operations in the current-fed push–pull, but at the price of having a (sometimes rather large) extra inductor.

The push–pull is treated here, while the half-bridge isn't, because the push–pull has both its transistors ground-referenced. Although it was noted above that there are ICs available that will drive high-side transistors for synchronous rectifiers, they tend to have rather low maximum voltages. Since the push–pull and half-bridge use two transistors, presumably they have been selected because the power level is higher than in single-transistor topologies, which often means that the input voltage is higher. Driving a half-bridge may thus get back into discrete parts to generate the floating gate drive; the push–pull definitely has an advantage here.

Voltage-Fed

The voltage-fed push–pull converter works by having two transistors across a center-tapped transformer (see Figure 2.9). They are operated 180° out of phase. This *doesn't* mean that each one is on 50% of the time, just that they have the same duty cycle, with one going on half a switching period later than the other. If the left transistor in Figure 2.9 is on, the right transistor is off. Looking at the dots on the transformer, this means that V_{in} is applied across half the transformer, and so $2 \times V_{in}$ is applied on the drain of the off transistor. Continuing with the left transistor on, there is a positive voltage applied to the bottom diode, which is on, and the top diode is reverse-biased. Everything is then mirror-

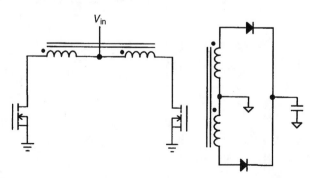

Figure 2.9 A voltage-fed push–pull.

imaged when the right transistor is on; since the two transistors are on for the same amount of time, if V_{in} is constant during a switching period, the volt-seconds across the transformer ideally sum up to zero, and the core operates symmetrically around zero gauss.

The biggest problem with this converter is the voltage rating needed by the transistors, which is at least double the maximum V_{in}. Operating from a rectified 120V line means that the transistors will see at least $2 \times 120V = 240V$. In practice, the line can be a very nasty place, as noted in Chapter 1, and so a 400V transistor might be a common choice here. This high voltage rating in turn means that the $R_{DS,on}$ is high, and so losses may be higher than desired. And in any case, the V_{in} need only surge above 200V for one switching period to blow out the transistors!

The other potential problem is that there must be a time (the dead time) between turning off one transistor and turning on the other. If both transistors were on at the same time, the transformer would be effectively shorted, and so the current would rapidly increase, limited only by the leakage inductance—this is a common cause of failure. The transistors must also be on equal amounts of time to avoid saturating the transformer; in practice this is accomplished by using current mode control (see Chapter 5 for the concept of saturation, and Chapter 6 for current mode control).

Current-Fed

The sensitivity to line voltage exhibited by the voltage-fed push–pull is obviated in the current-fed push–pull because it has an inductor between V_{in} and the transformer. Now when the transistor turns on, it gets a current set by the inductor current, as shown in Figure 2.10. This arrangement also gets rid of the problem of having to turn off one transistor before the other turns on, since even if both transistors are on simultaneously, the current is still limited by the inductor.

The downside of this converter is the addition of an extra inductor. Since this device must both carry the DC current of the converter and provide sufficient inductance to act like a current source during a switching period, it can easily grow to rather large (read expensive) size for moderate power level converters.

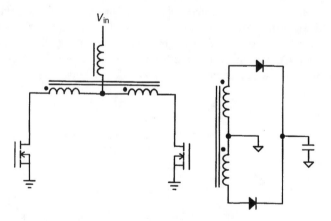

Figure 2.10   A current-fed push–pull.

Transformer Utilization

It should be observed that all the topologies discussed up till this section (the flyback, the forward, and the buck-boost) utilize only half the magnetics' cores: the flux density is ramped up to a maximum value and then back down to zero, never going negative. The push–pull utilizes the magnetics better, because the core's flux density goes both positive and negative, thus reducing the size of the magnetics for a given power level compared to the single transistor topologies.

RESONANT CONVERTERS AND SOFT-SWITCHING CONVERTERS

For quite a few years now, everywhere you turn there have been articles about resonant converters, how great they are, and how everyone ought to be using them. (The author feels, however, that this fad is finally passing.) If you are one of the braver souls, perhaps you've actually been in the lab, and spent several weeks or months trying to make a go of a resonant converter.

By way of contrast, there seems to be very little heard about soft-switching converters, and yet they seem much more practical; many of the converters in production that are called resonant are actually soft-switching. Another name for soft-switching is "quasi-resonant."

As noted at the start of this chapter, there are hundreds of different topologies that are resonant or soft-switching; for this reason, this section merely points to the sorts of feature it might benefit you to investigate.

The Difference Between Resonant and Soft-Switching Converters

A resonant converter is one in which the power waveforms (current and voltage) are sinusoidal. This is accomplished by letting inductances form a resonant tank with capacitances, the latter often (though not always) being parasitics. Switching occurs when the voltage and/or current goes through zero, ensuring an almost lossless switch transition. Resonant converters thus have had their main claim for usefulness in high frequency converters, where switching losses can dominate on-state losses of the switches. However, since switch transitions depend on the frequencies of resonant tanks, the actual switching frequency of the converter varies, sometimes quite dramatically, usually as a function of load and line.

A soft-switching converter is intermediate between a resonant converter and a PWM converter. Any of the topologies described in the sections above can be made soft-switching by suitable addition of components. A soft-switching converter always switches at the same constant frequency, like a PWM, but it creates a tank circuit for a portion of the switching period so that switch transitions still occur nearly losslessly.

Why You Should <u>Not</u> Use Resonant Converters

Resonant converters have quite a number of problems. Not least among these is the variation of switching frequency with load. In fact, for a common class of these converters, minimum switching frequency occurs at maximum load, so that EMI filtering has to be designed for the worst combination, minimum frequency and maximum current. The gain in size from operating at a high switching frequency may be lost when a realistic converter is designed including the EMI filter. The next time you are told about a resonant converter that does $100W/in^3$, ask what the power density is when a noise filter is included!

An even more serious problem arises because of the common use of capacitive strays as one of the elements of the resonant tank. This strategy almost *can't* be made to work on a production line, although it's great in the lab. The trouble is that these strays are not consistent from device to device; they can even differ between two *identical* devices from different manufacturers! This variation directly affects the operational frequency, which affects the output caps, the EMI filter, etc. The only way around it is to parallel some external capacitance with the parasitic, so variation of the parasitic is relatively unimportant. Unfortunately, this modification increases the tank period, and so the original motivation, operating at a high frequency, is destroyed.

Why You <u>Should</u> Use Soft-Switching Converters

In contrast with resonant converters, soft-switching converters operate at a fixed frequency, making their filtering requirements straightforward. They also typically use discrete capacitors, and so have quite reproducible characteristics from unit to unit. Figure 2.11 shows a fairly standard implementation of a soft-switching forward converter, with a sketch of a drain waveform.

Initially, the transistor is on, and the drain voltage is zero. When the transistor turns off, the primary inductance of the transformer forms a resonant tank with the external capacitor (in parallel with the drain–source capacitance of the MOSFET, but the external capacitor is designed to be larger than the MOSFET's capacitor). After completing a half-cycle of the ring, the core is reset: the L and C values set the ring frequency, and the volt-seconds required to reset the core determine then how high the voltage rings up. After the half-cycle ring is completed, the drain voltage remains at the input voltage, since there is now no energy stored in the transformer. It remains in this state until the transistor turns on again.

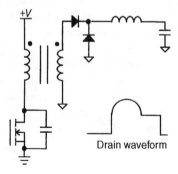

Drain waveform

Figure 2.11 A quasi-resonant or soft-switching forward converter.

What distinguishes this converter from a resonant converter is that it is still pulse width modulated: the transistor has a constant switching frequency. Of course, the capacitance and the inductance still have to be chosen carefully. If they are too big, the (half) period will exceed the switching period, and the core won't reset; if they are too small, the drain voltage will go excessively high, to get the necessary volt-seconds in a very short time. Even so, there is wide room for variation of the stray components within which the converter will work normally.

It may be noted that when the transistor turns on, the capacitor energy is dissipated into the MOSFET. If the capacitor is sufficiently small, however, this may not be too terrible. For example, if the capacitor is 100pF, the input voltage is 50V, and the switching frequency is 500kHz, the power lost because of the capacitor is only $P = (\frac{1}{2}) \times 100\text{pF} \times (50\text{V})^2 \times 500\text{kHz} = 63\text{mW}$.

Indeed, the only bad thing about soft-switching converters is the apparent dearth of ICs designed to operate them, although something can be rigged from a PWM designed to operate a synchronous rectifier. Perhaps as the word gets out (and certain potential patent issues become clarified) ICs implementing soft-switching will become common—at that time, they will make an excellent choice.

COMPOUND CONVERTERS

A compound converter is any converter that has two (or in theory more) stages in series. It is distinguished from merely two series converters in that there is usually only one control loop for the whole system. For example, one possible compound converter consists of a front-end buck operating from 160VDC followed by a push–pull (see Figure 2.12). The buck operates closed loop to produce an approximately fixed output voltage (say 50V); the push–pull operates at a fixed duty cycle to step down the voltage (say to 5V). The loop is closed by sensing the 5V output, and using its error signal to control the duty cycle of the buck. Thus, although the push–pull is seemingly operated open loop (since it switches at a

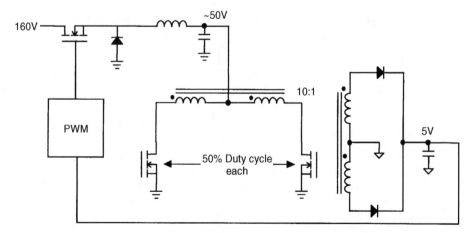

Figure 2.12 A compound converter consisting of a buck followed by a voltage-fed push–
pull; the buck's output capacitor serves as the push–pull's input capacitor.

fixed duty cycle) it is actually just a gain block inside the control loop, which is closed around it (in the example shown in Figure 2.12, it has a gain of $1/10 = -20\text{dB}$).

In some cases, the two converter stages may share components; in the example just given, the output capacitor of the buck is also used as the input capacitor of the push–pull. It is easy to imagine other combinations in which an inductor could be shared instead. As with the resonant and soft-switching converters, there are a large number of possible combinations for compound converters; instead of attempting an enumeration, I'll comment about when they might be useful.

When to Use Them

As the example given shows, having a compound converter is useful when you want to get a lot of step-down or step-up. It's already been mentioned that there are practical limits to the duty cycle you can get from a PWM, and to the size of the turns ratio you should try for on a transformer. If you need to make a voltage conversion beyond what's feasible within these limits, a compound converter offers a way to considerably extend the transformation range available.

A compound converter might be desirable, as well, when you need to get a fairly large conversion ratio (of input to output voltage) in a situation that also calls for input-to-output isolation. The two requirements together can make for a very challenging design, but by segregating the functions, you can make it much easier: For example, let the front-end converter do the voltage transformation, and then let the second converter do the isolation, perhaps with a 1:1 transformer. Since the second converter would always operate with the same input voltage and the same output voltage, its components could be optimized for this operation, and it could be very efficient. Indeed, this compound convertor may well be more efficient than a single-stage converter, because of the difficulties in the magnetics involved with simultaneous design of both large conversion ratio and isolation.

REFERENCES

1. Issa Batarseh, *IEEE Transactions on Power Electronics*, PE-9(1), 6 (1994).

3

Practical Selection
of Components

INTRODUCTION

There are many aspects of selecting components that somehow end up being mentioned only in vendors' application notes and hard-to-find books. It's not enough to know that if you're dissipating 0.7W in a resistor, you should pick a resistor that can handle 1W. You also should know, for example, that a wirewound device can handle pulse power much larger than 1W, and thus maybe doesn't need to be a 1W resistor if the 700mW is actually present for only a short time. But how do you find out *how long* a 0.5W resistor can take the 700mW pulse?

More or less every component used in power supplies has idiosyncrasies like this. The usual way of finding such information is through (sometimes sorry) experience or by having the good luck of talking with someone who has learned the hard way. Rather than advocating reliance on luck, this chapter collects together many of these topics for the following electronic items: resistors, capacitors, schottky diodes, rectifier diodes, BJTs, MOSFETs, op amps, and comparators. Hopefully, those relatively new in the field will find lots of useful items here, and even those with much experience will find it handy, if nothing else, to have all the information collected in one place. However, the author has refrained from stating the obvious, having assumed that if you're reading this book in the first place, you don't require to be told that electrolytic capacitors have a polarity and should not be put in backward.

RESISTORS

Values

10.2kΩ. 39.9Ω. Where did all those weird numbers come from for standard values? It turns out that the values are (approximately) logarithmically distributed across a decade (such as 1kΩ to 10kΩ). Actually, there are different numbers of resistors per decade, depending on the tolerance: for example, either 48 or 96.

There is a practical maximum to how large a resistor can be used on a PCB. The problem with very large values (although they are available, for specialized applications) is that there is current leakage on the board between any two points that are at different potentials and are close enough together physically. In severe cases, leakage can be the equivalent of a 1–10MΩ resistor. Thus, if you were to try to put a 100MΩ resistor in a circuit, it could be in parallel with this leakage, and you would end up with only the 1 or 10MΩ instead of 100MΩ. For a circuit that gets around this problem in the common case of an op amp feedback, see the section below on op amps.

> **Practical Note** Avoid using resistors bigger than 1MΩ unless special precautions are taken.

Types of Resistor

The oldest style of resistor is carbon composition (carbon comp), which nowadays you see only in hobby stores: these resistors are much bigger than metal film resistors of the same power rating, and are actually more expensive nowadays. Metal film resistors have the same frequency response as carbon comps, so be sure to tell your purchasing agent not to buy any carbons.

Then there are wirewounds. These range in size from tiny 1W packages to mammoth 1kW rheostats (see below for a definition). These resistors are called wirewound because they really are: if you cut one up, you will find a piece of (relatively) high resistance wire, usually wound around a core in a helix pattern. If you think this sounds like the description of a solenoid, that's because it is: wirewounds have plenty of inductance; as discussed below, it's also possible, by winding equal numbers of turns in opposite directions to produce a wirewound resistor having very little inductance. Table 3.1 lists the types of resistor discussed here and mentions some applications.

TABLE 3.1   Brief Resistor Selection Guide

Type	Suggested Applications
Carbon Comp	Not used anymore; use metal film instead.
Metal film	General purpose, use for most applications.
Wirewound (inductive) and rheostat	Use for load resistors.
Wirewound (noninductive)	Use for current sensing high frequencies, such as switching waveforms.
Shunt	Use for current sensing high currents.
PCB trace	Use for current sensing when cost is more important than accuracy.

Tolerance

It used to be that 5% resistors were the cheapest kind, and everyone used them for everything—not so today. Today, 1% resistors are both the most available and the cheapest—if you come across a purchasing agent who disagrees, suggest that a homework session is in order: there's no reason to ever use a tolerance greater than 1% on a resistor.

For that matter, during cost reduction efforts, people seem to come around to ask if you really need that 0.1% resistor, and couldn't you use a 1%? Send these people away. Unless you're making millions of this type of supply, the cost difference for a 0.1% versus a 1% is so small that almost <u>anything</u> else you change on the supply will have a bigger cost impact than changing that tolerance. Besides, you probably picked 0.1% to achieve the necessary output voltage tolerance or the like anyway.

Selecting Ratios

So far you've found out how to miff a purchasing agent. Here's a way to please one. As we'll discuss in the chapter on monitoring circuitry, frequently you don't care about the actual values of the resistors you use, you just want a voltage divider (i.e., a ratio of resistances). Picking a standard value for one of the pair will considerably reduce the number of different values in a design, which doesn't affect performance but makes the supply cheaper by enabling larger quantities to be purchased. If there's no reason to choose any particular impedance, for example, I always use $10k\Omega$ as one part of a divider.

Maximum Voltage

Believe it or not, resistors have a maximum voltage rating. And it's not always just set by the power dissipation; resistors can actually arc. This problem is especially severe when surface mount resistors are used, because of the close spacing between the ends. So if you're dealing with voltages above, say, 100V in a supply, you might check that any resistors attached to high voltage nodes have the necessary rating.

Temperature Coefficient

Most resistors have pretty small temperature coefficients (say, $50-250ppm/°C$), although these can be important when you're trying to do worst-case analysis (Chapter 10). Wirewounds, however, can change quite a bit when they get hot, so read the specifications carefully.

Power Rating

Everyone knows not to put a half-watt of power into a quarter-watt resistor. But what exactly *is* a quarter-watt resistor? The military decided that to increase resistor reliability, nobody would be allowed to put more than half the rated power into a (carbon or metal film) resistor. To meet this requirement, companies that design for the military apply their own derating; for example, that no one is allowed to put more than 70% of the *military* rated power into the resistor. To aid in this, some companies produce military-style resistors (e.g., RN55 or RN60) that are already derated the 50%; that is, what is really a half-watt resistor they call a quarter-watt resistor. Completely confused? The moral of the story is just that you need to keep a sanity check on resistor ratings—does it *look like* a quarter-watt resistor? Get a standard catalog, and check up on your buyers when they select alternates, to be sure the resistors you get will fit in the PCB holes.

While we're at it, what about putting 0.25W into a quarter-watt resistor? After all, the data book says the device can handle it! And so it can. However, resistors can get *extremely* hot—wirewounds are rated to operate at 275°C! Quite aside from not wanting to accidentally touch something at this temperature, resistors also give off unpleasant smells when they get too hot, and drift in resistance value very considerably.

> **Practical Note** A good practical limit is to follow the lead of the military and, whenever possible use a resistor only to half its rated steady-state power.

Pulse Power. While putting 1W into a 1W wirewound is not a good idea, this limitation is only for steady state (e.g., many seconds or more). For short times, a wirewound can take much more power than its rating without failing. This is *not true* for resistors of other types! You should strictly adhere to the maximum power rating of nonwirewound resistors, although for short times it's OK to put the full rated power into one; for example, you can safely put 100mW into a 100mW nonwirewound resistor for 100ms.

EXAMPLE

Suppose I have a 40V one-shot pulse across a 10Ω resistor for 100ms. This is a power of $P = (40V)^2 / 10\Omega = 160W$. Do I really need a 200W resistor? Dale has provided a guide to selecting power resistors (the table from which is reproduced as Figure 3.1). To use this table, first we calculate the energy that goes into the resistor, $E = P \times t = 160W \times 100ms = 16J$, and then the energy per ohm, $E/R = 16J/10\Omega = 1.6J/\Omega$. We now use the table's first column to find an energy per ohm larger than this: the first one is 2.46J/Ω. Reading across, we find the resistor value larger than 10Ω, which is 10.11Ω; and reading up, we see that this can be put into a G-10 resistor, which is a 10W type, a considerable size savings!

Note: Dale says that this is valid only up to pulses about 100ms long, and for standard wirewounds; longer pulses should be based on "short time overload" ratings, while noninductive wirewounds can take *four times* the pulse ratings given by this table.

Rheostats: A What? Rheostat is the proper name for a variable power resistor. In the lab you'll typically see rheostats that range from maybe 100W to 1kW. As with potentiometers, they have a center tap that shorts out part of the winding. Not to belabor the obvious, this means that if you are using half the resistance of a rheostat (e.g., 50Ω on a 100Ω rheostat), you can put in only half the power, too! (If it was a 300W rheostat, you wouldn't put in more than 150W in this condition.) This restriction most often gets people in trouble when they have a constant output voltage supply, and a rheostat as the variable load. Idly twirling the rheostat's knob in such a setup is not advisable. The best solution here is to put a fixed power resistor in series with the rheostat, so that even if it were set to 0Ω, it wouldn't dissipate too much power. The math is straightforward; don't be too lazy to do it right.

Energy–Resistance Chart

Energy per ohm [J/ohm or (W·s)/ohm]	Resistance (ohms)									
	EGS-1 RS-$\frac{1}{4}$ G-1 per ohm	EGS-2 RS-$\frac{1}{2}$ G-2	EGS-3 RS-1A G-3	RS-1B	RH-5 ESS-2B RS-2B G-5	RS-2C RS-2C	RH/PH-10 G-6 G-8	RH-25 EGS-10 RS-5 RS-5-69 G-10	RS-7 G-12	RH-50 ESS-10 RS-10 RS-10-38 G-15
13.9×10^{-6}	3480	4920	10.4K	15K	24.5K	32.3K	47.1K	90.90K	154K	265K
20.3×10^{-6}	2589	3659	7580	11.4K	18.69K	24.19K	31.79K	69.40K	1114.9K	197K
28.7×10^{-6}	1999	2829	5840	7960	14.19K	18.29K	26.99K	51.70K	8K	152K
39.5×10^{-6}	1549	2189	4630	6190	10.89K	13.69K	20.69K	40.40K	68.59K	111K
53.1×10^{-6}	1239	1749	3630	5280	8600	11.39K	16.69K	31.40K	54.39K	93.50K
70.0×10^{-6}		1414	2920	4280	6980	9250	13.59K	25.90K	44.19K	75.50K
90.6×10^{-6}	1000	1149	2740	3510	6550	7560	11.09K	24.50K	36.79K	71.50K
145×10^{-6}	670	947	1960	2870	4650	6260	8910	17.30K	29.50K	50.60K
221×10^{-6}	492	684	1420	2060	3370	4560	6570	12.70K	20.59K	37.40K
324×10^{-6}	355	502	1040	1510	2460	3270	4820	9220	15.69K	26.90K
460×10^{-6}	272	384	792	1160	1860	2480	3640	7000	11.89K	20.40K
632×10^{-6}	206	291	615	909	1340	1920	2840	5460	9240	15.70K
850×10^{-6}	167	236	487	713	1150	1530	2260	4310	7320	12.40K
1.12×10^{-3}	131	186	393	572	935	1201	1800	3850	5900	10.0K
2.07×10^{-3}	96.3	136	283	415	571	910	1250	2840	4260	7540
3.54×10^{-3}	65.1	92.0	192	255	454	601	875	1690	2870	4920
5.67×10^{-3}	45.7	64.5	134	196	313	424	617	1160	2030	3460
8.65×10^{-3}	33.2	47.0	97.7	142	227	307	444	843	1470	2510
12.7×10^{-3}	23.8	33.6	71.1	103	168	222	310	622	1073	1840
20.4×10^{-3}	17.9	25.3	51.8	75.8	122	163	237	447	777	1340
33.2×10^{-3}	12.2	17.2	36.1	52.8	85.5	113	165	320	544	932
56.7×10^{-3}	8.22	11.6	24.2	34.6	57.8	76.3	111	215	364	618
55.3×10^{-3}	6.06	8.566	16.9	25.6	42.1	55.5	70.3	156	263	451
90×10^{-3}	4.47	6.32	12.3	19.4	31.6	40.5	51.0	116	201	343
0.153	2.98	4.07	8.52	13.1	21.1	27.9	40.8	78.5	133	229
0.245	2.18	3.09	6.28	9.19	14.8	19.6	28.6	55.4	95.0	160
0.374	1.50	2.13	4.57	6.49	10.8	14.2	21.0	40.2	68.2	117
0.589	1.12	1.59	3.27	4.89	7.86	10.3	14.9	22.0	49.0	84.1
0.9443	0.780	1.10	2.31	3.13	5.46	7.22	10.6	20.0	34.4	59.3
1.52	0.542	0.773	1.61	2.35	3.80	5.13	7.40	14.1	24.2	41.5
2.46	0.383	0.538	1.13	1.67	2.69	3.56	5.47	10.11	17.2	29.4
3.76	0.271	0.394	0.829	1.22	1.99	2.61	3.81	7.36	12.4	21.4
5.98			0.591	0.861	1.41	1.84	2.15	5.24	8.87	15.1
9.77										11.29
6.57	0.178	0.280	0.423	0.644	0.999	1.36	2.00	3.52	5.49	7.09
16.6	0.105	0.121	0.210	0.366						

Figure 3.1 Dale's guide to derating power wirewound resistors. (From Ref. 1, p. 5.)

Energy per ohm [J/ohm or (W·s)/ohm]	EGS-1 RS-G-1 per ohm	EGS-2 RS-$\frac{1}{2}$ G-2	EGS-3 RS-1A G-3	RS-1B	RH-5 ESS-2B RS-2B G-5	RS-2C RS-2C	RH/PH-10 G-6 G-8	RH-25 EGS-10 RS-5 RS-5-69 G-10	RS-7 G-12	RH-50 ESS-10 RS-10 RS-10-38 G-15
					Resistance (ohms)					
20.9					0.529	0.784	1.04			
8.04								2.01	3.19	5.50
20.9			0.170	0.259	0.370	0.499	0.675	1.27	1.46	3.69
33.2								0.639	0.984	1.86
42.2			0.081	0.114						
83.8					0.189	0.259	0.344			
25.1								0.484	0.697	1.45
67.8					0.099	0.129	0.179	0.329	0.514	0.949
169					0.063	0.079	0.100	0.209	0.319	0.579
335								0.139	0.209	0.399

Figure 3.1   (*Continued*)

Noninductive Wirewound Resistors

As mentioned, resistors have inductance too; it's not usually of any concern unless you want to use one for a current sensor, and decide that the power dissipation calls for a wire-wound device. Because they are wound with wire, resistors of this type can have inductance so large that at typical power supply switching frequency, the inductive reactance is larger than the resistance, which then gives nonsense readings of current.

There is an alternative here: some manufacturers produce a special type of wirewound resistor that has very low inductance (although not zero) by specially winding the wire—of course, these resistors cost a bit more.

Shunts

When you go to really high current (and still don't want to use a current transformer, perhaps because there is DC current involved) you will want to use a shunt, which is a big piece of metal with an almost zero temperature coefficient (manganin) attached to heavy-duty brass terminal blocks. Shunts come in any size you could ever want: the author once had a 1500A job that could have had another life as a boat anchor. However, in addition to resistance, shunts also have inductance, which is very limiting again. As an example, consider a 100A shunt that produces 100mV at full current (100mV and 50mV at full current are the two standard types). It obviously has a resistance of $100mV/100A = 1m\Omega$. But the metal itself is about an inch long, which corresponds to about 20nH. So the transfer function of this device has a zero at a frequency of $f = 1m\Omega/(2\pi \times 20nH) = 8kHz$. All you can do here directly is get a shunt that produces a higher voltage (this increases R) or one that consists of multiple stacked pieces of metal, which reduces L. Chapter 7, on monitoring, shows a technique for differential amplification of the signal from a shunt that removes the effect of its inductance.

Using a Trace as a Resistor

Of course a trace is just a piece of copper, so it has some resistance, too. Sometimes, you don't need very accurate current sensing, perhaps for a converter's overcurrent limit. A trace might work just fine in such a case: it's there anyway, so there are no additional losses, and it doesn't cost anything. Of course, the resistance is only as accurate as the trace is cut, and copper has a temperature coefficient of 0.4%/°C.

Practical Note The resistance of a trace is approximately given by the formula:

$$R = 0.5\text{m}\Omega \; \frac{\text{length}}{\text{width}} \; (1 \text{ oz. copper})$$

at room temperature. Two-ounce copper is half this, etc.

CAPACITORS AND THEIR USAGE

There are quite a number of different capacitors used in power supplies, and each type has its own idiosyncrasies. It's really not possible to use only one type of capacitor; different kinds must be used in different applications if you're going to have a successful design. We'll cover some of the main points, paralleling the selection guide presented in Table 3.2.

Types of Capacitors

One common type of capacitor is the electrolytic capacitor used for the input or output of a supply. There are a variety of choices available. The most common (and cheapest) is the aluminum electrolytic. (You'll find that some people mean "aluminum electrolytic" when they just say "electrolytic.") There are also tantalum electrolytic capacitors, which are available in solid and wet varieties. The aluminums are available in the widest variety of values and voltages and can have gigantic values (millifarads, and hundreds of volts) but

TABLE 3.2   Brief Capacitor Selection Guide

Type	Suggested Applications
Aluminum electrolytic	Use when large capacitance is needed and size is unimportant, such as input and output capacitors on a converter.
Tantalum electrolytic	Use for moderately large capacitance, such as input and output capacitors on a converter.
Ceramic	Use for timing and signal applications.
Multilayer ceramic	Use for lowest ESR (e.g., in parallel with an electrolytic at the input or output of a converter).
Plastic	Use for high dV/dt, such as in quasi-resonant converters.

they are correspondingly gigantic in size. Tantalums have substantially better high frequency performance than aluminum, but cost more and are limited to about 100V and a few hundred microfarads. Nowadays, the best choice for a medium-power power supply may be to have an aluminum as the input capacitor for a supply, and a tantalum chip as the output. (Chips of course have much smaller capacitance and voltage than discretes.)

Then there are ceramic capacitors. These are used for timing and bypass. The ordinary variety come in a range from a few picofarads to 1μF. But also on the verge of affordability is the MLC (multilayer ceramic) variety, which has extremely low ESR and much larger values available, up to a few hundred microfarads.

Let's also mention plastic capacitors, particularly polypropylene, which are used in circuits that have very high dV/dt values (but see below) such as in quasi-resonant converters.

Standard Values

Not at all like resistors, there are only a few standard values for capacitors, (1.0, 1.2, 1.5, 1.8, 2.2, 2.7, 3.3, 4.7, and 6.8, with an occasional 5.6 and 8.2). So when you're calculating a time constant or a loop compensation value, select one of these values and adjust your resistors to get the values needed—it'll be a lot cheaper than trying to synthesize that 347pF cap.

There are some practical limits to how small a capacitor you can usefully use, just as we found for maximum value resistors, and for the same reason. Again, two surfaces in close proximity form a capacitor, and for very tiny discrete capacitors, the parallel capacitance that is formed can swamp out the value you're trying to use. So again,

> **Practical Note** Avoid using capacitors smaller than 22pF unless special precautions are taken.

Tolerance

Capacitor initial tolerances are typically ±20%, and can be substantially worse for electrolytics. You need to look very carefully at any electrolytic, to verify that it's going to be OK in production. Examine the tolerance over the temperature range even more carefully: some types lose 80% of their capacitance at −40°C!

ESR and Power Dissipation

Modern manufacturers of electrolytics specify ESR (equivalent series resistance) of their caps, and you should try to use only those that specify it at a high frequency, such as 100kHz.

> **Practical Note** *You will have no idea what the ESR of a cap is at 100kHz from data given at 120Hz.* This ESR, in addition to being a function of frequency, also depends on temperature. At −25°C, the ESR can be almost triple its value at 25°C! To come close to predicting capacitor ESR, you need data at least within an order of magnitude of your intended operating frequency.

EXAMPLE

I have an output ripple current of $1A_{pp}$ at 100kHz, and I need an output voltage ripple of $50mV_{pp}$. First off, I have a charge that could be as large as $1A \times (1/100kHz) = 10\mu C$, so even ignoring ESR, I need a capacitance of $C = Q/V = 10\mu C/50mV = 200\mu F$. Let's assume, then, that I'm going to use at least two $100\mu F$ electrolytics. Typically, a capacitor this size may have an ESR of something like $100m\Omega$ at room temperature. To get down to 50mV, I need an ESR of $50mV/1A(=50m\Omega)$, which is the two caps in parallel. *But*, at −25°C, the caps have more like 300mΩ ESR each, so I actually need six caps. With six caps, then, the ripple due to ESR is 50mV at temperature, and the ripple due to capacitance is only about 17mV; since resistance and capacitance are out of phase, the total ripple will be about $I_{total} = [(50mV)^2 + (17mV)^2]^{1/2} = 53mV$. Clearly, when you're designing a bulk filter, ESR can often be more important than total capacitance.

Aging

Although the matter of aging is easy to overlook, those specs that say "life 1000 hours" really mean something on electrolytics. If you are going to run a supply at elevated temperatures or for many years, you need to pick electrolytics that are designated as 2000h types at least, or better, 5000h. What happens is that as you approach the age rating, the capacitance goes down, and your ripple goes up until the supply ceases to meet spec. This is not an old wives' tale, either. You may not be about to wait around a year to see how bad it gets, but accelerated life tests quickly show up the differences between capacitors.

Fortunately, though, the life of the capacitor doubles with every 10°C drop in temperature, so a type rated 2000h at 85°C will last $2000h \times 2^6 = 128,000h = 16$ years at 25°C average temperature.

> **Practical Note** Make sure you use the *average* temperature the supply sees over its lifetime for this calculation, not the maximum temperature the supply will see, nor the rated temperature—otherwise you'll find there are no caps available that will meet spec over life!

dV/dt

A different type of usage of capacitor that is growing more common is the use of a metallized plastic cap for a quasi-resonant converter. In this application, there can be substantial dissipation in the ESR of the cap, and this is in fact the limiting factor on the capacitor size. Whereas electrolytics frequently are rated with a ripple current (which is basically determined by the ESR I^2R loss and the thermal characteristics of the package), plastic caps have the equivalent rating in terms of dV/dt [since charge $Q = C \times V$, current $I = dQ/dt = C(dV/dt)$]. To be sure that your cap is adequately rated requires measurement in-circuit. Whether you measure the current through the cap or its dV/dt depends on the circuit configuration—you may need a large-bandwidth differential amplifier to measure accurately dV/dt, but you need a loop to measure current, which can introduce unwanted inductance. In any case, make sure you get a capacitor rated for the dV/dt you're applying. Otherwise the capacitor can self-destruct!

Putting Caps in Series

If I can't get the voltage rating needed for a cap, how about putting two (or more) capacitors in series? Remember that two capacitors in series form a (reactive) voltage divider, and so if one is smaller than the other, it will carry a greater percentage of the total voltage. This sort of design is not really recommended, but if you need it, try putting a resistor in parallel with each cap, as shown in Figure 3.2. This will tend to balance the voltages.

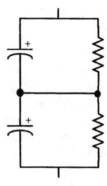

Figure 3.2 Practical method for placing capacitors in series.

SCHOTTKY DIODES

Schottkys are great as output rectifiers, because they have a low forward voltage and no reverse recovery time, right? Although it's true that they have no reverse recovery time *as such*, they often do have substantial *capacitance* from anode to cathode. This capacitance has to be charged and discharged every time the voltage across the schottky changes (it's largest when the schottky has almost no voltage across it). Current flowing into this capacitance looks a whole lot like reverse recovery current of an ordinary rectifier. So depending on your circuit, there can be times when it's less lossy to use an ultrafast rectifier than a schottky.

You might also take note that the anode–cathode capacitance, although low-Q, can still resonate with stray inductances in the circuit—this property is used intentionally in some resonant designs. So it may be necessary to add a snubber across the schottky, dissipating even more power.

> **Practical Note** Schottkys are very leaky at high temperatures and as the applied reverse voltage increases toward its rating. This leakage can look like a short on a forward's secondary, and indeed the leakage current is the main reason that no one uses germanium rectifiers today. So as a practical limit, you shouldn't try to use a schottky at more than about three-quarters of its rated reverse voltage, nor with a die temperature above about 110°C.

Given this tip, what about using something like a 100V schottky? Look carefully at the specs—as of 1996, the high voltage schottky tended to have a forward voltage comparable to that of a regular rectifier, so you might not be buying much with such a device.

RECTIFIER DIODES

Someone has just announced to you, the design engineer, that the output of that 12V rail is going to need 1.6A, not 1A. Rather than try to get a new part, and worrying about whether it will fit in the old holes, we'll try to just parallel up two of the old 1A diodes, OK? After all, our buddy John says he did it many years ago, and it worked out. Bad idea! As diodes get hotter, their forward voltage decreases, so the one that is conducting the most current at the start will get hotter, have a lower V_f, and conduct yet more, and so on, until it tries to conduct the whole current and fails—positive feedback, remember? So although it is possible to parallel rectifiers by very careful thermal management (i.e. by ensuring that there is minimal thermal resistance between them), *in practice*, these schemes never work out very well.

> **Practical Note** Bite the bullet and get a single diode that can handle the whole current.

Although you can get single diodes of almost any size, it's worth noting that MOSFETs *do* share current, because as *their* temperature goes up, their resistance goes up too. Thus a FET carrying more than its fair share of current will have a higher drop than a parallel device, and will thus correct itself—a negative feedback. This is one of the attractive features of synchronous rectifiers.

Reverse Recovery

We've mentioned that schottky diodes don't have a reverse recovery time; all other diodes, however, do. That is, after a diode has been conducting current in the forward direction, it will be able to conduct current in the opposite direction (yes, from cathode to anode) for a short time afterwards, and this time is called the reverse recovery time. Figure 3.3 illustrates this anomaly, which clearly would be very bad for converter efficiency and

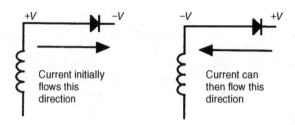

Figure 3.3 After current flows from anode to cathode, applying a reverse voltage to the diode can cause current to flow from cathode to anode.

must be avoided. There are different grades of diode (fast, ultrafast, etc.), depending on speed of recovery.

> **Practical Note** Converters are almost always going to use either ultrafast diodes or schottkys in their output stages.

Not mentioned in the practical note was synchronous rectification. The reason is that MOSFET body diodes usually have very slow reverse recovery, often about 1μs. They are thus not suitable for rectification, and this is why a schottky is usually paralleled with a MOSFET synchronous rectifier: the schottky takes almost all the current during the time the MOSFET is off, which means that the body diode doesn't have to reverse recover.

Is Faster Better?

This certainly *seems* like a generic rule, for after all, a diode that recovers faster will have lower losses. In the case of a rectifier used in an off-line bridge, however, it is not a good idea to use an ultrafast rectifier. The problem is that the fast recovery time also generates fast edges: read EMI. So for this particular case, your best bet is to use that old-fashioned regular bridge rectifier with a recovery time of 5–10μs. After all, it recovers only 120 times a second, so who cares if it's a little slow?

TRANSISTORS: BJTs

Pulse Current

If you're using power bipolars at all, you are presumably aware that they take substantially more care and attention than is required in designing with MOSFETs. Let's talk about some performance aspects of BJTs that are often not mentioned in data sheets. First, many small-signal BJTs, and power bipolars not designed specifically for switching, tell you their maximum DC collector current but don't give any curves or numbers relating to <u>pulse</u> currents.

> **Practical Note** When the manufacturer doesn't (or won't) give a pulse rating for a bipolar, a reasonable guess is that the device can take twice the rated DC current for a pulse. If this were based on the fusing current of the bond wire, you would think it would depend on the time; in fact, the limit seems rather to be set by localized current hogging. You'll be safest not to exceed the 2× limit even with short current pulses.

How Much Beta Can I Get?

The beta of a BJT (not referring to darlingtons, now) depends on all sorts of parameters—collector current, aging, temperature, not to mention initial tolerance. If you figure up all these parameters together, you may find that your bipolar has almost no gain left at all!

> **Practical Note** If you want to make a safe design, that is, one you don't have to sweat over in worst-case analysis, assume that your BJTs have a minimum beta of 10, regardless of what the data sheets seem to say.

Don't Forget Collector Leakage Current

And don't forget that this current, too, increases with the "double for each 10°C" rule. I recently saw a design that used a 4.7MΩ pull-up on the collector of a bipolar. It seemed to work in the lab, but as soon as it saw any sort of temperature rise above ambient, the collector voltage went to zero! In practice, you had better plan on a leakage of up to 1mA, depending on the size of the device.

Emitter—Base Zenering—Is It Bad?

Another limit on BJT performance is the emitter–base voltage V_{eb}, that is, how much negative voltage can be applied to the base of a bipolar with respect to its emitter. The manufacturer will usually say this limit is 5V or 6V. But what really happens if this value is exceeded? The base–emitter junction is a diode, and if you apply enough voltage to it, it will zener. (You can test this in the lab with a current-limiting resistor.) You might actually want to do this in a converter, because turning off a BJT involves sweeping out the current from the base region; the more negative the voltage on the base, the faster you can turn off the transistor. The limit, of course, is that the fastest possible turnoff occurs when the base–emitter is zenering.

> **Practical Note** You can apply any voltage emitter to base you care to, as long as you don't exceed the power rating of the die; that is, the real limitation on zenering is on the product $V_{eb} \times I_{eb}$. In practice this means ensuring that there is some sort of base resistor, to limit the current. Manufacturers typically refuse to guarantee this as a specification, but that's what they will tell you privately.

Fast Turnoff

Better than sweeping the base charge out fast is ensuring that there isn't too much base charge in the first place. Unfortunately, the easiest tactic, running the transistor at nearly its actual beta, conflicts with the assumption that your transistor is going to have a minimum beta of 10, much lower than the typical beta. If you need to have fast turnoff, it may be worthwhile to try a Baker clamp, which is about the best you can do, although it dissipates some extra power.

The Baker clamp (Figure 3.4) works as follows. When the transistor is on, the base is one diode drop above the emitter, and so the driving source is two diode drops above the emitter. The extra diode from the driving source to the collector then assures that the collector is approximately one diode drop above the emitter, which is to say, the BJT is almost, but not quite, saturated. It can thus be turned off quickly; whether this fast turnoff decreases the circuit losses enough to compensate for the increased losses due to the increased collector–emitter voltage depends on the particulars of a given design. (Observe that these statements are only approximations, since the currents and the V_f values of the various diodes differ.)

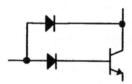

Figure 3.4 A Baker clamp prevents deep saturation, speeding turnoff.

TRANSISTORS: MOSFETs

Don't Confuse JFETs and MOSFETs

When everyone used bipolars and MOSFETs were new, it was fairly common to get the terms mixed up. Just to be sure: JFETs are small-signal devices with high on-resistance frequently used in rf-type work; MOSFETs, and specifically power MOSFETs, are what are used nowadays for power applications.

p-Channel and n-Channel

Most designs use n-channel MOSFETs, and if there's no indication otherwise, you can simply assume that all MOSFETs in a design are n-channel. One of the reasons p-channels are less popular than n-channels is that p-channels have higher on-resistance for the same voltage and die area, making them more expensive.

Still p-channels have a certain utility: they are turned off when their gate–source voltage is below a threshold (similarly to n-channels), but they are on when the gate voltage is <u>below</u> the source voltage, that is, negative. So in practice, they are used by attaching the source of the p-channel to a voltage (e.g., 5V) and letting the gate be at 5V to turn it off, or pulling it to ground to turn it on. The advantage is that whereas turning on an n-channel would require a voltage *higher* than 5V (such as 12V), the p-channel needs no extra supply, being turned on simply by pulling its gate to ground.

Bidirectional Conduction

Although MOSFETs are used routinely in synchronous rectification, perhaps it should be mentioned that they can conduct current in both direction, drain-to-source as well as source-to-drain, not counting the body diode. Applying a voltage from gate to source (for n-channel FETs) enables them to conduct bidirectionally. In synchronous rectification, this "reverse direction" conduction is explicitly used to short out the body diode, since the product of the current and the $R_{DS,on}$ of the FET is much smaller than the V_f of the body diode.

Calculating Losses: Conduction Loss

There are three sources of power dissipation in switching applications of power MOSFETs; the first to be discussed is conduction loss. When a MOSFET is fully on, it has a resistance from drain to source, and this dissipates power based on how much current goes through it, $P = I^2 R_{DS,on}$. However, you need to be aware that this resistance goes up with temperature [typically $R(T) = R(25°C) \times 1.007 \exp(T - 25°C)$]; so to find the actual junction temperature, you have to calculate the total power dissipated, figure out what temperature this causes (by multiplying by the thermal resistance), then recalculate the power based on the new temperature's resistance, and so on iteratively until the calculation has converged.

> **Practical Note:** A single iteration of this calculation is almost always good enough, because of limited knowledge of the actual thermal resistance. If it doesn't converge after one iteration you're probably dissipating more power than the device can take!

While on the subject of $R_{DS,on}$, you might take note that "logic-level" FETs are a little bit of a cheat. While their gate–threshold voltage is indeed lower than for a regular FET, their on-resistance is also higher than it would be if the gate were driven to a normal level. Typical logic-level FETs may have twice the $R_{DS,on}$ at 4.5V V_{GS} as at 10V.

Calculating Losses: Gate Charge Loss

A second source of loss, though not lost in the MOSFET, is due to the MOSFET having a rather substantial equivalent gate capacitor. (The losses are in whatever devices and resistors drive the gate.) Although the capacitance is actually a highly nonlinear function of gate voltage, many modern data sheets give a total gate charge Q_g, required to bring the gate voltage to a certain level V. Power lost by driving this charge into the gate at the switching frequency f_s is then $P = Q_g V f_s$. Note that there is no factor of 0.5.

> **Practical Note** If the gate voltage you actually drive the gate to differs from the one specified in the data sheet, it is probably a reasonable approximation to multiply the specified gate charge by the ratio of the two voltages; this works best if the voltage you are using is higher than that in the data sheet. (For the cognoscenti, the limiting factor in the approximation is how much charge is required to charge the Miller capacitance.)

Calculating Losses: Switching Loss

The third source of loss in switching MOSFETs, and the second that dissipates into the MOSFET, is switching loss. Whenever a (nonresonant) transistor turns off or on, it simultaneously has both voltage on it and current through it, resulting in power dissipation.

Practical Note An estimate of the switching losses can be had by assuming that the voltage is a linear function of time while the current is constant, in which case the power lost is $P = I_{pk}V_{pk}t_sf_s/2$ for discontinuous conduction mode converters, and double this for continuous conduction mode, where t_s is the transition time of the MOSFET drain-to-source voltage from on-to-off (and from off-to-on for continuous conduction converters); this is why driving the gate harder results in lower switching losses.

In summary, total losses associated with switching power MOSFETs are due to conduction loss, gate charge loss, and switching loss, of which only the first and last are dissipated in the FET. You can get a pretty good idea of the losses in the transistors by doing these calculations. Then by using the thermal resistance of the package, you should know whether the FET will be cool or hot or very hot; if it's not pretty close to what you calculate, there's something wrong!

The Need for Gate Resistors

You (hopefully) always put a gate resistor in series with the gate of a MOSFET. But if you have two FETs in parallel, can you still use just one resistor, maybe of half the value?

Practical Note You need an individual gate resistor for each MOSFET, regardless of whether the devices are in parallel, and even if they have some other current-limiting part, such as a bead, in series. The reason is that MOSFETs have both capacitance (gate–source) and inductance (in the leads). This potentially forms an underdamped resonant tank, and paralleled MOSFETs have been observed to oscillate at 100MHz! If you're using a digital oscilloscope and don't know to look for these oscillations, you may not even see them, but they can be lossy, and of course they wreak havoc in EMI. The gate resistor acts to limit the current the source has to source or sink to the gate, but its real significance is to damp the oscillations.

Maximum Gate Voltage

One last thing to avoid. On occasion people get the bright idea that to reduce switching loss, they're going to <u>really</u> drive that gate and use a 40V source or the like to ensure that it charges past the gate threshold voltage very fast. Don't even think about it. You end up having to stick a clamping zener diode on the gate to prevent it from exceeding its maximum voltage rating (always 20V nowadays), and that then throws away more power than you could possibly have hoped to save. The right solution is to get a gate driver with lower output impedance. In bare die form, power MOSFETs have been turned on in 10ns with the right driver!

OP AMPS

This section talks about the main parameters that can affect whether you get the anticipated operation out of your op amp design: offsets, limits on achievable gains, gain–bandwidth, phase shifts, and slew rates. Regardless of your application, you need to be familiar with these nonidealities.

Offsets: Input Offset Voltage

What's the story with offsets? Let's try to untangle how to use these specifications on op amps, and also give tips as to when they're important.

Consider Figure 3.5, the schematic for a noninverting amplifier with a gain of 10. (To make the discussion easy to follow, the input is grounded, but the effects of the offsets would be exactly the same if instead a nonzero voltage were used as the input.) Since its input signal is ground, we might naively expect its output to be zero volts also. But now consider that the LM2902 has a typical input offset voltage V_{os} of 2mV. (Plus or minus is always implied, if not explicitly stated.) What this means is that even with no input, the noninverting terminal will see (something between plus and minus) 2mV. Of course, the same thing applies at the inverting terminal when the op amp is used as an inverter. This 2mV gets amplified just like an ordinary, desired signal, and so at the output will appear as (something between plus and minus) 20mV. This signal is additive, so if we had applied 100mV at the noninverting terminal, at the output we would have, instead of exactly $100\text{mV} \times 10 = 1\text{V}$, somewhere between $(100\text{mV} - 2\text{mV}) \times 10 = 980\text{mV}$ and $(100\text{mV} + 2\text{mV}) \times 10 = 1.02\text{V}$. This value is clearly independent of the absolute values of the resistors used; it is dependent only on the gain. Thus, input offset voltage is important whenever small signals are to be measured and/or when high gain is needed.

Offsets: Input Offset Current

The same schematic (Figure 3.5) explains about input offset current, which is very similar to input offset voltage. Since the inputs to an op amp are not of infinite impedance, applying a voltage to them causes them to draw (or source) some current. The LM2902 has a typical I_{io} of 5nA. This means that the noninverting (or inverting) terminal will see (something between plus and minus) 5nA being pulled from the voltage source *different from the current being pulled by the other terminal*. In the case of the schematic, we are

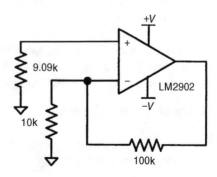

Figure 3.5 Op amp circuit for discussion of offset errors.

pulling 5nA from ground through a 9.09kΩ resistor, and so the noninverting terminal sees a voltage of $V = (5nA) \times (9.09k\Omega) = 45\mu V$ (again, this could just as well be $-45\mu V$). This then is amplified by the gain of 10, resulting in $450\mu V$ at the output terminal; this is in addition to the offset caused by the input offset voltage.

In this example, the input offset voltage was much more important for errors than the input offset current; but since the error due to the current is determined by the absolute values of the resistances used, in addition to the gain, it is clear that for large source resistances, the offset current becomes more important than the offset voltage.

Offsets: Input Bias Current

Now for input bias current, which is current pulled by <u>both</u> the inverting and noninverting terminals by the same amount. (It may help to think of input bias current as common mode current, and input offset current as normal mode current.) The LM2902 has a typical I_b of 90nA. The op amp schematic of Figure 3.5 has the same input resistance for both terminals $(100k\Omega\|10k\Omega = 9.09k\Omega)$, so the effect of pulling equal amounts of current from both is none. Suppose, however, that instead of 9.09kΩ to ground, the noninverting terminal had 19.09kΩ to ground. Then there is a difference of 10kΩ in the input resistances, and this results in an offset of $V = 90nA \times 10k\Omega = 900\mu V$, which gets multiplied by the gain to give an output error of 9mV, comparable in size with the error due to the offset voltage. This is the reason for trying to use the same input resistance for both terminals, even when they're virtually grounded.

What to Do About Offsets

To sum up, the output error of an op amp due to offsets is calculable as

$$V = [V_{os} + (I_{os} \times R) + (I_b \times \Delta R)]\text{gain}$$

where R is the average of the two input resistances, and ΔR is the difference of the two. Since gain is determined by operating needs, minimizing the error must involve three actions:

1. Ensuring that the resistor values being used are limited to the smallest feasible values; this limits the effects of I_{os} but also results in a need for greater currents from the sources being used to drive the signals.
2. Ensuring that resistor values to the terminals are matched eliminates the effects of I_b.
3. Minimizing V_{os}, which can be accomplished only through selection of the proper type of op amp.

Unfortunately, a low V_{os} is also invariably accompanied by a higher operating current of the op amp, a lower op amp bandwidth, or both. There are thus engineering trade-offs to be made in selecting the proper op amp for an application.

Limits on Large Resistances

Sometimes you want a large gain from an op amp and you might try something like the bad example shown in Figure 3.6.

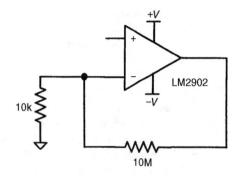

Figure 3.6 A circuit that won't work very well.

Let's assume that the op amp has adequate gain–bandwidth for your purpose (probably this isn't true; see below)—are you really going to get a gain of 1000? Probably not. The trouble is not with the op amp, or with any of the components—as explained in the section about resistors, it's rather with the PCB on which you mount them. For various reasons, the leakage around a resistor may exceed the amount of current being supplied through the 10MΩ resistor, effectively shunting it with a lower value.

Practical Note It is usually not effective to use a resistor larger than 1MΩ on a normal PCB, at least without taking special precautions. If you must have this gigantic gain, and can't reduce the 10kΩ source resistor to a 1kΩ, try instead the circuit shown in Figure 3.7.

The circuit of Figure 3.7 works as follows. Suppose you have 10mV at the noninverting input. Then the op amp forces the inverting input to have 10mV also (ignoring offsets in this calculation). With 10mV across 10kΩ, there must be a current flowing of 1μA. This current has to come from point A through the 90kΩ, so there must be a drop across that resistor of 1μA × 90kΩ = 90mV, which added to the voltage at the inverting terminal means that node A has to be at 10mV + 90mV = 100mV. Now 100mV at node A means that there must be a current of 100μA flowing into the 1kΩ resistor. This current (plus the 1μA flowing into the 90kΩ) must come from the output through the

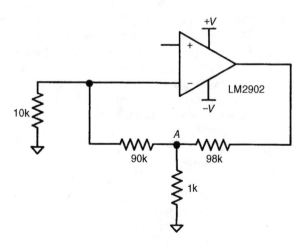

Figure 3.7 Practical circuit to get a gain of 1000.

98kΩ, which is therefore dropping $98k\Omega \times 101\mu A = 9.9V$, and the output voltage is this plus the voltage on node A, for a total of $9.9V + 100mV = 10V$, a gain of $10V/10mV = 1000$. No resistor in this circuit is larger than 100kΩ.

Gain Bandwidth

Suppose I use an op amp to construct a gain-of-10 amplifier. Suppose next that I use it to amplify a sine wave (ignoring slew rate for the moment, see below), and I keep increasing the frequency of this sine wave. At some frequency, the op amp itself will run out of gain and the output of the amplifier will stop being 10 times larger than the input. If I increase the frequency further, at some point the output will have the same amplitude as the input. This frequency is independent of the external components used to set the gain, and is called the gain bandwidth of the op amp.

One of the places you have to watch out for this parameter occurs when you use an error amplifier in a power supply. For example, the result of a calculation on closing the control loop, discussed in detail in Chapter 6, might be that you need a gain of 300 at a frequency of 20kHz. Well, a gain of 300 isn't so bad, and of course most op amps will work well at 20kHz; unfortunately, the two parameters together imply that the op amp must have a gain bandwidth of $300 \times 20kHz = 6MHz$, which may be beyond many of the error amps included in typical PWM ICs. This problem becomes quite noticeable as converter bandwidths reach into the tens of kilohertz. The symptom of having inadequate bandwidth in an error amp may be something like an instability in the converter, even though you have correctly compensated the loop.

Phase Shift

Even beyond gain bandwidth limitations of common op amps, there is an additional problem: as the sine wave frequency injected into the op amp in the thought experiment in the preceding section is increased, the output sine wave becomes more and more phase-shifted from the original. In the case of an op amp that is being used as the error amplifier in a converter, this translates to extra (unexpected!) phase shift in the loop, reducing phase margin. This too can cause a loop to be unstable even though apparently correctly compensated.

This is unpleasant enough, but worse yet, very few manufacturers give even typical numbers or curves for phase shift as a function of frequency, to say nothing of trying to do a worst case. It turns out that the phase shift is very dependent on the internal construction of the op amp; it is *not the case* that op amps with a higher gain bandwidth product necessarily have less phase shift at a given frequency than those with lower gain bandwidth! In fact, the only practical method for deciding whether a given op amp is going to give excess phase shift for a particular application is to measure it; for example, configure the op amp as a unity gain follower, and use a network analyzer, as described in Chapter 4.

Slew Rate

The last limitation of op amps we consider is the speed with which they can change from one output voltage to another. In the description of the gain-of-10 amplifier in the discussion of gain bandwidth product, it was assumed that the input signal was tiny.

Suppose instead that the input was $1V_{pp}$; then the output would have to be $10V_{pp}$. If, for example, the frequency of the sine wave was 200kHz, then in one quarter of the period, $(\frac{1}{4}) \times (1/200kHz) = 1.25\mu s$, the output has to go from 0V to maximum, a change of 10V; this implies that the op amp needs a slew rate of at least $10V/1.25\mu s = 8V/\mu s$, to use the common units. Many common op amps, particularly low power devices, can't slew this fast.

When is this important? One place, again, is in high bandwidth converters. As discussed in Chapter 6, it's not enough for a converter to be small-signal stable, it also has to have adequate response to a transient. When a transient occurs, the output voltage of the error amp has to change levels. If the device happens not to have the slew rate needed to do this, you will be left puzzling about why your fast converter is so slow.

In summary, then, gain bandwidth product and phase shift for an op amp used as an error amp are related to the small-signal performance of the converter; slew rate is related to the large-signal, transient performance.

COMPARATORS

Hysteresis

The same offsets and biases discussed for op amps apply in exactly the same way for comparators. Comparators are unique however, in that their outputs can be expected to be either high or low, not anything in between (No, *don't* try to use that spare op amp as a comparator, or vice versa! Distinct parts are built for a reason.) Actually, since comparators are real devices, on occasion they oscillate between these two states, sometimes at surprisingly high frequencies. The usual reason for this behavior is that the comparators don't have hysteresis. This can cause all sorts of problems that take time to debug.

Practical Note Always use hysteresis on comparators unless they are intended to run a latch: that is, if the first time the comparator trips, it is intended to cause something from which there is no recovery.

EXAMPLE

For small amounts of hysteresis, you can easily guess hysteresis values. For the circuit of Figure 3.8, since $1k\Omega/100k\Omega = 0.01$, the amount of hysteresis will be about 1% of the reference voltage.

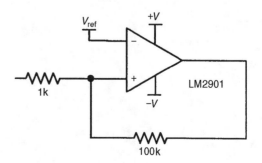

Figure 3.8 It's easy to guess the hysteresis of this comparator.

Output Saturation Voltage

One other unique aspect of comparators is that when they go low, they often don't go to 0V. Inspection of the data sheet of the common LM139 shows that its output is only guaranteed to be 0.7V if it is sinking 6mA. So when designing hysteresis, make sure to check how much current the output is intended to be sinking; if it's more than about 1mA, you need to include the saturation voltage in determining the hysteresis resistor values.

Saturation voltage also is important in driving an NPN transistor from the output of the comparator; at 0.7V a "low" probably will suffice to turn on a base–emitter junction and have the transistor on, so you can't use the comparator to directly drive a bipolar! For this situation, you need a blocking diode and a pull-down base resistor. Figure 3.9 shows an arrangement that will work even in worst case (the worst case of this circuit is analyzed in Chapter 10). When the comparator pulls low, even to only 700mV, the diode is off, keeping the transistor off. The pull-down on the base is needed because the base would otherwise be floating when the diode is reverse-biased, and the transistor might be partially on through leakage currents.

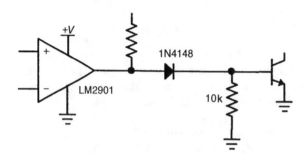

Figure 3.9 How a comparator should be configured to drive a BJT.

REFERENCES

1. *Pulse Handling Capability of Wirewound Resistors*. Dale Electronics, Columbus NE.

Practical Guide
to Instrumentation

INTRODUCTION

If you're like most of us, when you get a new piece of equipment, you play around with the knobs for a while, try it out on some unsuspecting circuitry, and then turn your attention to something more pressing. For items such as fancy oscilloscopes with lots of menus, you may occasionally have to look in the manual to find out where something is. Generally, though, well-designed equipment should be usable intuitively without any special training.

Even so, a number of considerations in the use of equipment and in measuring technique won't be in a manual, simply because they relate not so much to the design of the instrument as to how and when one particular instrument should be used rather than another. These instrumental considerations range from the general issues that apply to all instruments, such as the question of accuracy versus precision, to the specific, such as under what circumstances to distrust your AC power meter. This chapter offers practical guidance on general questions; it doesn't try to tell you how to use your voltmeter.

CALCULATORS AND CALCULATIONS

How Many Digits?

"I added the numbers four times, and here are the four answers."

We smirk when we hear this old chestnut, but in fact a lot of people are guilty of something similar all the time. The question is, How many digits should I write down when I make a measurement? We'll talk about accuracy versus precision in the next section about DVMs; for now, let's assume that your voltmeter is absolutely accurate, so that when it says the voltage is 15.426V you know that it is (for sure) somewhere between 15.4255V and 15.4265V.

Should you write down 15.426V? Or 15.4V? Or maybe just 15V? The answer depends on the purpose of recording the data. If you're checking that an op amp has the proper supply voltage, and you're using that op amp for general purpose only and don't care whether it has 14V or 16V as long as it works, then just writing down 15V is perfectly adequate—if indeed you bother to write it down at all. But the more common case is this: you're measuring both voltage and current, because you want to know power. Let's suppose you're using a handheld meter for the current, and it has only three digits, reading 2.02A. This means that you know the current only to three significant places—it's somewhere between 2.015A and 2.025A. Since in this case your knowledge of the current (three decimal places) is less than your knowledge of the voltage (five decimal places), the current controls your accuracy. *This means that your final answer, power, can be known only to the same three decimal places that your least accurate measurement is known to.* The correct thing to do (in this example) is to write down the voltage measurement to one more decimal place than the current, multiply, and then round off the answer to the three decimal places: $V = 15.43$V, $I = 2.02$A, so $P = 15.43$V $\times$ 2.02A $= 31.1686$W, and the answer recorded should be 31.2W. Pay real close attention here!

The final result of the calculation CAN'T have more digits than the LEAST accurate measurement!

This is because the uncertainty is greatest in the least accurate measurement, and this in turn controls the accuracy with which you can know the answer.

Do I Care?

The question of uncertainty is not just one of those dull things you forgot in high school and have thereafter ignored with impunity. To rub in the point, consider how far off the calculation *could* be. If the voltage and current were *both* at the low end, even though the meters were reading correctly, $P = 15.4255 \times 2.015$A $= 31.08$W; and if both were at the high end, $P = 15.4265$V $\times$ 2.025A $= 31.24$W, a difference of 160mW, *entirely due to the limited number of digits on the meters.* This doesn't seem like a big deal until you realize that you might be trying to measure the efficiency of an efficient converter. If the input power was 33.3W, then the efficiency is somewhere between $\eta = 31.08$W$/33.3$W $= 93.3\%$ and $\eta = 31.24$W$/33.3$W $= 93.8\%$—and this doesn't even include the inaccuracies in the input measurement! The difference between being able to report 94% efficiency rather than 93% efficiency can make or break a project. The correct thing to record is $\eta = 31.17$W$/33.3$W $= 93.6\%$, halfway between the minimum and maximum (note that the extra digit was again held over until the final calculation).

A Closely Related Problem

A closely related problem is not writing down *enough* digits. Maybe there's a little flicker in the last digit of the meter, and anyway there's not much difference between writing down 2.02A and just plain 2A, right? The example above shows that to be able to write down a number representing efficiency of an efficient converter to two digits requires writing down all the measurements to three digits. The reason here is slightly different from that given above: to calculate efficiency, two numbers that are very nearly equal are being divided, and so small inaccuracies in either one make the answer quite inaccurate—because you are presumably quite interested in whether the efficiency is 94% rather than 93%.

One More Problem to Avoid

A rather less common pernicious problem is the casual assumption that your measurement has unlimited precision: as we've emphasized, if a meter says 2.02A, that's what is meant, not 2.020000A! It's the same thing: your meter only has three digits, and there's no way to get a better number out of it by pushing buttons on a calculator. All you can do is get a better meter.

DVMs AND OTHER METERS

Accuracy versus Precision

In the foregoing discussion about how many digits to use in calculations, we assumed that what the meter showed was exactly right—that is, that the meter had *unlimited accuracy*. However, the meters showed only a certain number of digits (in the example, the handheld current meter showed three) and thus had a limited *precision*. But of course real meters have not only limited precision, they also have inaccuracies of various kinds, and problems of both types limit the validity of any measurements you make.

Averaging

It might be tempting to try to get a more accurate measurement in the case of a meter whose last (or several last) digit(s) are flickering by writing down the number several times and then averaging, as in Table 4.1. This idea is fine if you know for sure that the reason that the digits are flickering is due to white noise (random noise)—although in this case a better plan is to suppress the noise with a filter (see below). But if the noise is rather due to a periodic signal, such as an oscillation in the circuit at 1kHz, your meter may be reading the signal at the same point in each cycle, causing a systematic bias in the measurement, as in Figure 4.1. This is exactly the same thing as aliasing in an oscilloscope. In this case, you have an added inaccuracy, and filtering is essential; your "human averaging" is actually degrading the information.

TABLE 4.1   Sample Averaging Data

Trial 1	2.02A
Trial 2	2.06A
Trial 3	2.05A
Trial 4	2.00A
Average:	2.03A

Figure 4.1 If your DVM samples at a frequency related to an AC component of your waveform, you may get false readings.

How to Filter a DVM

To filter a DVM input, it's necessary to know what frequency noise you want to get rid of. Otherwise, you may be filtering the thing you want to measure! As an example of how to successfully filter a signal, suppose you want to filter a 100kHz noise source from a switching supply, and you need to reduce the noise by a factor of 10. This implies that the filter should have a frequency of about 100kHz/10 = 10kHz. This sets the product R times C, but not their individual values. The key here is that R is going to be in series with the input resistance of the meter. Therefore, to maintain a certain accuracy, R must be smaller than the input resistance by that amount. If the input resistance of the meter is 10MΩ, a typical value, and you are trying to achieve 0.1% accuracy, the R you choose for the filter has to be less than 10MΩ × 0.1% = 10kΩ. Completing the example, with R = 10kΩ, the capacitor (see Figure 4.2) will be

$$C = \frac{1}{2\pi \ 10\text{kHz} \ 10\text{k}\Omega} = 1.5\text{nF}.$$

You may want to build up a few of these little circuits on perf boards with a pair of banana jacks on both ends, for easy availability when needed in the lab.

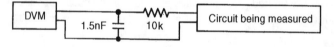

Figure 4.2 A filter for a DVM.

Measuring RMS and DVM Bandwidth

Your DVM updates its display a couple of times per second. However, this information doesn't necessarily have anything to do with its bandwidth, that is, the maximum frequency signal the instrument is able to measure. You find out the bandwidth by looking in the manual, but one thing to check is that the meter has adequate bandwidth for the measurement you're trying to make: if the bandwidth is 1kHz, the meter will certainly read a 10kHz signal as smaller than it really is.

Meters used in AC power measurements are a special case of this potential inadequacy. They frequently have very limited bandwidth, and so if you've attached, for example, a discontinuous flyback converter to the AC line, you can expect to get false readings unless you put a large capacitor in front to smooth the pulsating current.

Of course, putting a large cap in front is exactly the opposite of what you want to do to measure the power factor. In fact, measuring the input power and the power factor of an off-line converter may require two separate measurements, each with its own setup.

Another point to observe with RMS measurements is that many AC meters have a maximum *crest factor* they can tolerate; that is, if the peak (current) is very much higher than the average, they also give false readings—read the specs on this carefully.

Finally, it is worth observing that many types of meter have their internal circuitry somehow upset by high frequency noise, such as that generated by a switching power supply. (Isn't that convenient?) Almost all measurements on a converter are going to require filtering and careful attention to meter limitations.

Measuring Efficiency: Cross-Calibration

Here is a practical method for getting rid of accuracy problems where they are most important, during converter efficiency measurements. In measuring efficiency, you have to measure an input voltage and current, and an output voltage and current. If you were to simply write down the value of a meter reading from each of these four measurements, you'd end up with quite a bit of inaccuracy in the efficiency, because each meter contributes its own piece of inaccuracy to the result. However, note that the efficiency is the *ratio* of the two voltages times the *ratio* of the two currents. Thus the absolute values are of not much concern (you don't care whether the input is 27V or 28V, etc.) If both the voltage (or current) meters are then 0.3% high, *this inaccuracy cancels out!* Thus, what you want to do is what the author calls "cross-calibration": that is, before making the measurement, you attach both DVMs being used for the voltage (or current) measurements to exactly the same point (pass exactly the same current through them, respectively); they should read exactly the same. If they don't, you can find a scale factor for one of them that makes its reading equal to that of the other. If you now use the scale factor when measuring the efficiency, the inaccuracies still cancel out.

> **Practical Note** If you wanted to do it just like calibration people do, after the cross-calibration, you would next either ensure that the meter stays on the same scale throughout the measurement or cross-calibrate it with itself on the other scale, the one it's going to be used on. But practically, this isn't necessary, cross-calibration seems to work just fine without going to this extreme. In real-life a more serious problem occurs when someone comes by overnight, uses your meters, and puts them back in a different order. Now in the morning the cross-calibration is wrong, and you don't even know it! The author doesn't have a suggestion to fix this problem.

Where to Put the Probes

> **Practical Note** Put the DVM probes on separate leads from the power leads. Don't jack them in to the load.

The idea here is that since the power leads are carrying current, they have a voltage drop that increases, the further along the wire you go. So when you're doing a precision measurement (like efficiency, again), bring out separate wires from the output for the measurement, as shown in Figure 4.3. The same should of course be done for the inputs; often on converters, attention to this matter alone can be responsible for increasing the efficiency measured by 1 or 2% (the larger number is the correct one).

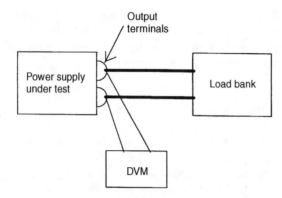

Figure 4.3 Use separate connections for carrying current and measuring voltage.

The same reasoning should be extended to the case of a small connector to which you must attach both the power connection and the meter, either input or output. Since there will be a voltage drop along the pin due to the current, the correct way to measure the efficiency is to attach the probes closest to the power supply under test, and then attach the power connections further away.

Measuring Very Low Resistances

Exactly the same technique should be used to measure a very small resistance. For example, you may need to know the resistance of a PCB trace, or the winding resistance of a transformer. Although a four-wire ohmmeter could be used, these instruments are frequently not conveniently available in a lab. The best way to do this measurement is to pass 1A (or 10A, or whatever) through the part or trace being measured, and use a DVM to measure the voltage drop—but be sure to have the DVM probes inside the power connections, as shown in Figure 4.4.

Using a Shunt for I > 10A

Most DVMs can't measure a current greater than 10A. A good choice here is to use a current shunt, and measure the voltage with a DVM. Shunts are discussed briefly in the components chapter, Chapter 3. The shunt typically has separate leads for power connections versus sense connections: use them! Although shunts are usually 1% tolerance, you can achieve better accuracy by cross-calibrating the shunt together with the DVM you're going to be using in the measurement. That is, pass (say) exactly 1A

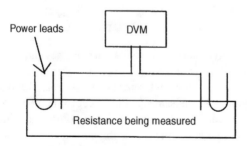

Figure 4.4 You can measure small resistances with a current source and a DVM.

through the shunt, and measure the voltage, calculating the resistance of the shunt, which amounts to the scale factor in this case. Just be sure to keep the shunt and DVM together as a pair thereafter. Otherwise you will lose the calibration.

How to Use a DVM to Measure a MOSFET

Well of course you're not going to be able to actually *characterize* the MOSFET with a DVM, but you can find out if it's "busted" or not. The trick is that on their resistance settings, mains-powered DVMs produce enough voltage to turn on the gate of a FET, at least a little. (Battery-powered DVMs produce a lower voltage, so this trick won't work with them, unless you have a logic-level MOSFET.)

To check the FET, first measure the resistance from drain to source. Here, "from" means putting the positive terminal of the DVM on the drain, and "to" means putting the negative terminal of the DVM on the source. The resistance should be something like 10MΩ or more. (If it's much lower, it's busted.) Now measure the resistance "from" the gate "to" the source: it should also be 10MΩ. Then, without letting the gate touch anything, measure the drain to source again. If the MOSFET is OK, you now read something like a few ohms up to maybe 2 or 3kΩ. If it reads open again, chances are the MOSFET is dead, since measuring the resistance of the gate to source should have applied enough gate voltage to turn it somewhat on.

Note: If in this last step (measuring drain–source after having measured gate–source) the measurement shows 20 or 30kΩ, the MOSFET is probably also busted, although in a weird way that doesn't show up well except in-circuit. You should try measuring its drain–source breakdown voltage with a curve tracer; generally, such a measurement with the DVM indicates that this FET too should be thrown away, although you might want to send it to Failure Analysis so they have something interesting to do.

ELECTRONIC LOADS

Why Is My Stable Converter Oscillating?

Electronic loads are convenient. You don't have to find that unusual resistor value in a high power package, and you don't need to find a fan to cool it either. But it's wise to recognize that these instruments have some significant limitations. Otherwise you may waste a lot of time looking in circuitry for problems that really lie in the instrumentation.

An electronic load is basically a bunch of power transistors in parallel, controlled by a feedback loop or loops, and operated in the linear region so that they are dissipative. The kind of control loop determines whether they appear as a resistive load, as a current sink, or as a constant voltage.

Regardless of mode of operation, electronic loads are always being controlled in a feedback loop, and of course this feedback loop has finite bandwidth: in typical units this bandwidth is somewhere in the vicinity of 1–5kHz. If your converter has more bandwidth than your electronic load, the load will not be able to make its transistors look resistive; as a result, your converter sees some unusual type of load impedance and may well start to oscillate. If your stable converter is oscillating, think about the load!

> **Practical Note** During converter development, try to use resistive loads if possible; reserve the use of electronic loads for the production line, after the bugs have been worked out. If it's necessary to use an electronic load, at least try to hang the anticipated load capacitance on the load's inputs, to reduce the load's impedance at the high frequency end.

Minimum Input Voltage

Electronic loads typically require some minimum input voltage to operate properly—read the manual to find out what this is if you're going to use an electronic load on a rail of less than 5V (and they usually can't stand negative input voltages at all). Typically, this minimum is in that range of 2–3V. Some types of electronic load are especially pernicious in that they will appear to operate at less load voltage than their minimum but won't have the proper impedance characteristics. You can waste a lot of time trying to debug your converter with something like this.

OSCILLOSCOPES

Aliasing

If you don't know or aren't sure what "aliasing" means, try this little experiment. Set the output from a function generator producing a 100kHz sine wave and put it into your digital oscilloscope with the scope set on 10µs/div. You see 10 cycles of the sine wave. Now start increasing the sweep time, to 100µs/div, then 1ms/div. When you get to 10ms/div. you may suddenly see a nice sine wave again. (If not, try a few more turns of the sweep speed knob.) This effect occurs because the oscilloscope can display only a finite number of points, and if it displays for a long enough period, it may end up *looking* like something it isn't. (A textbook will explain the mathematical details.)

Aliasing happens when your oscilloscope either can't take enough samples per second to catch everything your signal is doing or, more likely for power supplies, doesn't have enough memory to store the entire waveform occurring in a sweep period. For example, if the scope has 1000 points per channel, and you're set at 10ms/div, with 10 divisions displayed, the sweep time is 10ms/div × 10 divisions = 100ms, and since it only has 1000 points, it can only display intervals of 100ms/1000 points = 100µs; anything happening in less than this time can be aliased. That is, you may miss the event entirely, or it may appear to be at a lower frequency than it really is.

The practical point here is that just because your digital oscilloscope *says* your signal is doing something, this isn't necessarily happening. If you don't know what to expect, you can be seriously fooled. This is particularly likely to happen when you have 60Hz pickup and you're triggered in such a way and at such a time base that you don't see anything at that low frequency; you try to figure out why the waveform is different when you check it twice! The best plan when looking at a brand new signal is to sweep over a very broad range of time bases to ensure that there isn't something unexpected happening. Or, be an old fuddy-duddy: try using an analog oscilloscope for the early stages of investigating a new signal; *it* won't alias.

NETWORK ANALYZER

A network analyzer is an instrument for measuring the response of a system to a sine wave; that is, it measures the transfer function by producing a sine wave whose frequency varies slowly with time, then measuring the magnitude and phase response of the system to this signal. Network analysis can be as simple as measuring the impedance of a capacitor as a function of frequency, or as complex as measuring the closed loop response of a converter.

A network analyzer is a must-have for the loop measurements we're going to be doing in the chapter on stability, Chapter 6. Since they are complex instruments, and not nearly as familiar as oscilloscopes, we're going to give detailed instructions for operating the HP3562A, a typical instrument in the medium price range. The HP3562A is not particularly convenient for measuring impedances, but it works fine for measuring loops, which is what the instructions will be targeted for. Other popular models (such as those of Venable Instruments) are quite similar in concept. Thus, although the detailed instructions regarding which buttons to push will differ, the general procedure will be the same.

Step-by-Step Instructions

In the 10-step instruction set that follows, the hardware, or hard, buttons labeled on them on the front panel are indicated by the capitalized word BUTTON, whereas the soft (i.e., software-generated) buttons that appear on the display screen in response to pressing a BUTTON are designated by the capitalized word SELECT.

1. The analyzer takes about a minute to warm up and perform its self-checks. The very first thing to do with the HP3562A is to push the BUTTON Cal, and SELECT Auto Off. This particular machine, unlike others, will otherwise calibrate itself without warning, often splat in the middle of your measurement. This can cause your supply being tested to explode, since calibration is accompanied by the generation of signals.

2. The next step is to select the measurement mode. To measure the loop response of a converter, you want the analyzer to produce a time-varying sine wave. Push the BUTTON Meas Mode, and SELECT Swept Sine. Other models may require you to select network analyzer mode, or gain–phase mode.

3. Next we set the frequency range over which the transfer function is going to be measured. A typical sort of range for a moderate bandwidth converter might be from 10Hz to 10kHz, three decades. We also have to set how quickly the sweep is going to be made. On this machine, a reasonable compromise between signal-to-noise ratio and operator patience might be 30 seconds per decade, for a sweep time of 1.5 minutes. You can also select how much averaging is to be done (how many times the same band is averaged before going on to the next frequency), but we'll not use this in this example. On fancier machines, you may be able to select directly the windowing bandwidth, which is accomplished in this machine with the sweep speed. Thus, press the BUTTON Freq and SELECT Start Freq. On the keypad, press the BUTTONS for 10, and then SELECT Hz. Next, SELECT Stop Freq, press the BUTTONS for 10, and SELECT kHz. Finally,

SELECT Sweep Rate, and use the BUTTONS Up/Down to get to about 30s/Dc.

If the plots look scraggly, which happens usually at the lower end of the frequency spectrum, you can sweep more slowly, and/or average; but of course either ploy increases the time needed for the measurement.

4. Next we set up the display. We're trying to get a Bode plot, so we need two traces: one for magnitude, the other for phase. Other machines may do this automatically in gain–phase mode. Start by selecting BUTTON A, for the A trace. Then push BUTTON Coord, and SELECT Mag(dB). Then push BUTTON Meas Disp, and SELECT Freq Resp, since we are sweeping frequency.

5. Now we can do the same for the second trace: select BUTTON B, push BUTTON Coord, and SELECT Phase. Then push BUTTON Meas Disp and SELECT Freq Resp.

6. To turn both traces on simultaneously, push BUTTON Active Trace A/B; this produces the magnitude trace on the upper half of the screen and the phase trace on the lower half, the usual display style for a Bode plot. Other machines produce a single screen with both gain and phase on a single plot, with two axis scales.

7. For convenience, it is helpful to let the machine control the vertical axes scales (gain and phase), rather than worrying about it yourself. Push BUTTON Scale and SELECT Y Auto Scale. If you have special display requirements (e.g., not showing what happens below 0° phase, as we do in the stability chapter, Chapter 6), you can turn off this autoscaling on either trace independently by pushing BUTTON A or BUTTON B, and then SELECTING Y Fixed Scale, and pushing BUTTONS on the keypad for the minimum and maximum display range; the analyzer clips any measurement outside the selected range.

8. Now we set up the characteristics of the signal output that's going to be used to drive the system. For a closed loop measurement, a level of about 100mVAC is suggested as a starting point. Push the BUTTON Source, and SELECT Source Level, then press the keypad BUTTONS for 100 and SELECT mV; or you can use the BUTTONS Up/Down, or use the dial to accomplish the same thing. This machine powers up with the DC Offset = 0, but for the open loop measurement, this can be changed if desired.

The most common cause for scraggly looking plots at moderate frequencies is insufficient source drive level; try increasing it until you get a nice smooth plot. However, you need to observe the cautions below.

9. Finally, to turn on a cursor (useful not only for your measurement, but also for displaying information in a presentation), push the BUTTON X.

10. Some machines (although not the HP3562A) require you to set the input impedance and the input attenuation for each input channel. Input attenuation can be set to any value (usually either 0dB or 20dB) as long as the same one is used for both channels. An "input overload" warning that appears while the sweep is being run indicates that the input attenuation should be increased. The input impedance should be set to 1MΩ for both channels. Occasionally you will come across an instrument that has only a 50Ω input; this type CAN'T BE

USED for loop measurements, because the 50Ω load disturbs the loop components too much.

The network analyzer itself is now ready to go. But there are a few more things to know before you begin operation. The most important is to avoid thinking that the loop can be temporarily closed without injecting a signal by turning off or disconnecting the Source. **Don't do it!** With the mixer method (see the chapter on stability, Chapter 6) disconnecting the Source causes the output voltage of the mixer to double, causing the output of your supply to double! The correct way of removing the AC signal is to set it to 0V with the BUTTON Source. This caveat is irrelevant if you are using the transformer method.

Another step you'll certainly want to take is to monitor the gate drive signal with an oscilloscope while the analyzer is sweeping. Although the output of the analyzer is a constant amplitude, the response of the converter to this signal is not a constant; it happens not infrequently that what seemed a reasonable drive level at low frequencies causes the duty cycle to fluctuate wildly, and to go to zero at frequencies near the converter's bandwidth. *You have to avoid this*, because if the duty cycle ever goes to zero, the converter isn't operating, and you're no longer measuring the transfer function. This is the reason for watching the gate's duty cycle while sweeping, to ensure that the duty cycle is OK. A symptom of duty cycle collapse (if you're looking at someone else's measurement) is a sudden, discontinuous jump in the Bode plot.

Practical Note A good starting point for signal amplitude (source level) is to set the oscilloscope time base so that you're looking at a single cycle of the duty cycle (and trigger on the rising edge, as shown in Figures 4.5 and 4.6) and then increase the source level until you can just make out a little movement on the following edge. The figures show good and bad levels of drive. Figure 4.5 shows the gate drive of a converter being driven properly: the dither on the falling edge is caused by the modulation of the loop. Figure 4.6 shows the gate drive being overdriven: not only is the dither enormous, but the duty cycle goes down to 0% during a portion of the low frequency cycle.

With all of this set up, you can now turn the system on, in this order: mixer power supply, converter input power, and then analyzer sweep, by pushing the BUTTON Start. If you stop the sweep (by pushing the BUTTON Pause), reverse the order, by first turning off the converter input power and then the mixer's supply. Rigidly following this order prevents the converter from operating in open loop mode, where it might very well self-destruct, since the mixer is in the feedback loop, and it is of course an open when unpowered.

Nyquist Plots

The HP3562A can also be used to generate a Nyquist plot from the data. For this function, you need only press the BUTTON Coords, and SELECT Nyqust (sic). Since it is a single graph, it's best to turn on just A. Otherwise you will have two half-sized plots of the same thing. Not all analyzers have the ability to display Nyquist plots.

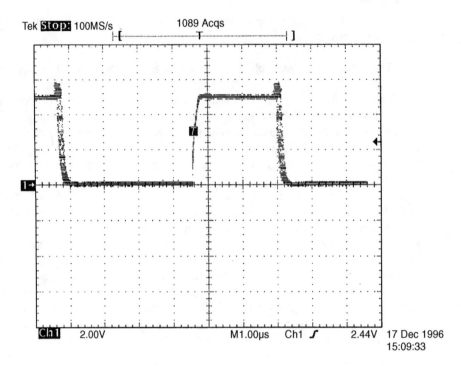

Figure 4.5   Gate waveform, showing proper network analyzer drive level.

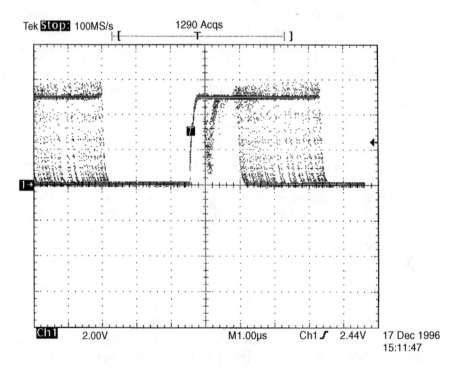

Figure 4.6   Gate drive waveform, showing too high a drive level.

5

Practical Design
of Magnetics

FUNDAMENTALS OF MAGNETICS

Introductory Comments

Designing a real piece of magnetics seems to take a lot of time. There are many decisions to be made: core material, core style, type of conductor, etc., and there won't always be a single best choice. When the design has been completed, performance has to be checked in the lab. And <u>then</u> you have to make sure the design can be produced at a reasonable cost!

Remember, though, that you can spend quite a bit of time designing even a window comparator: looking at resistor tolerances and temperature coefficients, leakage currents and offset voltages, and so on. So don't expect a magnetics design to jump into your lap either!

That said, though, this chapter gives a lot of practical information that will make your magnetics design, if not easy, at least straightforward. Although up to now knowledge of the basics has been assumed, in the field of magnetics, confusion among engineers is so common that it's best to begin with a review. The emphasis, however, remains strongly on the aspects of the theory that are essential for the practical design of magnetics. Indeed, after the introductory material, the rest of the chapter can be taken to be step-by-step instructions to producing good magnetics designs, including a final section about making your design manufacturable.

One last comment—This chapter cannot be a complete description of everything known about designing magnetics. Instead, it concentrates on aspects that are key for making a good, workable, solid design; to learn about proximity effect, field distributions and other advanced topics requires specialized study.

Ampere's Law

Let's start with the basics, then. All of magnetics is governed at a fundamental level by two laws, Ampere's and Faraday's.

Referring to Figure 5.1, imagine that we have N turns of wire wound onto a coil of circumference Length, and we're putting I amps of current through it. (The rectangle is just a former, something to hold the wire in place, plastic if you like; it will become a core later when we talk about permeability.) Ampere's law relates these parameters with the magnetic field, H, generated by the coil:

$$\ell H = IN$$

$$\text{Length} \times H = I \times N$$

By increasing the number of turns or the current, we can increase the field.

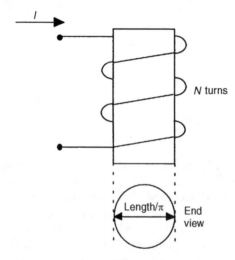

N turns

Length/π End view

Figure 5.1   A coil of wire of N turns carries a current of I amps. The coil has a circumference of length equal to "Length".

Faraday's Law

The second law needed for magnetics is Faraday's. Referring to Figure 5.2, imagine that we have a loop of wire enclosing an area A with N turns on it. If the magnetic flux through that loop changes (e.g., by being coupled to another loop with a changing flux), then Faraday's law relates these parameters to the voltage developed at the terminals of the coil:

$$V = N \frac{d\phi}{dt}$$
$$\phi = BA$$
$$\therefore V = NA \frac{dB}{dt}$$

$$\frac{d\Phi}{dt} = \frac{d(BAN)}{dt} \rightarrow$$

$$V = NA \frac{dB}{dt}$$

where V = rate of change of magnetic flux.

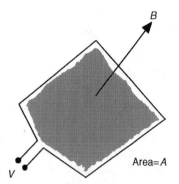

Figure 5.2 A loop of wire enclosing area A with voltage V and flux B.

Area=A

About Inductance

From the fundamental laws of Ampere and Faraday, we can derive the equation governing the behavior of an inductor. First, there is a relationship between B and H. What are these two anyway? We called them both "the magnetic field" above without being very specific. In fact, it's only a historical accident that they have different symbols, since they're really the same thing: H is the magnetic field in free space, B is the magnetic field when it's inside a magnetic material. But they're exactly the same thing. The relationship between them is given by a property of the magnetic material, the permeability μ. You can think of μ as being the "gain" of the magnetic material, because it makes the field inside stronger than it would be if the material wasn't there:

$$B = \mu H$$

We can put this in Faraday's law (μ is assumed to be a constant in this elementary discussion), to get

$$V = NA\mu \frac{dH}{dt}$$

From Ampère's law we know that

$$H = \frac{IN}{\text{Length}}$$

so

$$V = \frac{N^2 A \mu}{\text{Length}} \frac{dI}{dt}$$

Inductance is now *defined* as

$$\text{Inductance} = L \equiv \frac{N^2 A \mu}{\text{Length}}$$

Notice the expected dependence of inductance on the square of the number of turns. With this definition, we have

$$V = L \frac{dI}{dt}$$

the familiar relationship expressing rate of change of current as determined by the voltage applied across an inductor.

Units Confusion

Engineers routinely use volts and amps and don't have to worry about dividing them: you get ohms. Unfortunately, with magnetics there are two systems, CGS (centimeter-gram-second) and MKS (meter-kilogram-second), and magnetics designs routinely mix units from these two systems. The reasons are again historical. So for magnetics, you have to carefully watch the units, and be sure to use conversion factors, such as 10 or 4π. (The 4π comes from units used in Maxwell's equations.) Table 5.1 details the units.

TABLE 5.1   MKS and CGS Units Often Used in Magnetics

	MKS	CGS
Field (H)	tesla (T)	oersted (Oe)
Field (B)	tesla (T)	gauss (G)
Inductance	henry (H)	square second per centimeter (s^2/cm)
Voltage	volt (V)	statvolt
Current	ampere (A)	electrostatic unit per second (esu/s)
Area	meter squared (m^2)	centimeter squared (cm^2)

Note how common it is to use gauss and henry in the same calculation! It's this that causes the confusion, since these units are from different unit systems. But who ever heard of a statvolt? And while the MKS system has the name tesla for the magnetic field, CGS has two different names, oersted and gauss. Table 5.2 shows how to convert between the two unit systems.

TABLE 5.2   Some MKS-to-CGS Conversions

MKS	(equals)	CGS
$1\,m^2$		$10{,}000\,cm^2$
1 volt		1/300 statvolts
1 amp		3×10^9 esu/s
1 henry		1.113×10^{-12} s^2/cm
1 tesla		10,000 gauss

Just so you'll be prepared, you should be aware that you sometimes see a few other units not listed above. "Amp-turn/cm" is another name for oersted [because Length (cm) times H (oersted) $= I$ (A) times N (turn)]. And as if all this weren't bad enough, sometimes *English* units are used! So note that 1 circular mil $= 5.07 \times 10^{-6}$ cm^2. Here, "mil" refers to one one-thousandth of an inch.

Let's note that μ is dimensionless, for example with B in gauss and H in oersted, because these are really the same thing: permeability is just a number. And finally, with area measured in square centimeters and length measured in centimeters, it ends up that inductance in henrys is

$$L = \frac{4\pi}{10} \frac{N^2 \mu A}{\text{Length}}$$

Weird Words: The Three R's

If you ever read the literature on magnetics, you will probably come across "the three R's," Reactance, Reluctance, and Remanence, which have done as much any anything in all of engineering to confuse people. Let's take a quick look at these R's, primarily just to demystify them.

Reactance This has similarity to resistance, it's a type of impedance. The reactance of an inductor is $\chi = 2\pi f L$ (the Greek letter is pronounced "kai"); similarly to Ohm's law, we have $V = I\chi$ for an inductor. Don't forget that reactance and resistance are $90°$ out of phase, so that the magnitude of the total impedance of a system that has both reactance and resistance is

$$|Z| = \sqrt{R^2 + \chi^2}$$

Remanence This is a property of a magnetic material, a type of magnetic hysteresis. Suppose you start putting a magnetic field through a magnetic material (e.g., by winding a coil around it and passing current through it—Ampere's law). Next, you reduce the applied field back to zero. *The magnetic material will still have a field in it.* The magnitude of this remaining field is called the remanence. Who cares? Well, the field in, for example, a transformer is cycled up and down through zero all the time; in this case, remanence is related to the amount of power dissipated in the material by the cycling. We'll discuss these core losses further below.

Reluctance This term is used in an analogy between magnetic and electric circuits—its purpose was supposedly to make magnetic circuits, which can be confusing, look like electric circuits, which everyone knows how to deal with. It seems to have grossly failed in this purpose! In this analogy, we define reluctance to be

$$\mathfrak{R} = \frac{1}{\mu A}$$

Using Ampere's law and the definition of flux that $\Phi = BA$, we can calculate the effect of a current through a multiturn loop:

$$I_{\text{tot}} = IN = \text{Length} \times H = \frac{\text{Length} \times B}{\mu} = \frac{\text{Length} \times \Phi}{\mu A} = \mathfrak{R}\Phi$$

Thus, if we say that Φ "looks like" voltage, then reluctance "looks like" conductance (1/resistance), because their product is current. It is this "looking like" that is the basis of the analogy.

Warning! Some authors deal with the analogy the other way around: Φ is said to be analogous to current, and I_{tot} (called "magnetomotive force") is analogous to voltage, in which case reluctance is analogous to resistance rather than conductance. Clearly, this affects the way schematics using the analogy are drawn; but since it is just an analogy, both ways are acceptable, as long as you don't mix them!

In reality, engineers almost never use this analogy, but just stick with equivalent circuit models. An example of the usage of this analogy is given below in the discussion on leakage inductance.

THE IDEAL TRANSFORMER

Let's start our thinking about magnetics by dealing with an approximation, the ideal transformer. It's really a pretty good approximation for many purposes, and understanding it allows us to refine the model later to include nonidealities. A transformer is by definition a magnetic structure that *transforms*: whatever power goes in is what comes out, with no time delay. This is what distinguishes a transformer from an inductor, which can store energy for some time before releasing it.

The ideal transformer has two windings (signified by the curly shapes in Figure 5.3), which sit on a single core. The core is here shown as a magnetic material; if it were an air core, the two straight lines wouldn't be shown. Finally, the direction of current flow (or of applied voltage) is shown by dots: it makes no difference whether a dot signifies the start or end of a winding, as long as it is defined the same way for every winding on the transformer. Physically, this means that there are two ways to wind a wire onto a core (Figure 5.4): the start of the winding can go underneath the core or on top of it. When you actually wind the windings, you just pick one way or the other: if the dot means going underneath for the start, just follow that same rule for every additional winding. As long as you are consistent, the two possible end results are electrically equivalent.

Now let's consider Faraday's law for each side of the ideal transformer. For side 1, we have $V_1 = N_1 \times A_1 \times dB_1/dt$, and for side two $V_2 = N_2 \times A_2 \times dB_2/dt$. Now since the two windings are on the same core, they have the same area, $A_1 = A_2$. And since the

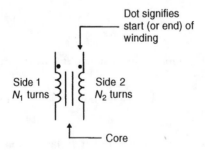

Figure 5.3 In a schematic, a dot signifies the start or end of a winding; its only significance is relative to another dot. The double lines between the windings signify a core.

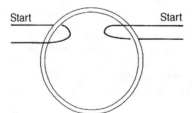

Figure 5.4 Two ways to wind a winding: by starting from the top (right side) or from the bottom (left side).

transformer is ideal, all the flux in one winding is (by definition of what we mean by "ideal") coupled into the other winding, that is, $B_1 = B_2$. Thus

$$\frac{V_1}{N_1} = \frac{V_2}{N_2}$$

which is why a transformer winding is calculated as so many "volts per turn." This equation shows that the volts per turn is the same for every winding on an ideal transformer.

Now an ideal transformer conserves energy, that is, there is no energy storage—exactly whatever is going in is what is coming out, with no time delay. Again, this is the defining property of a transformer. Stated mathematically, this means input power equals output power,

$$V_1 I_1 = V_2 I_2$$

turn ratio, $a = N_1/N_2$.

and combining the equations for V, N, and I shows that

$a = N_1/N_2 = V_1/V_2 = I_2/I_1$

$$I_1 N_1 = I_2 N_2$$

that is, <u>if voltage steps up, current steps down.</u>

EXAMPLE

If an (ideal) transformer has 48V in at 2A, and has 24V out, it must have an output current of 4A, because $48V \times 2A = 24V \times 4A = 96W$.

What About a Flyback "Transformer"?

As touched on in Chapter 2, a flyback transformer has the same *name* as a transformer but is physically different. A transformer transforms (power in = power out) an inductor stores energy. A flyback "transformer" acts like <u>both</u> an inductor <u>and</u> a transformer at different times during the switching cycle in a power converter! Perhaps it should have a different name. (Any suggestions? "Transductor" sounds good, since "informer" has another meaning!)

Consider the action of an (isolated) flyback in Figure 5.5 for a moment. When the switch is on, the flyback transformer acts like an inductor. Since the switch is ideally a short circuit when on, a positive voltage is imposed across the primary winding, and so current ramps up in it. Energy is stored in the primary inductance, $E = \frac{1}{2}LI^2$. When the switch is

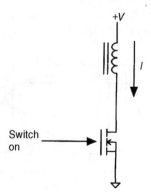

Figure 5.5 When the switch is on, an (isolated) flyback's "transformer" acts like an inductor, storing energy.

off, the flyback transformer acts as a transformer, as shown in Figure 5.6. Since the switch when off is ideally an open circuit, the current has no place to go on the primary, and instead is released on the secondary through the diode. Energy is transferred from the primary to the secondary. The flyback has thus acted as both an inductor and a transformer during a single switching cycle. We'll design a practical flyback transformer later.

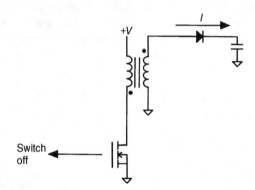

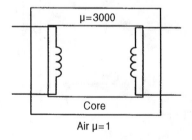

Figure 5.6 When the switch is off, the flyback's "transformer" acts like a transformer, delivering its stored energy to the secondary.

REAL TRANSFORMERS

Real transformers, as opposed to the ideal kind, have many nonidealities. These include nonperfect coupling to the core, core losses, and saturation. Perhaps the most fundamental of these nonidealities is imperfect core coupling; the others are dealt with in subsequent sections.

Nonperfect coupling to the core can come about because of coupling to the air. In Figure 5.7, the magnetic flux in the core set up by one winding doesn't "want" to make the right-angled bend, and a small portion of it escapes into air. Similarly, in a gapped core, the flux is forced to go through a small air gap and some of it does not return to the magnetic material on the other side of the gap, but rather continues out into the air, finding another path for its return. And in a toroid, although the flux is theoretically perfectly coupled to the core, in reality there is always a little bit of nonsymmetry in the winding, and this too causes a tiny bit of coupling to the air. Using the electrical analogy, the circuit of Figure 5.7 could be modeled as shown in Figure 5.8.

The voltage driving the first winding "looks like" a current source in the analogy. The permeability of the core "looks like" a conductance, so it is modeled as a resistor, with a

Figure 5.7 Not all of the flux goes through the core, some goes through the air, because the core has finite permeability.

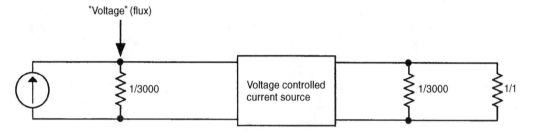

"Voltage" (flux)

1/3000   Voltage controlled   1/3000   1/1
                current source

Figure 5.8   The core in Figure 5.7 can be modeled with the electrical analogy.

resistance value that is the inverse of the permeability (1/3000). The resulting voltage (which is what the flux "looks like") is transformed back into a current source on the other side of the core. This reflected current then goes through both the core (resistance = inverse of permeability = 1/3000) and the air [resistance = 1/(the permeability of air), i.e., 1]. The analog of this is that the flux goes through the core and also through the air, with the relative amounts determined by the permeabilities of the two: 3000/3001 of the flux goes through the core, and 1/3001 of the flux goes through the air.

The part of the flux that goes through the air is called the leakage: in the analogy, some part of the current doesn't go through the core "resistor," so the voltage developed across the second winding is smaller than that generated by the primary winding. (The resistors are in parallel, and so the current generates a smaller voltage.) Since some of the flux is not coupled to the secondary, we can now go back and modify our original model of an ideal transformer to take account of this imperfect coupling. In the resulting schematic (Figure 5.9), we still have the perfect transformer in the center of the model. In series with the primary we are showing leakage inductance. The validity of this model is not affected by whether it is shown in the primary or secondary, since it is just subtracting from the voltage that appears on the secondary; here it is shown on the primary side.

EXAMPLE

If the primary has 10 turns and 100µH and 40V and the secondary 20 turns and 400µH and 80V, then the secondary has four times the inductance of the primary (inductance goes as the square of the number of turns). Thus if the primary is shown with a leakage inductance of, say, 1µH, on the secondary, this would appear as 4µH (square of the number of turns.) This makes sense because the

$$L = \frac{N^2 A_e \mu}{l_e}$$

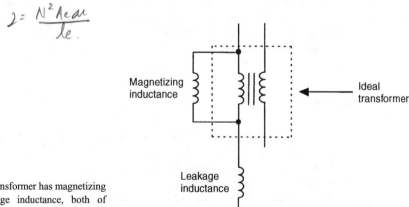

Magnetizing
inductance

Ideal
transformer

Leakage
inductance

Figure 5.9   A real transformer has magnetizing inductance and leakage inductance, both of which interfere with its ideal transformer action.

leakage inductance causes the same percentage voltage drop whichever side of the transformer it is on: $1\mu H$ corresponds on the primary to one turn $[(10 \text{ turns})^2 = 100\mu H$, so $(1 \text{ turn})^2 = 1\mu H]$, $4\mu H$ on the secondary corresponds to two turns $[(20 \text{ turns})^2 = 400\mu H$, so $(2 \text{ turns})^2 = 4\mu H]$, and on the primary this is $4V/\text{turn} \times 1 \text{ turn} = 4V = 10\%$ of $40V$, and on the secondary it is also $4V/\text{turn} \times 2$ turns $= 8V = 10\%$ of $80V$. Labeling Figure 5.9 makes this very clear—try it!

Practical Note Leakage inductance is caused by coupling through the air, not the core. This important fact implies that the amount of leakage inductance for a design depends only on the geometric shape of the coil; *the leakage inductance of a transformer is independent of the material on which the windings are wound.*

Also shown in Figure 5.9 is the magnetizing inductance. Since the core material has finite permeability, the primary has finite inductance (and so, for that matter, has the secondary). This means that applying a voltage to the transformer generates a current, the "magnetizing current" that is merely wasted as far as the transformer action goes (it is not coupled to the secondary). This is why it is shown in parallel with the primary (where the primary is assumed to be the winding with the impressed voltage, not the load). The magnetizing current I_m is determined by

$$V = L_m \frac{dI_m}{dt}$$

Thus, ultimately, both magnetizing inductance and leakage inductance are associated with losses, because they refer to energy that is required to use the transformer but that doesn't end up on the secondary where it can be applied to the load. These inductances are part of what makes the efficiency of a real transformer less than 100%.

Core Materials

Another aspect of a real transformer (or inductor) is its use of real core materials. Not only do real core materials have finite permeability, they have losses, they saturate (what this means is discussed in the next section), and at least some types have permeability, losses, and other properties that are temperature dependent! Incorporating all these factors properly requires some experience and knowledge. Later in this chapter we execute several practical magnetics designs to explore these issues in great detail. For the moment, let's consider Table 5.3, an overview of some practically important types of core materials and some of the pros and cons of using them.

Saturation

The preceding section mentioned "saturation" several times, so I'll explain it right away. Saturation is what happens to a core when it has more than a certain flux density: its permeability is reduced from a high value to approximately 1. This in turn means a radical reduction in inductance, which would clearly be disastrous in some circuits; complete saturation of a core is thus to be avoided in most cases.

TABLE 5.3 Core Materials: Pros, Cons, and Usage

Material	Consideration
Air	*Pro*: Air core magnetics can't saturate!
	Con: The permeability of air is one, so you can only get a small inductance. Practically, this means a couple of microhenrys tops is all you can expect to get from an air core winding. Further, there is of course a lot of fringing, almost by definition! This causes losses, and EMI.
	Used: The primary use of air core magnetics is in rf circuits, where a few microhenrys goes a long way. There has also been occasional talk of applications in ultrahigh frequency power converters, but this could never be practical because of EMI considerations.
Ferrite	*Pro*: Ferrite materials (made by a wide variety of vendors) have high permeability and thus can be used to generate high inductance. The permeability is relatively constant with flux density, and there exist a variety of ferrites optimized for minimal power dissipation in various frequency bands. The poorly controlled initial permeability of ferrites is frequently not a problem, as ferrite cores are often gapped.
	Con: Ferrite saturates hard.
	Used: Ferrites typically are used in power transformers, or for noise filters.
Molyperm (MPP)	*Pro*: MPP cores have a soft saturation. A wide variety of different permeabilities is available, and the permeability can be very well controlled by the manufacturer.
	Con: At typical power supply switching frequencies, MPP cores have much higher losses than ferrites.
	Used: MPP cores are used for inductors or noise filters at high DC currents.
Powdered iron	*Pro, Con*: Powdered iron saturates slightly harder than MPP, and while a variety of permeabilities is available, these are typically lower than what can be had from MPP. This means a powdered iron inductor will be larger than a device having the same inductance and current capacity but built on an MPP core. The big plus is that powdered iron cores are cheaper than molyperm cores.
	Used: The same places that use MPP cores, but where cost is more important than size.
Steel laminations	*Pro*: Steel has a very high saturation flux density, producing very high inductance. Don't ignore this material just because it's old! In some applications, such as very high density converters, steel laminations may be the only way to go.
	Con: For many applications, steel is unaffordably expensive, not to mention heavy. It also saturates hard and has higher losses at high frequency than ferrite. On the other hand, take a look at the new amorphous material, which overcomes some of these limitations.
	Used: Power inductors, low frequency power transformers.

Handwritten margin notes:

$\mu = $ based on $\frac{4\pi}{10}$

$\times 1 \cdot 2 \#$.

when $Ae = cm^2$

$le = cm$.

otherwise, $\mu = 4\pi \times 10^{-7}$

when $Ae = m^2$, $le = m$

$\mu = \mu_0 \mu_r$

"Saturation" has a fairly clear meaning for ferrites and steel laminations because the core saturates rather abruptly (hard): an extra oersted or two of flux density, and suddenly the permeability plummets (but bear in mind that even for these materials saturation flux density is a function of temperature).

For MPP cores, however, the reduction in permeability as a function of flux is very gradual (soft saturation), and indeed MPP cores are routinely run at reduced permeability intentionally; for this material, the term "saturation" really doesn't have a strict meaning.

Practical Note From a practical standpoint, if current flow has reduced the permeability of the core below, say, 20% of the permeability it has with zero current, the core may be considered to be effectively saturated.

EXAMPLE

The ferrite material 3F3 made by Philips [1] can take > 5000 gauss at 25°C. Applying additional flux (H = oersteds = amp-turns/cm) does not result in much increase in B, as indicated in Table 5.4.

TABLE 5.4 As Flux Increases, Permeability Drops: 3F3 Material

H (Oe)	B (G)
0.5	1000
1.0	2000
1.5	3000
2.0	4000
2.5	5000
3.0	5100

Starting from 0 flux, adding half an oersted at a time increases B by 1000G at a time, until suddenly the core saturates at 5000G: adding an additional half-oersted increases B by only 100G; another half-oersted might add only a few gauss, until you get only one gauss per oersted, that is, a permeability of 1; the core is saturated!

Other Core Limitations

Let's also mention a few of the other nonlinearities of cores that can prove important in practical applications.

Curie Temperature This is the temperature above which the core becomes "demagnetized" and irrecoverably loses its permeability. For 3F3 material the Curie temperature is above 200°C, so typically bobbins would melt or even wire insulation fail before this point was reached. On a toroid, however (since there is no bobbin), it might be possible to reach this temperature using high temperature wire insulation; obviously this is a no-no.

Core Losses Whenever there is a changing flux in a core, there is some power lost, power that goes into heat. The amount of power dissipated is a complicated function of many variables, such as peak-to-peak flux density, temperature, frequency, and of course core material. Observe however, that DC flux density <u>does not</u> cause core loss: a DC inductor with no AC ripple current through it has <u>no</u> core loss!

Practical Note The curves and equations shown in core materials' data books for power loss are for sine waves only! If there is a DC component to the flux, or if the flux is nonsinusoidal, the losses will be different because the *B-H* loop is different. No one really knows how to calculate the losses for the cases (you can't just decompose the flux into its frequency components as in a Fourier spectrum, because loss is nonlinear in *B*). Use the sinusoid as an approximation—if you have to know core losses exactly, measurement is the only choice.

Another Limit MPP permeability has a frequency dependence, too.

Optimum Design

It can be shown that minimum power is lost in a magnetic structure when

    A. Core losses = copper losses

    B. Primary copper loss = secondary copper loss

Practically, these conditions have three implications:

1. For a given magnetic, if the power loss in the core is much less than the copper losses (primary and secondary windings together), you need to decrease the number of turns; this increases flux density and core losses, while decreasing copper losses. The result will be that the <u>total</u> losses decrease.
2. Conversely, for a given magnetic, if the power loss in the core is much greater than the copper losses (primary and secondary together), you need to increase the number of turns; this decreases flux density and core losses, while increasing copper losses. The result will be that the <u>total</u> losses decrease.
3. Allot the same winding area to the primary and secondary; if the secondary has more turns, it must have proportionately smaller wire. If there are multiple secondaries, allot their winding area by output power (i.e., higher output-power outputs get more winding area, so that each secondary has the same I^2R loss).

Naturally, these are only guidelines; in most cases additional considerations (such as being able to get only integer numbers of turns on a winding) will prevent you from following these suggestions exactly. But you don't want losses to be unbalanced by, say, $3 : 1$; if they're different by 20–30% that's pretty good.

PRACTICAL DESIGN OF A DC INDUCTOR

Throughout Chapters 5 and 6, much of the design work is targeted at a specific design, a buck converter. Concentrating on this design will help to focus our efforts, because at the end of the design, in Chapter 6, we look at measurements of the converter as built in the lab, and compare them with the results expected from the design work in these two chapters. The measurements will turn out to compare very closely indeed with the designed results.

With all the foregoing background material under our belts, we're ready to design a real DC inductor. A DC inductor is by definition a magnetic structure that has a single winding, invariably on a core, and it carries primarily DC current; that is, the ripple current (AC component of the current) is relatively small.

For our design of a DC inductor, we are going to be working on the choke for the buck converter we are designing. The specific requirements are set by the design: we need 35μH at a DC current of 2A. The power dissipation we've allotted for this component of the design is 300mW, so the maximum resistance should be less than $(2A)^2R = 300\text{mW} \rightarrow R = 75\text{m}\Omega$. Observe that at a 250kHz switching frequency, with 15V at the input and 5V on the output (so that duty cycle = 5V/15V = 33%), the ripple current is $dI = V(dt/L) = (15\text{V} - 5\text{V})(33\% \times 4\mu s)/35\mu H = 0.377\text{A}$ peak-to-peak, which is small

$$V_L = L\,\frac{di}{dt}. \qquad \delta = 0.33$$

$$\delta i = \frac{V_L\,\delta t}{L} \qquad t_{on} = 1.32\mu s.$$

$$\delta t = t_{on}.$$

$$V_L = E_i - E_{out}$$

relative to 2ADC output, satisfying the requirements for this to be a DC inductor. In addition, since we know that some core types (in particular MPP) used for DC inductors can change permeability with flux, let's require that the core not swing more than 20%. This means that the inductance should not lose more than 20% of its value as the current increases from 0A to 2A; that is, the inductance with no DC current should be 44µH (44µH × 80% = 35µH).

$$x\,(0.8) = 35\mu H.$$
$$\therefore x \approx 44\mu H *$$

Core Selection

First, let's choose a core material. Since this is a DC inductor, the typical choice would be either MPP or powdered iron. To keep this chapter to a manageable size, we're going to say that getting a small inductor is more important than cheapness, which points to the choice of MPP. In reality, you might try it both ways, to see what makes sense given the overall dimension and cost budget available to the design. Exactly the same procedure detailed in the following sections would be used to design a powdered iron inductor.

First Try

We're going to use a recent Magnetics Inc. catalog [2] to design our inductor, since its selector guide (Figure 5.10) provides a convenient starting point. Without a selector guide, we would have to rely on experience with previous designs for our first guess. As will become apparent, however, making a good first guess is not essential, it merely reduces the amount of work you have to do.

The selector guide (Figure 5.10) bases its guidance on the amount of energy the inductor will have to store (actually twice that amount). The selector guide wants the inductance in millihenrys: 35µH = 0.035mH; at 2A, (twice) the energy is $(2A)^2 \times 0.035mH = 0.14mJ$. Tracing along the guide as in Figure 5.11, we find a recommendation of a 200µ core (200 is the initial permeability). In Figure 5.12, we find the core number is 55127.

So our first try is going to be the core 55127. Looking at Figure 5.12, the A_L for the core is 85. What is A_L? It is a convenience provided by the manufacturer, telling you how many millihenrys you get on this core for 1000 turns, or equivalently, how many nanohenrys you get for 1 turn (inductance goes as N^2, so the 1000 : 1 turns ratio means 1,000,000 : 1 for inductance, the same ratio as mH to nH). So to get 35µH, we need:

$$L = N^2 A_L.$$

$$N = \sqrt{\frac{L}{A_L}} = \sqrt{\frac{35\mu H}{85nH}} = 20.29 \rightarrow 20 \text{ turns}$$

[*Check*: (20 turns)^2 × 85nH = 34µH. The turns are rounded off because of course only an integer number of turns is possible on a toroid winding.]

Now we will calculate the flux density, so we can find out how much the permeability changes between 0 and 2A of DC current. First looking at Figure 5.11, we have that $H/NI = 0.467$. (We can check this, or calculate it for manufacturers who haven't provided it: $H/NI = 0.4\pi/\text{path length} = 0.4\pi/2.69\text{cm} = 0.467$. This is clearly a constant that partially describes the core.) Thus the magnetic field being applied is $H = H/NI \times N \times I = 0.467 \times 20 \text{ turns} \times 2A = 18.7 \text{ Oe}$.

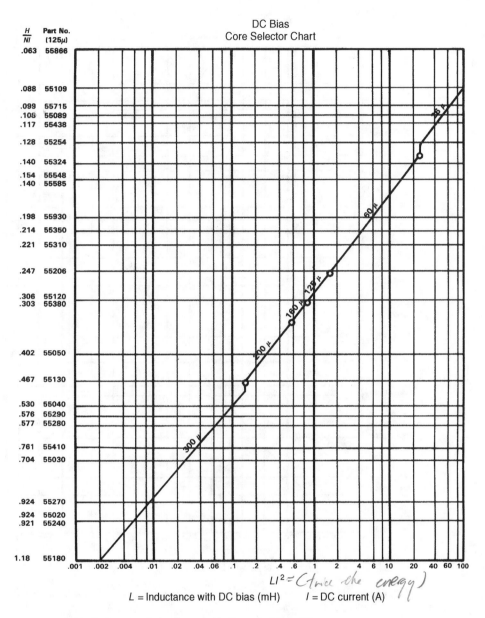

The following table accompanies the chart:

$\frac{H}{NI}$	Part No. (125μ)
.063	55866
.088	55109
.099	55715
.108	55089
.117	55438
.128	55254
.140	55324
.154	55548
.140	55585
.198	55930
.214	55350
.221	55310
.247	55206
.306	55120
.303	55380
.402	55050
.467	55130
.530	55040
.576	55290
.577	55280
.761	55410
.704	55030
.924	55270
.924	55020
.921	55240
1.18	55180

DC Bias
Core Selector Chart

$LI^2 = (\text{twice the energy})$

L = Inductance with DC bias (mH) I = DC current (A)

Figure 5.10   A vendor's selector guide (From Ref. 2, p. 31).

$B = uH.$

We could also calculate the flux density, B, inside the core (it is just the permeability times H), but we will be interested in that only when we get to core losses. For the moment, we need to get the inductance right, and for that we want only the percentage of initial permeability due to the DC current. *Note*: Some manufacturers give percent permeability at just one or two points, making it difficult to know exactly where you are in inductance; I recommend staying away from such materials.

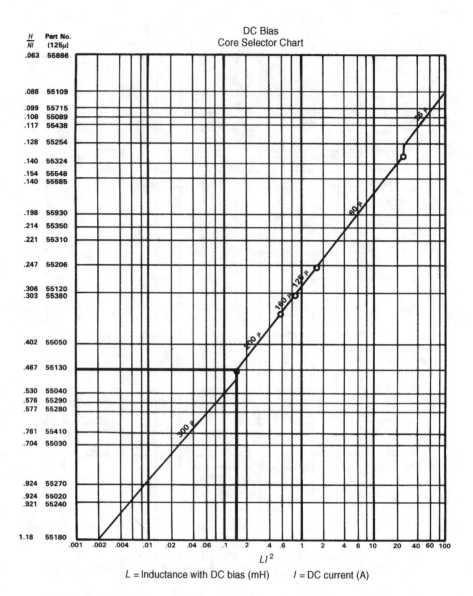

Figure 5.11 Using the vendor's selector guide to make an initial guess for the core. (From Ref. 2.)

Practical Note Manufacturers nowadays also provide equations (as opposed to curves) that describe the permeability as a function of flux; because these equations are fits to data, not based on theory, below about 20% of initial permeability the equations start giving seriously erroneous errors. **Always use the manufacturer's curves, not the equations.** As a further specific note, I observe that the version of the Magnetics MPP catalog I was using had the numbers for the equation for 300µ material with errors in it!

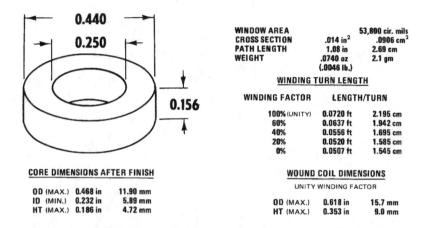

MAGNETIC INFORMATION

PART NO.	PERM μ	INDUCTANCE @1000 TURNS (mH±8%)	NOMINAL DC RESISTANCE (Ohms/mH)**	FINISHES AND STABILIZATIONS*	GRADING STATUS 2% BANDS	B/NI (Gauss/amp-turn)
55133–	14	6	4.10	A2	*	6.54 (<1500 gauss)
55132–	26	11	2.23	A2	*	12.1 (<1500 gauss)
55131–	60	26	.945	ALL	*	28.0 (<1500 gauss)
55130–	125	53	.464	ALL	YES	58.4 (<1500 gauss)
55129–	147	63	.390	ALL	YES	68.6 (<1500 gauss)
55128–	160	68	.361	ALL	YES	74.7 (<1500 gauss)
55124–	173	74	.332	ALL	YES	80.8 (<1500 gauss)
55127–	200	85	.289	ALL	YES	93.4 (< 600 gauss)
55125–	300	127	.194	A2 & L6	YES	140 (< 300 gauss)

14 through 160μ types are available as high flux cores.

WINDING INFORMATION
FOR UNITY WINDING FACTOR**

AWG WIRE SIZE	TURNS	R_{DC} (Ohms)	AWG WIRE SIZE	TURNS	R_{DC} (Ohms)
17	22	0.00808	31	460	4.34
18	28	0.01276	32	560	6.54
19	34	0.02000	33	695	10.31
20	43	0.03192	34	885	16.63
21	54	0.04958	35	1,098	26.2
22	66	0.07747	36	1,355	40.5
23	83	0.1210	37	1,655	61.0
24	102	0.1896	38	2,069	96.5
25	127	0.295	39	2,663	162.4
26	158	0.467	40	3,363	259
27	199	0.737	41	4,138	393
28	245	1.150	42	5,275	630
29	299	1.747	43	6,405	987
30	374	2.80	44	7,370	1,374

*Further stabilization and grading information available from the vendor.
**The nominal DC resistance and the R_{DC} are theoretical values not attainable in practice.

Figure 5.12 Vendor's data sheet that applies to the core selected, number 55127. (From Ref. 2, p. 54.)

From this, we can find the percent of initial permeability from a. curve the manufacturer provides (Figure 5.13).

The 55127 core is 200μ, so referring to Figure 5.13, we are going to use curve 8. With 19 Oe, the percentage of initial permeability of this core is 75%. This means that the inductance at 2A is reduced to only 75% × 34μH = 25.5μH. To increase this inductance, we would have to add turns—but we are already past the 80% swing point. Adding turns would

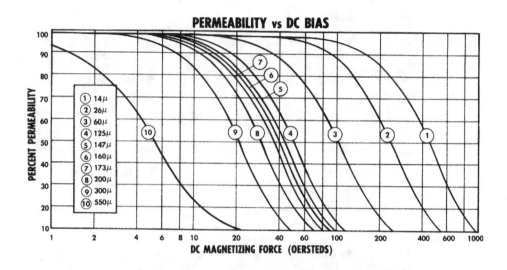

General equation:

$$\mu_e = \frac{\mu_i}{100} \sqrt{\frac{a+cH+eH^2}{1+bH+dH^2}}$$

where H = DC bias in oersteds

		μ_i	a	b	c	d	e
High Flux		14	10004	.0027514	26.879	.000011888	.041784
		26	9914.0	-.000088616	2.4260	.000037542	.012877
		60	10159	.00058116	-41.642	.000047498	.050984
		125	9952.5	-.0046907	-59.727	.00041074	.11038
		160	9993.9	.0017796	-107.06	.00047937	.29598
MPP		14	9949.6	-.0018420	-22.199	.0000045774	.013253
		26	9979.7	-.0039552	-42.541	.000018943	.050104
		60	10067	-.0054844	-63.702	.00012792	.10098
(Graph above)		125	10174	-.015802	-169.63	.00051688	.76876
		147	10279	-.016889	-221.49	.00054472	1.2934
		160	10238	-.018887	-220.62	.00074733	1.2676
		173	9996.2	-.017441	-157.84	.0012421	.34560
		200	10025	-.027999	-304.90	.0012754	2.5101
		300	10021	-.034600	-386.56	.0011600	4.2854
		550	9956.8	-.016354	-1054.6	.044933	34.653

Figure 5.13   Determining the percentage of initial permeability of the design according to the vendor's data. (From Ref. 2, p. 29; references to material not included in this book deleted.)

increase the flux density, even further increasing the swing. So instead, let's try a core with a lower permeability.

Second Try

For a second try, let's use a 125μ core (60, 125 and 300μ seem to be the easiest perms to get hold of). In this core size, this is the 55130 core. This core has an $A_L = 53$nH, so we need:

$$N = \sqrt{\frac{L}{A_L}} = \sqrt{\frac{35\mu H}{53nH}} = 25.7 \rightarrow 26 \text{ turns}$$

Again calculating, $H = 0.467 \times 26$ turns $\times 2A = 24$ Oe. This is higher than before, but remember that this is a lower perm core, and therefore a higher flux density doesn't necessarily mean a lower percent permeability!

Looking at Figure 5.13 again, a 125µ core is curve 4. At 24 Oe we have 80% of initial permeability. Now the actual inductance achieved is $L = A_L \times N^2 \times \%\text{perm} = 53\text{nH} \times 26^2 \times 80\% = 28.7\mu\text{H}$. We need to get this up to 35µH, so remembering that inductance goes as turns squared, we need to increase the turns to:

$$N = \sqrt{\frac{\text{desired inductance}}{\text{actual inductance}}} = \sqrt{\frac{35\mu\text{H}}{28.7\mu\text{H}}} = 29 \text{ turns}$$

We have $H = 0.467 \times 29$ turns $\times 2A = 27$ Oe, which is still 80% permeability, and, at last, $L = 53\text{nH} \times 29^2 \times 80\% = 35.7\mu\text{H}$. As a sidelight, $B = H \times \mu \times \%\text{perm} = 27$ Oe $\times 125 \times 80\% = 2700\text{G}$. Remember that this is DC flux density, and thus does not contribute to losses.

Practical Note The most common cores seem to be 60, 125 and 300µ. If you're in a rush to get a sample, you may find it best to select one of these.

Let's suppose that after a couple iterations like this (they take only a minute each), we find that the lowest perm core in this size doesn't make it. Or suppose the 60µ core doesn't make it, and we don't want unusual core types. Or again, suppose we didn't follow the selector guide and need to get the absolutely smallest possible core for the application. We then have three choices.

1. We could relax the criterion we had pre-established concerning the maximum swing in the core, allowing the inductance to start at a higher value. The effect of this is that the ripple current in the inductor, and thus the ripple voltage on the output capacitor, changes more from minimum to maximum load—perhaps not a big deal. It also means that the double-pole frequency set by the inductor and the output capacitor will move more—but again, perhaps this can be lived with.
2. We could go to a *high-perm* core, which are those (for Magnetics, Inc.) that start with a 58XXX rather than a 55XXX. These cores take a higher flux before saturating. Since, however, most of the improvement is in the range of 50% initial perm and up, this probably isn't going to help unless you've already implemented suggestion 1. In addition, all the high perm cores are special order, and cost somewhat more.
3. The final choice, obviously, is to go to the next core size up, and try again.

All these options take only a few minutes to explore, so a core can usually be selected within a quarter-hour.

Selecting the Wire

Now that we have selected a core and the number of turns to go on it to get the inductance specified, we can calculate the wire size that fits on this core, and thence the power dissipated. The process of wire selection is similar for all magnetic structures, so we're going to do it in great detail here, refering you back to this section when it's time to select wire for other magnetics designs.

From the data book (our Figure 5.12), the winding area of the 55127 core is 53,800 circular mils. (You were *warned* that these crazy units show up sometimes!) Now for a toroid, you can't actually fill up this entire winding area, because you couldn't get a winding tool into the tiny hole that's left when the core is wound. Besides, wire doesn't lay (pack) neatly. In practice, then, the best filling you can get on a toroid is 45–50% of the winding area (this is called the *fill factor*: see Figure 5.14).

Can't get more wire in

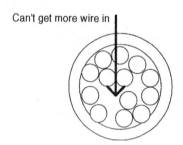

Figure 5.14   Wire can't fill entirely the winding area; 50% is typical maximum fill factor.

Don't forget, you also have to include the cross-sectional area contributed by the wire insulation! There's double (heavy), triple, and quad insulation, and all have different areas. It's surprisingly common for a designer to just pull out a table for bare copper wire, make a selection without thinking about it, and end up not being able to get those last couple of turns on. Also, small wire has its insulation as a greater percentage of its total cross section, and with the multiple thin wires known as litz, insulation can take up 50% of the available winding area!

So the cross-sectional area available for a single turn is going to be half the total winding area divided by the total number of turns:

$$A_L = \frac{\text{winding area fill factor}}{\text{number of turns}}$$

$$= \frac{53,800 \text{c.m.}/0.5}{29} = 928 \text{ c.m./turn}$$

Referring to Figure 5.15, we select the closest size, 22AWG, rounding <u>down</u> in area to avoid exceeding our 50% fill factor.

Calculating the Resistance

Having selected the wire gauge, we can now calculate the resistance of this winding on this core. Referring again to Figure 5.12, we are going to use the "100% fill factor" length per turn number. This choice has both a practical and a theoretical justification. Theoretically, our 50% fill factor is going to just about fill up the core, again because of insulation, packing, etc. Thus the 100% number is closer to reality. Practically, it has been found by winding many different cores over the years that the 100% gives a better approximation—and it's usually better to have an overestimate of the winding resistance than an underestimate.

Wire Table

AWG WIRE SIZE	RESISTANCE (ohms/foot)	WIRE AREA*		CURRENT CAPACITY (amperes)	
		Circular mils	cm² (×10⁻³)	(1)	(2)
8	.00063	18,000	91.2	22.0	44.0
9	.00079	14,350	72.7	17.5	35.0
10	.00100	11,500	58.2	13.8	27.6
11	.00126	9,160	46.4	11.0	22.0
12	.00159	7,310	37.0	8.71	17.4
13	.00200	5,850	29.6	6.91	13.8
14	.00252	4,680	23.7	5.48	10.9
15	.00318	3,760	19.1	4.35	8.70
16	.00402	3,000	15.2	3.44	6.88
17	.00505	2,420	12.2	2.74	5.48
18	.00639	1,940	9.83	2.17	4.34
19	.00805	1,560	7.91	1.72	3.44
20	.01013	1,250	6.34	1.37	2.74
21	.0128	1,000	5.07	1.083	2.17
22	.0162	810	4.11	.853	1.71
23	.0203	650	3.29	.681	1.36
24	.0257	525	2.66	.539	1.08
25	.0324	425	2.15	.427	.854
26	.0410	340	1.72	.337	.674
27	.0514	270	1.37	.269	.538
28	.0653	220	1.11	.212	.424
29	.0812	180	.912	.170	.340
30	.104	144	.730	.133	.266
31	.131	117	.593	.1056	.211
32	.162	96.0	.487	.0853	.171
33	.206	77.4	.392	.0672	.134
34	.261	60.8	.308	.0530	.106
35	.331	49.0	.248	.0418	.0836
36	.415	39.7	.201	.0333	.0666
37	.512	32.5	.165	.0270	.0540
38	.648	26.0	.132	.0213	.0426
39	.847	20.2	.102	.0163	.0326
40	1.07	16.0	.081	.0128	.0256
41	1.32	13.0	.066	.0105	.0210
42	1.66	10.2	.052	.00833	.0166
43	2.14	8.4	.043	.00645	.0129
44	2.59	7.3	.037	.00533	.0107
45	3.35	5.3	.027	.00412	.00824
46	4.21	4.4	.022	.00330	.00660
47	5.29	3.6	.018	.00259	.00518
48	6.75	2.9	.015	.00233	.00466
49	8.42	2.25	.011	.00200	.00400
50	10.58	1.96	.010	.00130	.00260

* Based on maximum diameter of heavy Formvar wire with insulation.
(1) Based on 750 cir mil/amp. (2) Based on 375 cir mil/amp. Current capacity will vary according to the geometry and wire size, and can range from 375 to 1000 circular mils per ampere.

Figure 5.15 Typical vendor's table for selecting a wire gauge. (From Ref. 2, p. 13.)

> **Practical Note** When the manufacturer doesn't give the length per turn for 100% fill factor, or (more commonly) doesn't tell you what fill factor the length per turn is for, a good approximation for all core sizes can be made as follows: length per turn = $OD + (2Ht)$, where OD is the unwound core outer diameter, and Ht is the unwound core height.

The catalog (Figure 5.12) lists the length per turn as 0.072 ft. The resistance per length of #22 wire, again from Figure 5.15, is 0.0162Ω/ft. The resistance (at 20°C) is thus

$$R = \text{length/turn} \times \text{number of turns} \times \text{resistance/length}$$
$$= 0.072\text{ft} \times 29 \text{ turns} \times 0.0162\Omega/\text{ft} = 34\text{m}\Omega$$

about half the 75mΩ we initially calculated as absolute maximum permissible.

Power Loss

So far we've calculated the DC flux density and the resistance. To find total power loss in the inductor (aside from temperature, which will be done iteratively, see below), we still need the AC flux density, which determines the core losses. Let's calculate this next.

Recall that our switching frequency is 250kHz, which is a period of 4μs. The duty cycle was 33% (because $V_{out}/V_{in} = 5\text{V}/15\text{V} = 33\%$), and so the peak-to-peak ripple current was 0.377A.

So the core has a peak-to-peak AC flux density of $H_{AC} = H/NI \times N \times I_{AC} =$ 0.467 × 29 turns × 0.377A = 5.1 Oe. Since the permeability is 125 × 80% = 100 (because the permeability has been reduced by the 2ADC current), the AC core flux density is $B_{AC} = H_{AC} \times \mu = 5$ Oe × 100 = 500G_{pp}.

Following the theoretical discussion above, we cannot find out what the core losses for this situation are really because the current waveform is triangular, not sinusoidal. Still, since all we have is losses for sinusoids, we're going to go ahead and get an approximate idea of the core losses by approximating the triangular waveshape with a sinusoid of the same peak-to-peak amplitude.

> **Practical Note** This approximation is one of the main reasons it's necessary to go to the lab and really measure your magnetics. It simply isn't possible to get really good power loss calculations for the core (you'll be doing very well if you're within 10–20%). Note however, that you can do much better when the magnetic piece really is a DC inductor, because if the AC ripple is zero, then so is the core loss.

Referring now to Figure 5.16, another chart from the Magnetics catalog, we find that with a flux density of 500G_{pp} at 250kHz, there is a core loss of approximately 30W/lb. [*Note*: This is a pretty crazy unit, huh? Other manufacturers give it in W/m^3.] The core has a weight of 0.0046 lb, so the core losses are about 140mW.

To get the total losses for the design, let's add in the copper loss: $P = I^2R$ = $(2A)^2 \times 34\text{m}\Omega = 136\text{mW}$ (at 20°C). Notice that the copper losses are just about the same as the core losses. Following our rule for optimal design, this means we have done a good job. If the ripple had been much smaller, yielding a smaller core loss, this would have told us to decrease the copper loss at the expense of increasing the core loss, which we would accomplish by removing turns, using a higher perm core, and letting the inductance swing more—just the direction we initially started from. In practical terms, this would mean that our restriction of not letting the inductance swing down to less than 80% of its initial

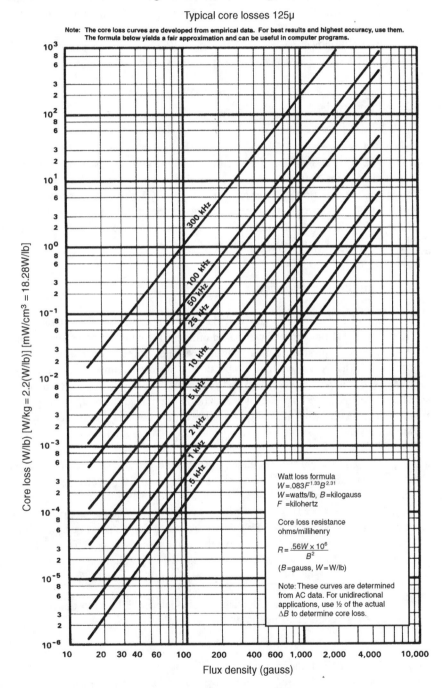

Figure 5.16 Calculating core loss. (From Ref. 2, p. 22.)

value would have been causing unnecessary losses. Of course, there may be a perfectly valid reason for limiting the swing, which in the case of a flyback is to prevent the pole set by the inductance from moving too much, as will become clear in questions of stabilizing the loop in the following chapter. At any rate, even though the losses are optimized already, at this point in the calculation it won't hurt to revisit this percent swing limitation to see if it can be usefully relaxed any.

The total power losses are $P = P_{core} + P_{wire} = 140mW + 136mW = 276mW$, and so we can estimate the temperature rise with the formula:

$$\Delta T = \left[\frac{(P(mW))}{SA(cm^2)}\right]^{0.833} = \left(\frac{276}{2.5}\right)^{0.833} = 50°C$$

where SA is the (wound) surface area of the inductor, which is listed in the Magnetics catalog [2, p. 4]. If the power loss and thence temperature rise were dominated by the copper losses, and if the temperature rise had proven to be excessive, we would also have been pushed in the direction of fewer turns. Realistically, in this case it might be necessary to go to the next core size up. Conversely, if the temperature rise seemed acceptably low, the entire calculation could be repeated for the next core size down, to see if a smaller (and therefore cheaper) core would work.

Temperature Dependence

With the 50°C rise, we can now calculate the copper losses as a function of temperature. (Remember that the 136mW was based on the assumption that the wire was at 20°C.) The goal here is to produce a final power loss and temperature rise estimate that is self-consistent. That is, we want the temperature at which the power loss is calculated to be the same as the temperature at which that power loss implies the core is going to be operating. The equations governing the two equations are transcendental, so they can't be given a convenient form; but in reality, for all practical designs the temperature can be solved for iteratively, in just one or two cycles. Let's do that here, so you can see an explicit example.

The temperature rise calculated by our first estimate, ΔT, was 50°C. So the resistance should be multiplied by a factor of $(1.0039)^{50} = 1.21$, because copper has a positive temperature coefficient of 0.39%/°C; that is, the resistance at 20°C + 50°C = 70°C is 34mΩ × 1.21 = 41mΩ. The new power loss is 165mW in the copper, which is 305mW total, for a temperature rise of 55°C. This is close to the temperature at which we calculated the copper resistance, and so the whole calculation is now self-consistent. If the core operates only at 25°C, this 55°C temperature rise is perfectly acceptable.

Practical Note In practical applications, however, it is often desirable to limit the magnetics temperature rise to about 40°C.

For example, if the inductor is going to operate in an ambient temperature as high as 70°C, the inductor will be getting up over 125°C, and so you need a cooler design. Don't forget about maximum ambient temperature when calculating the wire resistance, either!

Conclusion

As you see, there can be quite a bit of work involved in the design of even the simplest magnetic structure, a DC inductor. People who do such designs frequently tend to use computer programs. All the major manufacturers offer such design programs for their cores, although the software is of widely varying quality and usefulness—caveat emptor!

PRACTICAL DESIGN OF A FLYBACK TRANSFORMER

Although we're not using a flyback transformer in our design of a buck converter (obviously), we'll give an exemplary design for one, because a flyback transformer is halfway between an inductor and a transformer, as indicated above, and deserves it own treatment for clarity. The presentation of the design work will be slightly less detailed than that for the DC inductor, but only on the aspects that are truly the same. Note that the design is for an isolated flyback; however, the design of a nonisolated flyback's inductor would be almost the same, except for the absence of a secondary. Let's suppose the following design requirements: a 48VDC input (for simplicity, we'll assume there is no line variation) and desired power output of 10W. Switching frequency is 250kHz. You've allotted 0.2W for losses (based on total losses you can allow to meet the converter's efficiency requirements), so the transformer has to be 98% efficient ($0.2W/10W = 2\%$). This sort of efficiency is going to give you a moderate sized piece of magnetics; if the transformer has to be smaller, the efficiency will go down.

You can design the primary of an (isolated, discontinuous conduction mode) flyback transformer with just these four pieces of information: power output, switching frequency, losses, and input voltage. (They are also sufficient for designing the inductor of a nonisolated flyback.) Note that nothing has been said about inductance! Inductance is determined by the other parameters, as will become apparent below.

Let's say you're using the PWM chip UC3845, (a moderately priced 8-pin device), so the maximum duty cycle is 45%. The choice of maximum duty cycle is going to be related to the decision of whether this flyback is going to operate in continuous mode or discontinuous mode; we'll calculate it below. Our goal is going to be discontinuous mode for this example.

Let's set one more design goal: the transformer should be low profile, perhaps because of height constraints. It turns out that transformer design is not as straightforward as inductor design; there are always quite a few different magnetic cores that could be used to achieve the same electrical parameters. In this case, other criteria must be used to choose a core, based on size, or cost, or something else.

Equations Governing the Flyback

Let's do some basics first. As described in the theoretical portion at the beginning of this chapter, when the switch attached to the flyback transformer primary is on, the primary is acting like an inductor. Thus, we have a voltage applied across the inductance of the primary, and that results in a current that ramps up for as long as the switch is on:

$$I_{pk} = \frac{V}{L}t_{on} = \frac{V \times DC \times T}{L} = \frac{V \times DC}{f \times L}$$

where DC is the duty cycle, f is the switching frequency, and $T = 1/f$ is the switching period. This equation is valid because we are designing a discontinuous mode flyback. Remember that the current in the primary looks like the sketch in Figure 5.17.

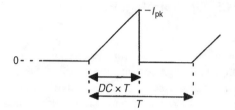

Figure 5.17 Current in a discontinuous mode flyback.

Now the energy stored in the primary inductance depends on the peak current:

$$E = \frac{LI_{pk}^2}{2} = \frac{V^2 DC^2}{2f^2 L}$$

and since this energy is delivered once every cycle,

$$P = Ef = \frac{V^2 DC^2}{2f L}$$

This equation is fundamental for the discontinuous mode flyback. It says that once the input voltage has been determined, to increase output power you have to either decrease the frequency or decrease the inductance; there are no other choices. Once the switching frequency has been chosen, all you can do to increase power is to decrease the inductance. Since there is a practical minimum to the inductance (set by, say, 10 times the stray inductances—let's say 5µH), there is a practical maximum amount of power you can get out of a discontinuous mode flyback converter, on the order of 50–100W.

Practical Note At low input voltages above about 50W, you shouldn't be trying to design a flyback converter.

We've assumed that we're switching at 250kHz (perhaps set by switching transistor limitations). Calculating,

$$10W = \frac{(48V)^2(0.45)^2}{(2 \times 250,000)L}$$

or $L = 93\,\mu H$. We can now find I_{pk}:

$$I_{pk} = \frac{48V \times 0.45}{250kHz \times 93\mu H} = 0.93A$$

Selecting a Core Material Type

Now we need to select a core material to achieve this inductance. Since the switching frequency is relatively high, we pick ferrite; another possibility would be MPP, and a full-blown design would properly consider that too, repeating all the steps herein. For simplicity of presentation, only the ferrite is considered, since it will probably turn out that the ferrite design is substantially smaller for the same efficiency than the MPP core design would be.

We already know that (in engineering units of centimeters, amps, and gauss)

$$B_{max} = \frac{0.4\pi I_{max} N \mu}{l_m} \tag{5.1a}$$

and

$$L = \frac{0.4\pi N^2 A_e 10^{-8} \mu}{l_m} \tag{5.1b}$$

with l_m the magnetic path length. Now for the small ferrite cores that we will be using, the magnetic path length is pretty tiny, with the result that B would be very large, probably saturating the core, and in any case certainly dissipating a lot of power. For this reason, *flyback transformers* (and any DC inductors that use ferrite) *always use an air gap*. The air gap greatly increases the effective magnetic path length because the permeability of air is so very much lower than that of ferrite. The effective path length for a core with an air gap is

$$l_e = l_m + \mu \times l_{gap} \tag{5.2}$$

In many practical cases it turns out that the second term of this equation is much larger than the first,

$$\mu \times l_{gap} \gg l_m \tag{5.3}$$

so that it is a reasonable approximation that

$$l_e \approx \mu \times l_{gap}$$

Note: This is only an approximation; it is not always true! You need to check that this approximation is true in every design, every time you use it.

Substituting in with this approximation, we have

$$B = \frac{0.4\pi I_{max} N}{l_{gap}} \quad \text{and} \quad L = \frac{0.4\pi N^2 A_e 10^{-8}}{l_{gap}} \tag{5.4}$$

Let's make it 100% clear about the usage of these equations: when there is an air gap in a ferrite (or other high perm) material, use equations 5.4, after verifying the validity of the approximation (equation 5.3); otherwise, use the fundamental equations shown in equations (5.1a) and (5.1b), remembering to use the effective path length (equation 5.2) when there is a very small air gap.

Core Selection

Unsurprisingly, it is usually necessary in actual practice to go through several different styles of cores to determine which is the best for a given application. The case we are designing for, however, had low transformer profile as a design criterion, which eliminates most styles from consideration. So we are going to go ahead and use the EFD style core (the name stands for "Economic Flat Design"); it would probably be reasonable to look at some other cores as well as this one when the design is finished, but we won't pursue that in the interest of space.

So let's pick the smallest EFD core, the EFD10, made, for example, by Philips [3], and see if we can squeeze the 10W out of it. If not, then we'll have to go up a core size. The information for this core is in the Philips soft ferrite cores catalog, reproduced as Figure 5.18.

Selecting Core Material

Now we can select a core material for this core. Referring to pages of the Philips catalog reproduced in Figure 5.19, we see that there are quite a few power materials from which to choose. In fact, if we look at other manufacturers' data books, there seems to be almost an endless variety, no two manufacturers making the same set of materials, not even materials with identical characteristics. How to choose?

Let's start by just talking about Philips's materials [1]. In the old days, everyone used a material referred to as 3C6A for everything in power. This material was pretty poorly characterized and had very high losses; it is now marketed as 3C80 and is used only in the most cost-sensitive applications. It was replaced by 3C8 material, which is now called 3C81. However, as converter switching frequencies continued to rise, Philips [1] came out with various new materials—remember that core losses grow faster than linearly with frequency. So nowadays, there is a whole set of power core materials, and we can pretty much choose one based on switching frequency alone.

This also answers the problem presented by the availability of so many differing sets of core materials from each manufacturer. Closer examination will show that all have (at least roughly) similar materials for each frequency range, and indeed it is not uncommon in a magnetics specification to state that the core material used can be any one from a listed set, one from each manufacturer. Small differences in the materials are swallowed up by the tolerances of the various parameters in the construction of the magnetic core material.

Since we said that the switching frequency of this flyback was going to be 250kHz, we look across the soft ferrite materials selection table (Figure 5.19), and find that the recommended material is 3F3 (or, again, an equivalent from a different manufacturer). This material is very good, with losses half those of 3C85 at the same frequency; but things keep changing in this field, and you need to stay aware of the materials currently available. Perhaps there will be a better choice by the time you read this, but for our EFD10 core, we will choose 3F3 material.

Selecting the Gap

Having selected the core shape and material, we next select an air gap. The natural way to go about this might seem to be to target a peak flux density (based, e.g., on losses) and then

EFD Cores

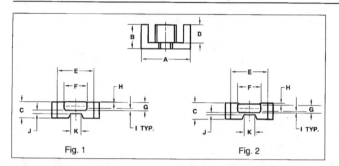

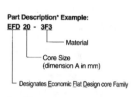

Part Description* Example:
EFD 20 - 3F3

— Material

— Core Size
(dimension A in mm)

— Designates Economic Flat Design core Family

* Part Description is for a core half.

Fig. 1   Fig. 2

CORE DESCRIPTION	DIMENSIONS										
	A in/mm	B in/mm	C in/mm	D in/mm	E in/mm	F in/mm	G in/mm	H in/mm	I in/mm	J in/mm	K in/mm
EFD10 (Fig. 1)	.413 ±.012 10.5	.205 ±.004 5.2	.106 ±.004 2.7	.148 ±.006 3.75	.301 ±.01 7.65	.179 ±.006 4.55	.057 ±.002 1.45	.008 ±.004 0.2	.008 ±.004 0.2	.031 ±.004 .8	.118 REF 3.0
EFD12 (Fig. 2)	.492 ±.012 12.5	.244 ±.004 6.2	.138 ±.004 3.5	.179 ±.006 4.55	.354 ±.01 8.99	.213 ±.006 5.4	.079 ±.004 2.0	.008 ±.004 0.2	.008 ±.004 0.2	.031 ±.004 .8	.138 REF 3.5
EFD15 (Fig. 1)	.591 ±.016 15.0	.295 ±.006 7.5	.183 ±.006 4.65	.217 ±.010 5.5	.433 ±.014 11.0	.209 ±.006 5.3	.094 ±.004 2.4	.008 ±.004 0.2	.020 ±.004 0.5	.031 ±.004 .8	.138 ±.004 3.5
EFD20 (Fig. 2)	.787 ±.022 20.0	.394 ±.006 10.0	.262 ±.006 6.7	.303 ±.010 7.7	.606 ±.020 15.4	.350 ±.008 8.9	.142 ±.006 3.6	.007 ±.004 0.2	.031 ±.004 0.8	.031 ±.004 .8	.177 ±.008 4.5
EFD25 (Fig. 2)	.984 ±.026 25.0	.492 ±.006 12.5	.358 ±.008 9.1	.366 ±.010 9.3	.736 ±.024 18.7	.449 ±.008 11.4	.205 ±.006 5.2	.024 ±.004 0.6	.039 ±.004 1.0	.039 ±.004 1.0	.197 ±.008 5.0
EFD30 (Fig. 2)	1.181 ±.031 30.0	.591 ±.006 15.0	.358 ±.008 9.1	.441 ±.012 11.2	.882 ±.030 22.4	.575 ±.010 14.6	.193 ±.006 4.9	.030 ±.004 0.8	.039 ±.004 1.0	.039 ±.004 1.0	.236 ±.008 6.0

CORE DESCRIPTION	EFFECTIVE CORE PARAMETERS				A_L(nH) FOR UNGAPPED CORE SETS		
	le in/mm	Ae in²/mm²	Ve in³/mm³	C1 in⁻¹/mm⁻¹	3C85 ±25%	3F3 ±25%	3F4 ±25%
EFD10	.933 23.7	0.011 7.2	0.01 171	83.82 3.30	—	500	280
EFD12	1.12 28.5	0.018 11.4	0.02 325	63.5 2.50	—	700	380
EFD15	1.34 34.0	.023 15.0	.031 510	58.26 2.27	—	700	400
EFD20	1.85 47.0	.048 31.0	.089 1460	38.54 1.52	—	1150	580
EFD25	2.24 56.9	.090 58.1	.201 3300	24.89 1.00	2000	1800	
EFD30	2.68 68.0	.107 69.0	.287 4700	25.05 0.98	2100	1900	

Figure 5.18 A vendor's EFD core data sheet. For gapped core information, users are referred to pages 24 and 25 of Ref. 3; page 25 is reproduced below as Figure 5.21. (From Ref. 3, p. 18.)

Soft Ferrite Materials Selection Table

				FILTER INDUCERS			
PARAMETER[1]	SYMBOL	UNIT	TEST CONDITION	3B7	3B9	3D3	4C6
Suggested Freq. Range	f	MHz	—	< 0.3	< 0.3	< 2.5	< 20.0
Initial Permeability	μ_i	—	T = 25°C, B < 1mT	2300	1800	750	100
Saturation Flux Density @ Field Intensity	Bs @H	mT A/m	T = 25°C	410 250	350 250	370 1000	380 3000
Remanence	Br	mT	T = 25°C	150	125	160	200
Coercive Force	Hc	A/m	T = 25°C	15	20	80	250
Relative Loss Factor (x 10⁻⁶)	tan δ / μi	—	f = 100 kHz, B < 0.1 mT f = 300 kHz, B < 0.1 mT f = 1 MHz, B < 0.1 mT f = 3 MHz, B < 0.1 mT	≤ 5 12	≤ 5 16	— ≤ 10 ≤ 30	— — 25 ≤60
Power Loss Density[2] @ T = 100°C (Sinewave Excitation)	Pv	mW/cm³	f = 25kHz, B = 200mT f = 100kHz, B = 100mT f = 500kHz, B = 50mT f = 1MHz, B = 30mT	—	—	—	—
Temperature Factor (x 10⁻⁶) in the Temp. Range	TF ΔT	K⁻¹ °C	f = 10kHz, min max	- 0.6 + 0.6 +20 – +70	+ 0.9 + 1.9 -30 – +70	+ 0.5 + 2.5 +25 – +70	0 + 6.0 +5 – +55
Curie Temperature	Tc	°C	—	≥ 170	≥ 145	≥ 200	≥ 350
DC Resistivity	ρ	Ω.m	T = 25°C	≈ 1	≈ 1	≈ 2	≈ 10⁵
Density	δ	g/cm³	—	≈ 4.8	≈ 4.8	≈ 4.7	≈ 4.5
	Planar E Cores		Page 5	—	—	—	—
	Pot Cores & PT Cores		Pages 6, 7, 8, 9, 10	●	●	●	●
	PQ Cores		Page 11	—	—	—	—
Available	RM Cores		Pages 12, 13	●	●	●	●
Core	E, EC, ETD Cores		Pages 14, 15, 16,17	—	—	—	—
Shapes	EFD Cores		Page 18 (Fig 5.18, this book)	—	—	—	—
	EP Cores		Page 19	—	—	—	—
	U&I Cores		Page 20, 21	—	—	—	—
	Toroidal (Ring) Cores		Pages 22,23	●	—	●	—

NOTES:
1. Values shown are based upon measurements on toroidal test cores with OD = 25mm, ID = 15mm, HT = 10mm. Products generally do not fully comply with the material specification. Deviations may occur due to shape, size, grinding operations etc.
2. Typical values. See detailed material specification for guaranteed power losses. Each core in our catalogs has a guaranteed power loss specification.
3. For detailed material information, request our Soft Ferrite Material Selection Guide, PC1062.

Figure 5.19   Catalog pages showing characteristics of the vendor's soft ferrite materials. (From Ref. 3, pp. 2–3.)

determine a gap that gives this flux. (What is meant, of course, is that knowing <u>both</u> the flux density and the desired inductance is what determines the gap—of course the flux density alone is insufficient because of its dependence on the number of turns.) The problem with this approach is that it ends up with an odd gap size that will have to be specially ground for this transformer—read money. Another potential problem with making a selection this way is that the gap could end up being very small, in which case the tolerance on the gap could have a significant effect on the flux density achieved, and thence the losses; there might even be the potential for saturation of the core.

Soft Ferrite Materials Selection Table

WIDE BAND & PULSE TRANSFORMERS, EMI INDUCTORS				POWER TRANSFORMERS & INDUCTORS					MAGN. AMP.	
4C4/4C65	3E2A	3E25	3E5	3C80	3C81	3C85	3F3	3F4	3R1	SYMBOL
—	—	—	—	< 0.1	< 0.1	< 0.2	0.2–0.5	0.5–3.0	—	f
125	5000	6000	10000	2000	2700	2000	1800	900	800	μ_i
380 3000	410 250	380 250	360 250	500 3000	500 3000	500 3000	500 3000	450 3000	450 3000	Bs @H
200	100	100	80	150	100	150	150	150	340	Br
250	5	5	5	20	15	15	15	60	40	Hc
— — 40 ≤ 80	≤ 10 25 — —	≤ 25 ≤ 200 — —	≤ 75 (≤ 25 @ f = 30kHz) — —	—	—	—	—	—	—	$\tan\delta / \mu_i$
—	—	—	—	100 — — —	90 @ 50°C — — —	80 90 — —	50 180	180 140	—	Pv
—	—	—	—	—	—	—	—	—	—	TF
≥ 350	≥ 170	≥125	≥125	≥ 200	≥ 210	≥ 200	≥ 200	≥ 220	≥ 200	Tc
$\approx 10^5$	≈ 0.5	≈ 0.5	≈ 0.5	≈ 1	≈ 1	≈ 2	≈ 2	≈ 10	≈ 1	ρ
≈ 4.5	≈ 4.8	≈ 4.9	≈ 4.9	≈ 4.8	≈ 4.8	≈ 4.8	≈ 4.8	≈ 4.7	≈ 4.7	δ
—	—	—	—	—	—	●	●	●	—	Planar E
—	●	●		—	●	●	●	●	—	P, PT
—	—	—	—	—	●	●	●		—	PQ
—	●	●	●	—	●	●	●	●	—	RM
—	●	●	—	●	●	●	●		—	E, EC, ETD
—	—	—	—	—	—	●	●	●	—	EFD
—	—	●	●	—	●	●	●	●	—	EP
—	●	●	—	●	●	●	●		—	U&I
●	●	●	●	—	●	●	●		●	T, RCC

Figure 5.19 (*Continued*)

Practical Note It's not really practical to specify an air gap less than 10–20 mils (thousandths of an inch; i.e., 0.25–0.5mm) because the tolerance on the grinding is 1–2 mils (0.025–0.05mm). Below this value, your only safe bet is to buy a pregapped core for which the manufacturer guarantees an A_L rather than a gap size.

Even with a pregapped core, you have to worry about how much this gap will change when the two core halves are clamped together if the gap is too small: a glue will add to the gap length (especially if the glue thickness varies from unit to unit), and if you pot the core, it may expand. There are all sorts of problems; designing with a gap larger than 20 mils avoids many of them.

Practical Note When you buy a core set that has a given A_L, it frequently has one half gapped and the other half ungapped. Thus, for lab work, you can achieve A_L values equal to half those listed in the book by putting together two gapped halves. Of course, then you're stuck with a bunch of ungapped halves.

Practical Note When you build your own gapped core in the lab, a common "gotcha" occurs when you try to put spacers in each of the two outer legs of the core (e.g., with multiple layers of 2-mil Mylar tape) and make each spacer equal to the desired gap. You need to remember that the gap you calculate is the total air path length, which is the sum of the center post path and (either one of the) outer post paths. (There are two complete paths, one through either side of the structure.) Since putting gaps on the outside legs also creates a gap in the center post, the gap you put into each leg should be half of this (see Figure 5.20).

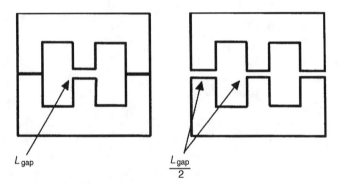

Figure 5.20   A center gap is equal to twice a side gap.

Practical Note If you want to have the equivalent of a 50 mil gap at the center post, you need to put spacers in the sides each of thickness 25 mils.

Returning to selecting a gap for our core, and looking at another page of the Philips catalog (Figure 5.21), we see that for the EFD10, there are five different A_L values available as standard products. Without thinking about it very deeply, we might suppose that 93μH seems like a lot of inductance on such a physically small core, so let's start by trying the core with the highest A_L. Since this implies it will have the fewest turns, it will also have the lowest winding resistance, which sounds promising. The highest A_L for this core is listed as 160nH. To get 93μH we need

$$N = \sqrt{\frac{93\mu H}{160nH}} = 24 \text{ turns}$$

Standard A_L Values For Gapped E Core Families
FOR 3C80, 3C81, 3C85, 3F3 MATERIALS

PART DESCRIPTION[1] New/(Old)	A_L(nH) ±3% / µe				
E CORE SETS					
E13/6.4-"M"-A_	40	63	100	160	250*
(814E250PA_-"M")	44	69	109	175	273
E19/4.7-"M"-A_	40	63	100	160	250*
(813E187PA_)	56	89	141	225	352
E19/8.7-"M"-A_	63	100	160	250	315
(813E343PA_-"M")	48	77	123	192	242
E25/6.4-"M"-A_	63	100	160	250	315
(812E250PA_-"M")	64	102	163	255	321
E25/7.2-"M"-A_	100	160	250	315	400
(New)	89	142	222	280	356
E30/6.9-"M"-A_	100	160	250	315	400
(782E272PA_-"M")	91	145	227	286	363
E31/9.4-"M"-A_	160	250	315	400	630
(New)	95	148	187	237	373
E34/9.3-"M"-A_	160	250	315	400	630
(E375PA_-"M")	109	170	214	272	428
E41/12-"M"-A_	160	250	315*	400*	630**
(E21PA_-"M")	66	104	131	166	262
E42/15-"M"-A_	250	315	400*	630*	1000**
(783E608PA_-"M")	108	136	172	271	431
E42/20-"M"-A_	250	315	400	630*	1000**
(783E776PA_-"M")	84	105	134	211	334
E47/16-"M"-A_	250	315	400	630*	1000**
(E625PA_-"M")	76	95	121	191	302
E50/15-"M"-A_	250	315	400	630*	1000**
(New)	106	133	169	267	424
E55/21-"M"-A_	315	400	630	1000*	1600**
(E55PA_-"M")	88	112	176	280	448
E56/19-"M"-A_	315	400	630	1000*	1600**
(E75PA_-"M")	79	101	158	251	402
E65/27-"M"-A_	400	630	1000	1600*	2500**
(E65PA_-"M")	88	138	219	350	547
E80/20-"M"-A_	315	400	630	1000*	1600**
(New)	118	150	236	374	598
E83/38-"M"-A_	630	1000	1600*	2500**	3150**
(New)	121	193	308	482	607
PLANAR E CORE SETS (E CORE WITH PLATE)					
EI14/5.0-"M"-A_	25	40	63	100	160
(New)	23	37	58	92	148*
EI18/6.0-"M"-A_	63	100	160	250	315
(New)	26	41	65	102	129
EI22/8.2-"M"-A_	160	250	315	400	630
(New)	42	66	83	106	166
EI32/9.6-"M"-A_	160	250	315*	400*	630**
(New)	35	55	69	87	138
EI38/12-"M"-A_	250	315	400	630*	1000**
(New)	45	57	72	113	180
EI43/14-"M"-A_	250	315	400	630*	1000**
(New)	45	57	72	113	180
EI58/15-"M"-A_	315	400	630*	1000*	1600*
(New)	56	71	112	178	285

Part Description Example:

E 30/6.9 - 3F3 - A100

- A_L value (nH) or GAP size (µm)
  - A-unsymmetrical gap
  - E-symmetrical gap
  - G-mechanical gap
- Material
- Dimensions in mm
  - A/C† FOR E, I, U & T cores
  - A/2xB for P, PT, PTS, PTR & PQ cores
  - A for EC, EFD, EP and ETD cores
- Core shape

†For EI sets: "B" of E core + "C" of PLT core

PART DESCRIPTION[1] New/(Old)	A_L(nH) ±3% / µe				
EC CORE SETS					
EC35-"M"-A_	63	100	160	250	315*
(EC35PA_-"M")	46	73	117	184	231
EC41-"M"-A_	63	100	160	250	315
(EC41PA_-"M")	37	59	94	147	186
EC52-"M"-A_	63	100	160	250	315
(EC52PA_-"M")	29	46	74	116	147
EC70-"M"-A_	160	250	315	400	630*
(EC70PA_-"M")	65	102	130	165	256
EFD CORE SETS					
EFD10-"M"-A_	25	40	63	100*	160*
(New)	66	105	165	263	420
EFD12-"M"-A_	40	63	100	160*	250**
(New)	80	125	199	318	497
EFD15-"M"-A_	63	100	160*	250*	315**
(New)	114	181	289	452	567
EFD20-"M"-A_	63	100	160	250	315*
(New)	76	121	194	302	381
EFD25-"M"-A_	100	160	250	315	400
(New)	80	127	199	251	318
EFD30-"M"-A_	100	160	250	315	400
(New)	78	125	195	246	312
ETD CORE SETS					
ETD29-"M"-A_	100	160	250	315	400
(ETD29PA_-"M")	75	120	188	237	300
ETD34-"M"-A_	100	160	250	315*	400
(ETD34PA_-"M")	65	103	161	203	258
ETD39-"M"-A_	160	250	315	400	630*
(ETD39PA_-"M")	94	147	185	235	370
ETD44-"M"-A_	160	250	315	400	630*
(ETD44PA_-"M")	75	117	148	187	295
ETD49-"M"-A_	250	315	400	630*	1000*
(ETD49PA_-"M")	106	134	170	267	425
ETD54-"M"-A_	250	315	400	630*	1000**
(New)	90	114	145	228	361
ETD59-"M"-A_	315	400	630	1000*	1600**
(New)	95	120	190	301	481

NOTES:
      * means A_L tolerance = 5%   ** means A_L tolerance = 10%
1. Substitute selected material for "M" and fill in an A_L value after A in part description.
2. RM6R is also available in 4C6 with A_L=63, µe=41.
3. A_L measured @ f=10kHz, B≤1mT, T=25°C, Fill factor ≥ 80%, Clamping pressure ≅ 1N/mm² (≅ 150PSI).

Figure 5.21   Off-the-shelf pregapped EFD cores: vendor's table of A_L values. (From Ref. 3, p. 25.)

Note: The gap can be calculated by looking up $A_e = 0.072\text{cm}^2$, so that

$$160\text{nH} = \frac{0.4\pi \ (1 \ \text{turn})^2 \ 0.072 \times 10^{-8}}{l_g}$$

which yields gap $= 0.0057\text{cm} = 2.2$ mils—tiny! Clearly, this is not the sort of gapping you should try to achieve on your own.

Knowing the gap, we can now find the flux density,

$$B = \frac{0.4\pi \times 0.93\text{A} \times 24 \ \text{turns}}{0.0057\text{cm}} = 4970\text{G}$$

which is greater than the saturation flux density of the core at 100°C of 3300G. (Although on the other hand it just squeaks by under the saturation flux density at 25°C of 5000G— conceivably you could be fooled in the lab!)

Continuing through the available options with the same calculations we find the set of values listed in Table 5.5. The last ($A_L = 25\text{nH}$) is the largest gap pregapped core Philips offers. Of this list, only the last two have flux densities less than the 100°C saturation flux density of 3F3 of 3000G, so we won't consider any further the cores with $A_L = 63$ and 100nH.

TABLE 5.5 Calculating Flux Densities of Pregapped Cores

A_L (nH)	N	l_g (cm)	B (G)
100	30	0.0090	3848
63	38	0.0144	3070
40	48	0.0226	2463
25	61	0.0362	1956

Core Loss

How about core loss for our two choices, $A_L = 25$ and 40nH? In a flyback, as shown at the beginning of the chapter, current is unidirectional, and therefore so is flux density: it increases from 0 to B_{max} and then back to zero, so that the peak to peak flux density is half of B_{max}. For the 3F3 material at 250kHz, losses at $2463\text{G}/2 = 1231\text{G}$ are approximately 330mW/cm^3; at $1956\text{G}/2 = 978\text{G}$ they are approximately 170mW/cm^3. (The Philips catalog also describes 3F3 characteristics: see Figure 5.22).

How Did He Read That Little Graph?

No, the author can't read tiny little graphics any better than you can—the trick is to write an equation of the form mW/cm$^3 = a \times B^x$, where a and x are constants, and determine their values by selecting two points that cross axis lines exactly so you can read their values well. There are then two equations in two unknowns, easily solved by hand or with a math program.

To be specific, for 3F3 material at 200kHz, we can pick 500G, where the losses are 20mW/cm^3, and 800G, with 80W/cm^3. The two equations are:

$$20 = a500^x$$

$$80 = a800^x$$

1 SERIES 3F3 FERRITE MATERIALS

Core Loss vs. Flux Density

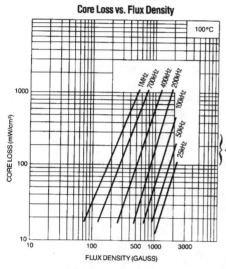

* Recommended operating range for loss limited designs.
Flux density for bipolar excitation is B.
Flux density for unipolar excitation is $\frac{Bp \cdot p}{2}$.

Core Loss vs. Temperature

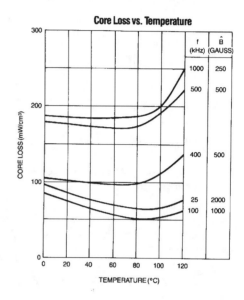

f (kHz)	B̂ (GAUSS)
1000	250
500	500
400	500
25	2000
100	1000

Permeability (μ_a) vs. Flux Density (B̂)

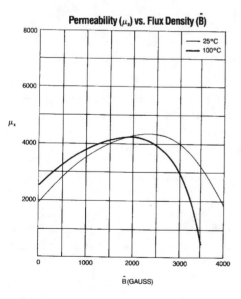

Hysteresis Curve

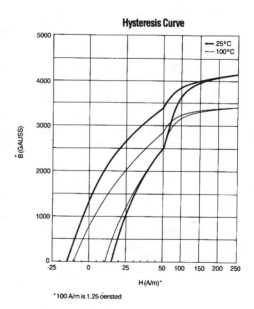

* 100 A/m is 1.25 oersted

Figure 5.22   Vendor's presentation of 3F3 characteristics. (From Ref. 1, p. 37.)

Multiplying the first equation by 4 on both sides gives

$$80 = 4a500^x$$

which combines with the second equation to give

$$4 \times 500^x = 800^x$$

Taking logarithms of both sides, we have

$$\ln(4) + x\ln(500) = x\ln(800)$$

which at once solves as $x = 2.94$. Substituting back into the original equation, $a = 2.19 \times 10^{-7}$. Thus, at 200kHz,

$$\text{mW/cm}^3 = (2.19 \times 10^{-7})B^{2.94}$$

Rather than try to interpolate based on frequency, we'll get into the right ballpark at 250kHz by simply multiplying this by a factor of $(250\text{kHz}/200\text{kHz}) = 1.25$, which is the source of the preceding estimates.

Can I Get Lower Core Losses by Lowering the Switching Frequency?

To answer this question, recall from the theoretical part of this chapter that losses depend nonlinearly on both frequency and flux density. A typical relationship might be

$$\text{losses/lb} = f^{1.2}B^{2.3}$$

So, for instance, let's see what happens if the switching frequency is cut in half:

$$f \to \frac{f}{2}$$
$$L \to 2L$$
$$N \to \sqrt{2}N$$
$$B \to \sqrt{2}B$$

because, respectively, we double the inductance to maintain the power level; which means root 2 times the number of turns to double the inductance; which increases B by root 2, because B is proportional to the number of turns.

Total losses, which are losses per pound times weight, therefore go as

$$\left(\frac{f}{2}\right)^{1.2}(\sqrt{2}B)^{2.3}(2L) \approx 1.92fBL$$

because core weight is directly dependent on the energy stored, which is linear in inductance. Thus core losses have almost doubled with a cut in half the switching frequency. On the other hand, a lower switching frequency does decrease switching transistor losses proportionately to frequency:

$$P_Q \approx K + Af$$

where K is set by the on-state losses and A by the switching speed. Therefore,

$$P_Q\left(\frac{f}{2}\right) \approx 0.5P_Q(f)$$

if the switching losses dominate over the on-state losses (as will be true at fairly high switching frequencies). The moral of the story is that in a typical situation, changing the switching frequency doesn't have huge effects on efficiency, though there may be an overall broad optimum to be found. The real benefits will be seen in the size of the magnetics, which decreases with increasing frequency.

Returning to the core losses calculation, the total volume of the core is $171\text{mm}^3 = 0.171\text{cm}^3$. Thus for losses for the first of the two cores we have $330\text{mW/cm}^3 \times 0.171\text{cm}^3 = 56\text{mW}$, and for the second, $170\text{mW/cm}^3 \times 0.171\text{cm}^3 = 29\text{mW}$. Total losses, you recall, were supposed to be only 0.2W, so this seems to be working nicely so far; let's pick the lower A_L core for our design.

Had the core losses been unacceptably high, we would have two choices: either try to increase the gap still further, by mating two ground pieces or with a custom gap, or go on up to the next size core. As the gap gets larger, though, we start to have significant fringing (the magnetic field couples through the air out of the magnetic structure), which is to say there is increased leakage inductance. The increased leakage inductance will start to contribute to losses in the other elements of the circuit, negating the benefits we thought we were getting with the more efficient transformer design. On the other hand, a larger core takes up more board area, and costs more. As always in engineering, there are trade-offs to be evaluated.

Winding Losses

We can now calculate the copper losses for this design. This style core doesn't list the winding area, so let's figure it up directly from the specified core dimensions, given in Figure 5.23.

When calculating the winding area, remember that the wire goes in on one side and then back out the other side to complete the loop on the other side, so the winding area for half the core, as shown in Figure 5.23 (the whole unit consists of two of these pieces mated together) is the shaded area. Total winding area (WA) for this core is then double this,

$$WA = \frac{0.301 \text{ in.} - 0.179 \text{ in.}}{2} \times (0.148 \text{ in.} \times 2) = 0.0181 \text{ in.}^2$$

For a core of this shape, we may be able to achieve a fill factor as high as 80%. (If you need primary-to-secondary isolation, you had better count on substantially less fill factor: first allot the necessary area for the tape, and then use 80% for the wire in the remaining area.)

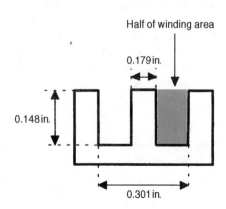

Figure 5.23 Calculating the winding area of an E core (not drawn to scale).

We can thus calculate the area per turn, remembering to use only half the winding area for the primary (so that we have half for the secondary):

$$\text{area/turn} = \frac{0.0181 \text{ in.}^2 \times 0.8}{(2)61 \text{ turns}} = 0.00012 \text{ in.}^2$$

$$= 28 \text{ AWG}$$

To get a conservative bound on the length per turn of the wire, let's assume that it goes from edge to edge of the winding area and is square in the third dimension (i.e., it would be bounded by a cube if removed from the core):

$$\text{length per turn} \approx 0.301 \text{ in.} \times 4 = 1.2 \text{ in. (conservative)}$$

So the resistance at 20°C will be not more than

$$R_{\text{DC}} = 1.2 \text{ in.} \times 61 \text{ turns} \times \frac{1000 \text{ ft}}{12,000 \text{ in.}} \times \frac{65.3\Omega}{1000 \text{ ft}} = 400\text{m}\Omega$$

The wire resistance of course goes up at higher temperatures. Supposing that the final magnetics temperature is 60°C (which can be figured out iteratively as was done in the DC inductor example above), the wire resistance will be

$$R = R_{20°C} \times 1.0039^{(60°C-20°C)} = 400\text{m}\Omega \times 1.0039^{40} = 467\text{m}\Omega$$

Usually, it is close enough to estimate the wire temperature from the ambient temperature and the power allotted for dissipation in the magnetic (using the surface area approximation demonstrated above). Otherwise, it can be done iteratively.

Do I Need to Worry About Skin Effect?

The skin effect causes current to flow in a sheath on the outside of a conductor. How deep the sheath is (the *skin depth*) depends on the frequency; at a low enough frequency, the skin depth is greater than the radius of the wire, in which case the entire cross-sectional area of the wire is being used. Thus at frequencies typical of switching power supplies, the skin effect can be important: doubling the cross-sectional area of a wire will not necessarily halve the resistance because the current stays on the outside of the wire.

On the other hand, going to multiple thin wires (litz) is not always a good idea either. Since each strand of the litz is individually insulated (if the strand weren't insulated, it wouldn't be an individual strand, it would be a funny-shaped solid wire), a lot of the winding area is potentially eaten up by the insulation. The number of strands that minimizes the resistance has to be decided on a case-by-case basis.

To decide whether to go with our design of 28 gauge wire, or use some kind of multiple-strand arrangement to decrease losses, we consider that the skin depth can be approximated by

$$\delta \approx \frac{6.61}{\sqrt{f}} \text{ cm}$$

For our switching frequency of 250kHz, the skin depth is $\delta = 6.61/\sqrt{250,000} = 0.13\text{cm} = 0.0052$ in. Now for the 28 gauge wire we selected, the bare wire radius is 0.0063 in. (obviously the insulation thickness is irrelevant, since the material is nonconducting).

So the current-carrying cross-sectional area of the wire is the unshaded annulus in Figure 5.24, which has an area of

$$A = \pi[(0.0063 \text{ in.})^2 - (0.0011 \text{ in.})^2] = 0.000121 \text{ in.}^2$$

Sometimes designers are advised to use wire smaller than the skin depth. Now what would happen if we did this and instead of a single #28 wire we used two strands of #31? (The wire scale is logarithmic, so increasing the wire gauge by 3 approximately halves the area.) Bare 31 gauge wire has a radius of 0.0044 in., which is less than the skin depth. Thus all the wire carries current, and the current-carrying area is $A = 2$ strands $\times$ $\pi(0.0046 \text{ in.})^2 = 0.000133 \text{ in.}^2$, about 10% larger than the effective cross section of the single strand of 28 gauge wire. But now let's include the wire insulation: the area of #28 wire with heavy insulation is 210 circular mils, and the area of two strands of #31, each with heavy insulation, is $2 \times 110 \text{ c.m.} = 220 \text{ c.m.}$, about 5% larger than the single strand of #28. Thus, even ignoring questions of packing (two round wires don't fit as well as one round wire), you really aren't buying much of anything by going to multiple strands of smaller wire. *Don't assume that going to litz is buying you something; you have to check in each case.* In this case, we decide to stick with the single #28 wire.

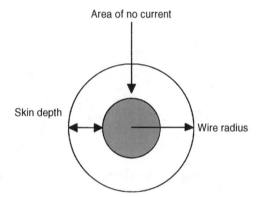

Figure 5.24 AC current only penetrates wire to the skin depth.

Copper Loss and Total Transformer Loss

Continuing with the evaluation of this design, remember that losses in the wire depend on the RMS current (Don't be confused on this one!) For the sawtooth current waveform shown earlier (Figure 5.17), the RMS current is

$$I_{RMS} = I_{pk}\sqrt{\frac{DC}{3}} = 0.93\sqrt{\frac{0.45}{3}} = 0.36\text{A}$$

Thus the power in the primary is $P_{pri} = (0.36\text{A})^2 \times 467\text{m}\Omega = 60\text{mW}$. Finally, since half the available winding area has been allocated to the primary, we may reasonably expect that the losses of the secondary will be equal to those of the primary, and we have the total power dissipated in the magnetic as $P_{TOT} = P_{core} + P_{pri} + P_{sec} = 29\text{mW} + 60\text{mW} + 60\text{mW} = 0.15\text{W}$. This is a transformer efficiency of 0.15W out of 10W, or 98.5%, meeting our original goal of transformer loss less than 0.2W.

Note that the copper losses are quadruple the core losses (0.12W vs. 0.03W). So, we really should be using fewer turns and a smaller gap; probably the $A_1 = 40\text{nH}$ would be optimal. Since the design is already meeting spec, we won't pursue this any further.

FLUX DENSITY: TWO FORMULAS?

Up till now, we have been dealing with cores that store energy in themselves (and in their air gap), that is, inductors. (Recall that a flyback is an inductor during part of the switching period.) Now we are going to deal with transformers, magnetics that don't store energy. A brief digression is called for. Usually, people use different formulas for calculating the flux density in a transformer than in an inductor. This leaves you wondering where the formulas came from in the first place, and how does anyone know which to use when? This section will show that the two formulas are in fact identical, and the one selected is purely a matter of convenience, depending on which variables are known.

In engineering units, we already know:

$$L = \frac{0.4\pi \times 10^{-8} \times N^2 A_e \mu}{l_m} \tag{5.5}$$

$$B = \frac{0.4\pi\mu IN}{l_m} \tag{5.6}$$

and

$$V = \frac{LI}{t} \tag{5.7}$$

Let's rearrange (5.5) to solve for μ:

$$\mu = \frac{l_m L}{0.4\pi \times 10^{-8} \times N^2 A_e}$$

Substituting into (5.6) gives

$$B = \frac{0.4\pi IN}{l_m} \frac{l_m L}{0.4\pi \times 10^{-8} \times N^2 A_e} = \frac{10^8 IL}{NA_e}$$

but (5.7) is the same as $L = Vt/I$, so

$$B = \frac{10^8 I}{NA_e} \frac{Vt}{I} = \frac{10^8 Vt}{NA_e} \tag{5.8}$$

Thus, equations (5.6) and (5.8) are equivalent. Normally you use (5.6) for energy storage (inductors) because you know the current, and you use (5.8) for transformers because you are driving them with a voltage for a certain time; but these two formulas are equivalent, and give the same result for flux density.

PRACTICAL DESIGN OF A FORWARD TRANSFORMER

As an example of the design of a power transformer, we're going to design a forward, although again, we're obviously not using this in our buck design. Let's consider the following design requirements: we want a forward converter that has 48VDC in (for simplicity, we won't consider a range of input line voltages), 5VDC out at 100W, and a switching frequency of 250kHz. The basic configuration is shown in Figure 5.25.

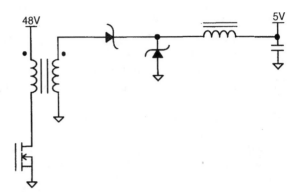

Figure 5.25   A forward converter.

Now the output current is $100W/5V = 20A$. Since the current is high, we'll be using a small number of turns on the secondary, to keep the winding resistance low. In turn, this implies that the turns ratio (number of primary turns divided by number of secondary turns) for the smallest possible number of secondary turns, one, is going to be an integer. So to get started, let's see what happens if we start looking at integer turns ratios.

Turns Ratio $= 1:1$ This case has the same number of turns on the primary and the secondary. When the switching transistor turns on, the full 48V is applied across the primary, which in this case implies that 48V also appears across the secondary (ignoring leakage inductance), in turn applying it across the freewheeling diode. *Practically,* however, the highest voltage schottky diode that can be obtained that has reasonably low forward voltage is 45V. To use 48V will require at least a 60V part, and maybe higher if there is ringing, or if the input line has variation to it. This higher voltage diode will then have a higher forward voltage, which in turn will decrease the efficiency of the converter.

This question of rectifier diodes' forward voltage is always a problem for low voltage outputs. The reason is easy to see: the current through the inductor is always coming either through the rectifier diode or through the freewheeling diode; in either case, then, there is a loss of $V_f I$ through these diodes, and that is out of a total power of $V_{out} I$, yielding an efficiency loss of V_f/V_{out} just from the diodes. The only way around this is to use synchronous rectifiers, but driving these is substantially more complex. (As V_{out} drops to 3.3V and lower, synchronous rectification becomes a necessity for just this reason.)

At any rate, for a reasonably high efficiency converter without synchronous rectifiers, a $1:1$ turns ratio is not a good choice.

Turns Ratio $= 2:1$ Now the primary has twice the turns of the secondary, so that the 48V applied across the primary yields 24V across the secondary and the diodes, so a schottky can be used. The duty cycle of a forward converter is approximately $DC \approx V_{out}/V_{sec} = 5V/24V = 21\%$ (ignoring the V_f of the schottky.) The peak current on the primary, and thus through the switching transistor, may be calculated by recalling from the first part of this chapter that when the voltage steps up (secondary reflected to primary), the current steps down. So when there is 20A through the secondary forward diode, there will be $I_{pri} = 20A/2 = 10A$ in the transistor. *Practically,* this may be too high for a MOSFET. (We won't be using a bipolar at 250kHz!) Since the MOSFET on-state losses go as the square of the current, the part will have $100\ A^2 \times R_{DS,on} \times 21\%$ losses, and a suitable FET may be too expensive to keep this loss to a reasonable level.

Turns Ratio = 3 : 1 Now the secondary diodes see only $48V/3 = 16V$, and the duty cycle is about $5V/16V = 31\%$. The primary current is $20A/3 = 7A$, so the on-state transistor losses are about three-quarters what they were at $2 : 1$, only $49\ A^2 \times R \times 31\%$. All parameters seem to be under control for this turns ratio.

Turns Ratio = 4 : 1 The secondary diodes see only $48V/4 = 12V$, and the duty cycle is up to $5V/12V = 42\%$. If you take into account the forward voltage of the diodes, or if the line can go lower than 48V, this will exceed 45%, which is the limit in duty cycle for PWM ICs such as the Unitrode UC3845. Thus *practically*, we have a limit from our choice of chips.

The conclusion from these calculations is that something like a $3 : 1$ turns ratio best meets the various practical limits on components. Let's thus choose a $3 : 1$ turns ratio.

Rather than going through the whole process of choosing a core, working through the gory details, seeing if some other core is better and so on, let's choose a suitable core to start with, assuming that all this other work has been done. Now we can concentrate on aspects of the problem that are novel in the design of the forward transformer.

Having said this, we choose an RM10 core with no center hole, which has an $A_e = 0.968\ cm^2$, and when using 3F3 material, has an $A_L = 4050nH$. With a three-turn primary, we have a primary inductance of $L_{pri} = (3\ turns)^2 \times 4050nH = 36\mu H$, which results in a magnetizing current of

$$I_{mag} = \frac{48V \times 31\% \times 4\mu s}{36\mu H} = 1.6A$$

The RMS of this current is added RMS onto the primary current of $20/3A$ reflected from the secondary. We have

$$I_{RMS} = \sqrt{I_{DC}^2 + \frac{I_{pk}^2 DC}{3}} = \sqrt{\left(\frac{20}{3}\right)^2 + \frac{(1.6)^2 0.31}{3}} = 6.686A$$

resulting in an increase in loss, which is proportional to I_{RMS}^2, of $(6.686/6.66)^2 = 1.006$ or 0.6%, which although quite acceptable, will still be reduced a little bit for the sake of the discussion. To reduce the magnetizing current, we will increase the primary inductance, and so we increase the primary number of turns while maintaining the same turns ratio.

Selecting next a turns ratio of $6 : 2$, the number of turns is doubled, so the primary has an inductance four times larger, $144\mu H$, resulting in a peak magnetizing current four times smaller, 0.4A. This now gives a truly negligible increase in I_{RMS}^2.

Now we can also calculate the core flux density (remember that the 48V is applied for a time equal to the period times the duty cycle),

$$B = \frac{(48V \times 31\% \times 4\mu s) \times 10^8}{6\ turns \times 0.968cm^2} = 1025\ G$$

which seems to be a practical level to have limited losses with 3F3; note that the three turns tried originally would have resulted in a flux density of 2050G, which would have had very high core losses, one real reason for increasing the number of turns on the primary.

Now, just as in other designs, this design should go on to calculate core and copper losses, compare them with the next step of a nine-turn primary, and see which is most efficient. The various other steps proceed as before.

PRACTICAL DESIGN OF A CURRENT TRANSFORMER

As a final piece of magnetics design, we will design a current transformer, which could be used to reduce the losses in sensing the primary current in a converter.

What's the difference between a current transformer and a voltage transformer? This question seems to cause even experienced magnetics designers to scratch their heads. The fundamental difference can be expressed by saying that the voltage transformer is trying to reflect a voltage across from its primary to its secondary, whereas a current transformer is trying to reflect a current; the voltage that the current transformer sees depends on its load.

Working this through for a practical design case should make this clear.

Let's suppose for specifications that we want to sense the primary current on a converter, and to develop 1V for a current of 10A. Of course, we could just use a 1V/10A = 100mΩ resistor, but this results in a loss of 1V × 10A = 10W, which is unacceptably high for almost all designs. So instead, let's use a current transformer arranged as in Figure 5.26.

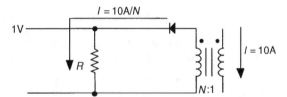

Figure 5.26 Using a current sense transformer to reduce losses.

Of course, we will use only one turn on the primary, to minimize the resistance, and many turns on the secondary, to drop the current down to a low level. If N is the number of turns on the secondary, by Ohm's law $(10/N)R = 1V$, and the power dissipated in the resistor is $P = (1V)^2/R$. Let's suppose that we limit the power dissipation to 50mW (e.g., so we can use a derated 100mW resistor). This sets R to be no smaller than 20Ω, and using this value, Ohm's law shows that $N = 200$.

Now let's look at the core. If we suppose that the diode is a plain rectifier, we might expect a forward voltage of about 1V at a current of 10A/200 = 50mA. So the total voltage the transformer sees is the 1V output, plus the 1V diode drop, or 2V. Then the flux density in the core, if we are operating at 250kHz, will be not greater than

$$B = \frac{(2V \times 4\mu s)10^8}{200 \text{ turns} \times A_e} = \frac{4}{A_e}$$

since the time the current is passing through the primary can't be greater than the period (otherwise the core could never reset). Thus A_e can be quite small without making B very large, and thus the size of the core is not determined in this case by the need to limit losses or prevent saturation, but more likely by the separation between primary and secondary required for isolation voltage. If isolation isn't required, the core size is probably limited by the 200 turns: you may be able to carry a 50mA peak current in a #40 wire, but this gauge is so thin that vendors will refuse to wind it.

Practical Note Don't use wire gauges smaller than #36 unless you absolutely have to.

So now how do we know that our device isn't a voltage transformer instead of a current transformer? Consider that we have 2V on the secondary, and therefore $2V/200 = 10mV$ on the primary. If the source driving the current transformer is, for example, 48V, then the 10mV across the primary is insignificant—you can get the 50mA from the secondary without affecting the drive to the current transformer's primary. Suppose on the other hand (unrealistically) that the driving source on the primary were only 5mV. Then it wouldn't be possible to generate 10mV across the primary, and you thus wouldn't be able to get the 50mA out of the secondary because the primary impedance (i.e., the reflected secondary impedance) is too large and is in fact determining the current. Even if the entire 5mV were dropped across the primary, only $200 \times 5mV = 1V$ would be generated on the secondary: it can't produce enough voltage to drive the current through the resistor. Therefore it would act as a voltage transformer.

Viewed the other way, when the source is 48V, something other than the voltage on the primary is determining the current through the current transformer.

A current transformer is a voltage transformer that is impedance limited.

Finally, what about errors in the current transformer? The answer to this follows from the fundamental statement of what a current transformer is.

Practical Note The diode and the winding resistance of the transformer secondary don't matter to the measurement of the current, because (as long as it is impedance limited) the same current is going to flow through the resistor no matter what else is in series with it.

Practically, this is why it often doesn't matter whether you use a schottky as the rectifier: the lower forward voltage affects only the transformer, not the current measurement.

Measurement error does arise, however, if there is finite inductance, that is, magnetizing inductance. Suppose that we want to be sensing current with a maximum error of 1%. Since the secondary current is going to be 50mA, this means we have to have a magnetizing current (on the secondary) of less than $50mA \times 1\% = 500\mu A$. The magnetizing current diverts current away from the resistor, and thus we end up not measuring it, which is to say it is in error. We thus need to have a minimum inductance on the secondary of

$$L \geq \frac{2V \times 4\mu s}{50mA \times 1\%} = 16mH$$

With 200 turns, this means we need an A_L of $16\text{mH}/(200 \text{ turns})^2 = 400\text{nH}$, which is easily achievable with normal small ferrites.

TIPS FOR DESIGNING MANUFACTURABLE MAGNETICS

So far in this chapter we've presented theoretical aspects of magnetics, followed by practical guidelines for making a design that will repeatably work in the lab the way you want it to. But unlike most other electrical components, magnetics also have to be custom-produced in a factory, often one at a time. So after you've designed something that works in the lab to your satisfaction, the next step should be to talk to a manufacturer and try to make the unit work to *his* satisfaction as well. The best design is of no use if it can't be produced reliably, and so this section will give you some pointers based on many years' work with manufacturers.

Manufacturers of custom magnetics have a lot of experience, and you should listen carefully when they make suggestions on how to wind something or pot it, etc. Almost invariably, these suggestions have to do with minimizing the cost of production of the magnetic, which is of course highly desirable for your design. On the other hand, don't take a manufacturer's word uncritically, because someone who designs magnetics for a living is not necessarily well versed in circuits that use magnetics. In particular, be very cautious about suggestions for reordering the layers in a multiwinding transformer, because this strongly influences coupling. The usual answer to a request to change the order of the layers should be no, or at best, send a sample and try it out.

Wire Gauge

We've already talked about this, but re-iteration in the new context will be helpful.

Practical Note It's best to limit wire gauges to a maximum of #20, and a minimum of, say, #38. Above #20, some machines can't wind the wire, upping your cost, and above about #18, bobbins can be cracked by the stiffness of the wire. Try multiple strands of #20 if you need greater wire cross-sectional area. Below #38, manufacturers will of course wind wire, but it becomes very hard for you to build your own sample magnetic in the lab. The wire is like a piece of hair, subject to twists and snaps when you've just got that second-to-last turn on.... You may be better off using #38 even if you've calculated that that 1mA winding only needs #45, just because of the difficulty of handling.

As long as we're thinking about wire gauges, consider the possibility of saving money (if you're producing a lot of units) by controlling the number of different wire sizes used. If you have a primary winding using 23 gauge wire and two secondaries, one with #24 and one with #22, you might consider whether the design would still work if all three windings went to #23, or even #24. The cost saving might be quite noticeable, whereas an extra few milliwatts of loss might be more easily made up elsewhere.

Wire Gauge Ratio

The author has never heard anyone (except for the technicians who actually have to wind magnetics) mention this, but winding can become awkward if there are radically different sizes of wire on the same piece. The trouble is that if you wind some very thick wire in a flat spiral, and then try to wind some very thin wire on top of it, the thin wire tends to fall into the crevices between the turns of the thick wire, so that the thin wire doesn't form a flat layer. This can affect coupling, making it different from unit to unit. No firm guide is possible, but:

> **Practical Note** Try not to use wire sizes more than about 10 wire sizes apart on adjacent layers.

Toroid Winding Limits

Winding a toroid takes a lot more effort than winding magnetics of other types. Indeed, the author jokingly tells people that it can be proven that it is *topologically impossible* to wind a toroid! Anyway, the hand work is substantial, not to mention the very real and annoying prospect of losing count of how many turns you have put on. I always advise technicians to go to a place where they can't be interrupted, and make a mark on a paper for every 10 turns wound. Additionally, because winding is so labor intensive:

> **Practical Note** Cut your technician (or yourself) a break. Don't design a toroid with more than 200 total turns if you intend to hand-wind a sample.

Tape versus Wire Insulation

Tape is commonly used on a transformer to provide isolation voltage between a primary and a secondary, and sometimes for isolation between secondaries. There are two slightly different reasons here. Many safety agencies require a high-pot test between windings that are connected to an AC mains and windings that connect to where people can get at them. Depending on the circumstances, this test voltage can be anywhere from 500V to 3000V. This isolation is a perfectly natural use of tape, and at the upper end of the voltage range it may even be best served with a flanged bobbin—that is, one that has a piece of plastic dividing the winding area into two pieces, permitting the primary and secondary to be wound in separated compartments.

Isolation between secondaries differs in that it is not mandated by a regulatory agency, but is rather imposed by the designer to avoid arcing. For example, consider a flyback transformer that is generating a $+30V$ and a $-160V$. In the same way that you keep the traces spaced apart to avoid arcing, the windings can't get too close together, either. There is about 200V difference between windings when the transistor is on, and possibly more when the transistor is off, depending on the details of the design: a forward has higher voltages inversely proportional to the duty cycle. Indeed, for a high voltage output such as the $-160V$, even individual layers of the wire may require insulation: you wind from left to right for one layer, than back from right to left for the next layer, and consider the maximum voltage from the underlying wire on the left side to the overlying wire on the same side.

While this second isolation requirement may also end up with tape, you should be aware that any layer of tape added to a design greatly increases cost because it is a hand operation. So for intralayer insulation, and also nonagency interlayer insulation, consider using heavier insulation on the wire, rather than tape. Standard insulation ("heavy") is a double layer, but both triple and quad are easily obtainable at not much cost increase, and they take less room than a layer of tape. The hard question is, How much insulation is enough for a given voltage?

Without getting into the details, the problem is that the voltage rating of magnet wire is given for 60Hz sinusoidal voltage, which is almost irrelevant for 100kHz square-wave operation, at which frequency little is known in any systematic way. Breakdown of the wire is also statistical, depending as it does on temperature and number of years of operation. Up to several hundred volts (peak), quad-build wire at switching–converter frequencies and waveforms appears to work fine. It should be good for almost all intrawinding insulation, and most nonagency interwinding insulation. This is the best I can tell you; the only way to be *sure*, is to run an accelerated life test in a real circuit.

Layering

The correct way of winding a multilayer winding has already been touched on: it should go left to right in one layer, then back right to left in another layer, and so on (this is not for a toroid, now). Although such a configuration is possible, consideration of the placement of the pins indicates that a winding should not end anywhere in the middle of a layer: if a winding started or terminated in the middle of a layer, it would have to cross over the rest of the layer to get to a side, where it could then exit the winding and make its way to a pin for connection. This crossover would be an uneven lump in the middle of the next winding on top, throwing it off. So part of the design-for-manufacturing process has to be selecting a wire gauge that enables you to get an exact integer number of layers; this consideration often dominates the desire to optimize resistance in the design of real magnetics.

Number of Windings

It is considerations of the kind just explored that compel manufacturable magnetics to have an absolute maximum of four to six windings. Not only is it difficult electrically to have more (because coupling becomes highly variable for the last couple of windings), but layering becomes difficult, and, bottom line, most bobbins have only 8–12 pins available! A custom bobbin is absolutely the last thing you want.

Potting

Potting is the process of filling up a volume surrounding a magnetic with a thermally conductive compound for the purpose of improving heat removal by providing a better thermal path, as well as by increasing the surface area of the magnetic mechanical structure. Potting is not to be confused with vacuum impregnation, which is used for insulation but doesn't do anything thermally.

Potting's big advantage is thermal and mechanical: it really helps get the heat out, and because it provides a flat surface, it can be very useful for mechanical mounting. (For example, a screw hole can be included in the potted shape.) There are also some potential problems with potting, which you should discuss with the vendor. The first is pretty obvious: potting compound is heavy, and your magnetic will weigh a lot more potted. Much less obvious, potting can change the magnetic characteristics of the magnetic. One problem much struggled with in the past is the shrinkage of potting material as it cures. This shrinking has been known to change the gap on gapped cores, causing the inductance to change! A similar problem is that ferrite cores, being rather brittle, can be snapped by the shrinkage. And a third problem along these lines is that MPP cores are strain sensitive, and their permeability can be affected by the shrinkage. There are various possible solutions for these problems, many of which revolve around proper selection of potting compound, but make sure your vendor is professionally dealing with these questions.

Specs

This last item is a peculiar one, really nothing that would occur to you as a reasonable designer—until you've experienced it a couple of times. It's quite challenging to write good magnetics specs. On your first couple of tries, you leave things out that you never imagined should be included (e.g., how far up the side of the bobbin should a layer of tape go?). Then on your next try, you put everything conceivable into the spec (which is now a 25-page book), and the vendor tells you that all this detail will cost you an arm and a leg.

You finally write something that satisfies you both, the vendor sends you a fourth sample, it works in your breadboard, the world is a good place. Now, your buyer finds a second source for the magnetic and sends them a copy of the spec to build to. They send you a sample, and it doesn't work at all! You take it apart to find out what's wrong, and you find that they've managed to misinterpret your masterpiece, building it to spec in a way that comes out completely different from your design.

This sounds like a horror story, but those with experience will recognize it as an every-supply occurrence. In fact, *the same vendor* can send you a sample built one way to a spec and then provide shipments to the same spec which are built another way! The only way the author has found that somewhat gets around these problems is to work with each vendor until something is produced that works, and then write into the spec that units must be built identically to the sample provided (number such-and-so). Constant vigilance is called for.

CONCLUDING COMMENTS

We thus see that there is nothing mysterious about (elementary) magnetics design. It just requires a lot of patience and attention to details—all the formulas really do work! But it is this need for patience and detailed work that is really the problem with magnetics design. If you design one or two magnetics once every other month, it perhaps is not too horrible to do it all by hand. But if you spend all day doing magnetics, and need to turn out two or three designs a day, it's not only tiresome, but impractical. The solution would be, of course, to let a computer do all the work. As suggested above, however, the available software doesn't seem to be adequate to the task. A worthwhile large-scale project for a group of engineers would be to design software that is technically accurate and has not only a modern user interface, but adequate documentation and a large enough database to be useful in designing at least the common types of magnetics covered in this chapter. The future awaits!

There are many advanced topics in the design of magnetics that were not addressed in this already long chapter. The author feels, however, that mastery of the practical techniques demonstrated here will suffice to generate most everyday magnetics designs. Following these steps should enable you to design a piece of magnetics that meets requirements the first time you build it, probably within 10–20%; this is the best that can be hoped for without very sophisticated and time-consuming analysis, which is done only for the most complex and critical designs. And to be truthful, the end result of many sophisticated analyses is still sometimes not as good as what can be accomplished by hand, based on the techniques in this chapter.

REFERENCES

1. *Soft Ferrite Materials Selection Guide*, publication PC 1062, 1994, Philips, Saugertties, NY.
2. *Power Core, MPP and High Flux Cores for Filter and Inductor Applications*, publication MPP-303X, 1995. Magnetics Inc., Butler PA.
3. *Soft Ferrite Cores Short Form Catalog '95*, publication PC060-2, 1995. Philips, Mount Prospect, IL.

6

Practical
Feedback Design

INTRODUCTION

Design of the feedback network of a converter is one of the most important aspects of a converter's design, and yet (with the exception of magnetics design) it is also the one most often misunderstood. Power supply designers can be classified into two groups: those who really understand what compensation (= feedback design) is about and those who don't. The former can compensate a converter within a few hours, and have it perform precisely as designed: this chapter will promote you into this group.

Feedback design is slightly more sophisticated mathematically than other aspects of power supply design, but this shouldn't frighten you off: the math is not used in day-to-day work, but is important only to be able to deal with new questions that sometimes arise. So to remind you of the necessary background, and unlike the other chapters, this chapter discusses some topics that aren't practical in the sense of being immediately visible in the lab; we start with a refresher on complex numbers, and ramp up to transfer functions, concepts that are essential to understanding what compensation is about. After this beginning, we show the practical part of feedback design in great detail: it really is possible to compensate a converter in a couple of hours, and have it perform exactly as desired on the first try!

REFRESHER

Logarithms and dB

Decibels are the standard unit for measuring the gain of a transfer function (which we'll define below), such as the open loop or closed loop gain of a converter. We start our refreshment with dB, and with logarithms, which are almost the same thing.

In engineering, the logarithm base 10 is almost always used, rather than the natural logarithm, which is base e. Remember what this means: if something gets 10 times bigger, its logarithm is increased by adding 1; multiplication is replaced by addition, and division is replaced by subtraction, making the system very convenient.

Decibels (dB) refer to logarithms that have been multiplied by 10 or 20 to make nice-looking numbers (i.e., approximately integers). For our purposes, the multiplying factor is always 20. Thus 10V is expressed in dB as

$$20 \times \log(10V) = 20dBV$$

100mV is

$$20 \times \log(0.1V) = -20dBV$$

Amplitudes less than 1 correspond to dB less than 0.

Decibels, being logarithms, convert multiplication into addition. So if you have a gain of 8 [$=20 \times \log(8) = 18dB$] and you want to reduce it to 4, you must multiply it by a factor of 0.5, so that in dB this is adding $20 \times \log(0.5) = -6dB$: multiplying corresponds to adding. Of course multiplying by 0.5 is the same as dividing by 2, so that in dB this is subtracting $20 \times \log(2) = 6dB$: dividing corresponds to subtracting. Either way, either multiplying by 0.5 or dividing by 2, the end result is the same, $18dB - 6dB = 12dB = 4$, as it must be.

Just as an aside, you sometimes hear people jokingly talk about "bels" which are taken to be 10 decibels each; no such unit is ever used in practice.

Complex Numbers

Complex numbers are constantly used during feedback design and measurement, although the practice is not always obvious. The most transparent case of use is in making a Nyquist plot, which is basically a graph of the imaginary part of the loop's gain versus its real part. Nyquist plots are discussed later in connection with Figure 6.34. For now, suffice it to say that complex numbers and functions are essential.

A complex number is an object that consists of two numbers, a real part and an imaginary part, written as:

$$(Re) + i(Im)$$

where Re is the real part and Im is the imaginary part. (Engineers call the imaginary unit j instead of i to avoid confusion with the symbol for current). For our purposes, we don't care about i being the square root of -1; all we need to know is that there are two numbers, Re and Im.

Since a complex number consists of two numbers, we can draw it on a graph with the amount of real on the x axis, and the amount of imaginary on the y axis, as in Figure 6.1. Redrawing this picture, we have Figure 6.2, from which it is obvious that a complex number can equally well be determined by two other numbers, one the distance from the origin (0,0), the second the angle counterclockwise from the positive real axis, which is to say a magnitude and a phase.

The upshot of this is that in electronics, whenever we need to represent something with both a magnitude and a phase (and this happens all the time), it is natural to use a complex number, which encodes both pieces of information together.

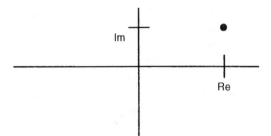

Figure 6.1 A complex number consists of
two numbers, so it can be shown on a graph.

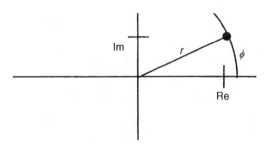

Figure 6.2 A complex number also can be
shown as a distance and an angle.

Complex Functions

Since we can use a complex number to represent simultaneously a magnitude and a phase, we can have this complex number depend on a parameter (in particular, magnitude and phase depend on frequency). For the functions of interest to us in stability design, there are two interesting aspects of these functions: At what parameter value (read frequency) are they equal to zero, and when are they equal to infinity? These two conditions are referred to as zeros and poles of the function, respectively.

EXAMPLE

$$\frac{x-2}{x-3}$$

Clearly, this function is zero when $x = 2$, so it has a zero at the complex number of magnitude 2 and phase $= 0$, (Re) $= 2$ and (Im) $= 0$. (Think about Figure 6.1.) It becomes infinite when $x = 3$, so it has a pole at the complex number of magnitude 3 and phase $= 0$.

As another example, we'll soon see that a capacitor has a complex number associated with it (its impedance) that is a function of frequency, $1/sC$ (here s is related to frequency); and an inductor has an impedance sL. Figure 6.3 shows the output filter of a switching converter (without ESR of the capacitor, or winding resistance of the inductor).

So, this forms a voltage divider whose attenuation depends on frequency, the output is equal to the input times

$$\frac{1/sC}{sL + 1/sC} = \frac{1}{s^2LC + 1}$$

If it is conceptually easier, think of this as if it were a resistor divider with one resistor having a value sL and the other a value $1/sC$. This function has no zeros, but it will have a pole if $s^2LC = -1$, or $s = \pm i/\sqrt{LC}$. So here, two poles occur at a magnitude equal to the resonant tank frequency, and at angles of 90° and 270° (being pure imaginary, no real part), as indicated in Figure 6.4.

The physical significance of this, of course, is that the LC tank has a resonance at this frequency, so that the output is indefinitely amplified from an input at this frequency. Of course, a real circuit always has resistance, and so the amplification is not infinite—that is, it doesn't really have two poles on the imaginary axis; it has some real part also.

For those already in the know, observe that there is no factor of 2π here, because s actually corresponds to $i\omega = 2\pi i f$, not frequency.

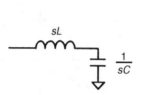

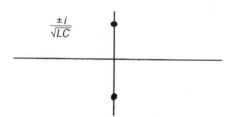

Figure 6.3 Complex impedance of a capacitor and an inductor.

Figure 6.4 An LC tank has poles at its resonant frequency.

What Is a Transform?

Now that we know about complex functions, we can turn to transforms, which we use, for example, any time we look at a frequency spectrum. Most generally, a transform is a connection between two different ways of representing the same data. For our purposes, the two representations are

As a function of time. (*Example*: What was the voltage during the first second?)

As a function of frequency. (*Example*: There was 15V at 60Hz, plus 3V at 180Hz.)

Any function of time can be represented as a function of frequency, and vice versa, so if we talk about a spectrum (which is the transform of some function of time), we have exactly the same information contained in the original (time) function, just encoded differently, and perhaps more conveniently for some purposes.

Two Transforms

For engineers' purposes, there are two types of transform, Fourier and Laplace. Suppose then that we have a voltage that depends on time, $V(t)$. The Fourier transform is

$$V(\omega) = \frac{1}{\sqrt{2\pi}} \int_{-\infty}^{\infty} e^{i\omega t} V(t)dt$$

while the Laplace transform is

$$V(s) = \frac{1}{\sqrt{2\pi}} \int_{-\infty}^{\infty} e^{st} V(t)dt$$

What's the Difference?

The difference between the two types of transform is that the Fourier transform considers all time; that is, it assumes that you've been measuring the (in this case) voltage forever. A Laplace transform considers only voltages that start at time $= 0$: that is, the voltage was turned on at time 0 and was zero before that time.

Practically, this means that a Fourier transform is used for something like power supply noise emission, which can be measured as slowly as you please. A Laplace transform is used to describe how a waveform changes with time: for example, what does the voltage on this capacitor do when the power supply is turned on?

In this chapter, we only use Laplace transforms, because we are interested in how a power supply responds when something is done to it at time 0, (e.g., a load step is applied at that time). Fourier transforms are used implicitly in the chapter on EMI.

Transform of C and L

It is straightforward to determine the Laplace transform corresponding to the impedance of a capacitor. Of course, this impedance, and that of an inductor, is used all the time in designing filters, and in particular in filters used inside the loop of a converter, as mentioned above. We know that

$$C\frac{dV}{dt} = I$$

If we let $V = e^{st}$, so that the voltage is a sine wave [this is the same because $e^{i\omega t} = \cos(\omega t) + i \sin(\omega t)$], we find that

$$I = Cse^{st} = CsV$$

or that impedance

$$Z \equiv \frac{V}{I} = \frac{1}{sC}$$

as promised before. We didn't have to actually evaluate the integral in the definition of the Laplace transform because the integration is implicit in the solution of the differential equation—but this is not at all a practical concern. Similarly, we can find the impedance of an inductor by knowing that

$$V = L\frac{dI}{dt}$$

and substituting e^{st} for V again and integrating,

$$LI = \frac{e^{st}}{s} = \frac{V}{s}$$

or $Z = sL$. This then justifies the voltage divider example above.

TRANSFER FUNCTIONS

What Is a Transfer Function and Who Cares?

A transfer function is a compact method for expressing what a linear system will do at its output when you do something at its input. For example, the box in Figure 6.5 might be a complete power supply, and so the transfer function represents audio susceptibility: that is, how much input noise is attenuated (or amplified!) into the supply upon injection.

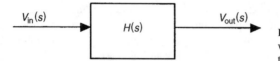

Figure 6.5 The transfer function describes what the system does to change the input into the output.

We already know that any function of time can be broken up into its constituent sine waves—that's what it means to take its transform. If I apply a sine wave of frequency ω to this system, the output will also be a sine wave of frequency ω, but with a magnitude and phase different from the input. The ratio of the output to the input is $H(s)$, the transfer function of the system. We use s, where s is complex, because it encodes both the amplitude change and the phase shift due to the system.

We can thus tell the response of the system to any input by breaking up that input into its constituent sine waves, applying $H(s)$ to each of them, and reassembling them at the output.

With power supplies, we are concerned when there is a small disturbance in the loop, or an error: instead of growing bigger, the disturbance should die away with time. This is what the transfer function can tell us. If the transfer function shows that a loop is unstable, as in Figure 6.6, then a disturbance will be amplified, with the result that the circuit oscillates.

Composition Law for Transfer Functions

When two systems are in series, there is an easy rule for deriving the composition of their transfer functions, as shown in Figure 6.7. This rule enables us to figure out the transfer function for a closed loop system like that of Figure 6.8, which could represent a power supply. The box labeled $H(s)$ is the power stage, since it transforms the input to the output, and the box labeled $G(s)$ is the feedback control, since it takes the output and uses it to control how much of the input the power stage sees. We know right away that $G(s)$ applied to Out is Out $\times$ $G(s)$, and we can then subtract this from In as shown in Figure 6.9.

But $H(s)$ times this has to equal Out, so we can solve:

$$H[\text{In} - (\text{Out} \times G)] = \text{Out}$$
$$(H \times \text{In}) - (H \times G \times \text{Out}) = \text{Out}$$
$$H \times \text{In} = \text{Out} \times [1 + (H \times G)]$$
$$T(s) \equiv \frac{\text{Out}}{\text{In}} = \frac{H(s)}{1 + H(s)G(s)}$$

10
8
6
V
4
2
0
100
200
300
400
500
t (μs)

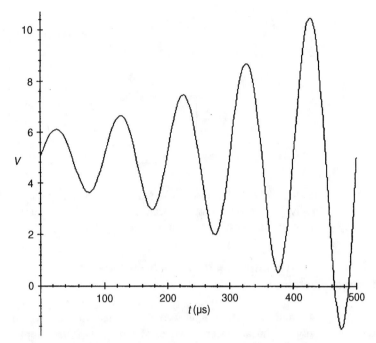

Figure 6.6 Response of an unstable system to a disturbance.

In
H(s)
G(s)
Out
Equals
In
H(s) G(s)
Out

Figure 6.7 Composition law for transfer functions: two in series are multiplied.

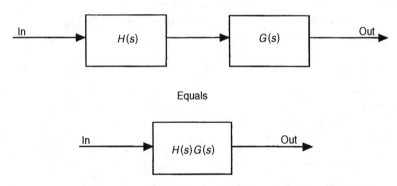

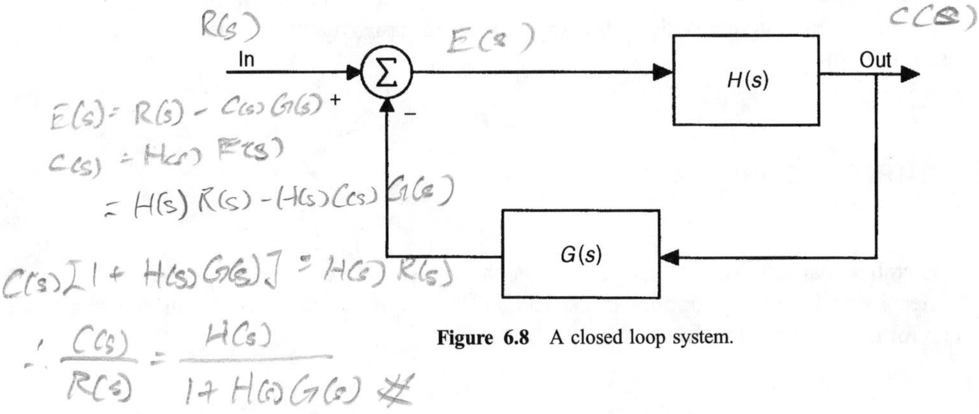

R(s)
In
E(s)
C(s)
Out
H(s)
+
−
G(s)
E(s) = R(s) − C(s) G(s)
C(s) = H(s) E(s)
= H(s) R(s) − H(s) C(s) G(s)
C(s) [1 + H(s) G(s)] = H(s) R(s)
∴ C(s)/R(s) = H(s) / (1 + H(s) G(s)) #

Figure 6.8 A closed loop system.

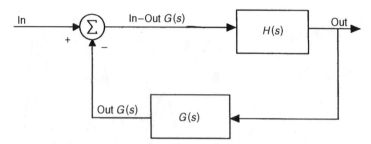

Figure 6.9 Calculating the transfer function of a closed loop system.

This transfer function, $T(s)$, will prove fundamental in determining the stability of a closed loop power supply. As an overview, you can say that if $T(s)$ becomes infinite at any frequency—that is, if the transfer function has a pole—the converter is unstable.

There's No Such Thing as a (Useful) Transform of a Nonlinear System!

Before we get carried away about how wonderful transforms are, let's note that they are really useful only for linear systems, which in terms of power supplies usually means small-signal (just what this means will be made more precise later). The typical problem with transforms usually occurs when part of the system depends on a parameter nonlinearly. Then the operating point of the system changes as the parameter changes, and the transform gives information about the system <u>only</u> at that one particular operating point, telling nothing about the new operating point.

EXAMPLE

A converter's input power source is a solar array. The input voltage changes as the logarithm of the current, $I = ae^{bV}$. If you do a transform on this system, it tells you only how the power supply operates at that one input voltage—**NOT** what happens at any other operating point! The transfer function does not provide useful information in this case. (But you might think about this: Could you devise a function that depended *both* on frequency *and* on the operating point?)

The usual solution to getting useful information from a nonlinear system is to time average it, so that the nonlinearities are averaged out—this is what state-space averaging does for power supplies. (We won't talk about state-space averaging in this book.) But for truly nonlinear systems, such as the solar array example, transform methods cannot be usefully used.

BASIC CONTROL THEORY

Remember that a closed loop system has the transfer function $H/(1 + HG)$. In most systems, and for power supplies in particular, H is given: it's the system you're trying to control (in our case, the power stage of a converter).

**The goal of control theory is to select *G*, the feedback, so
that the transfer function is always finite.**

⟹ i∩finite se∩t instability

The transfer function can become infinite only if the denominator is zero, which happens only if $HG = -1$. So the quantity we measure is $H(s)$, and then we select a $G(s)$ in such a way that when the magnitude of $|HG| = 1(= 0\text{dB})$ the phase is not $180°$ (i.e., -1). The amount by which it differs from $180°$ is called the phase margin of the system.

Phase margin determine sys. stability.

Bode Plots

Rather than work directly with the complex numbers that constitute a transfer function, engineers find it easier to deal separately with the real and imaginary parts, or magnitude and phase. There are several ways of doing this, but the most popular calls for the use of Bode plots. (There's been argument over how to pronounce this name, boh-dee or boh-day? The first is by far the more common.)

A Bode plot consists of two graphs: one is the magnitude of the transfer function (in dB) versus logarithmic frequency; the other is the phase in degrees versus logarithmic frequency. Since for the magnitude plot, both axes are logarithmic, a plot of the transform of a single pole (like a capacitor, its impedance is infinite at 0 frequency) or a single zero (like an inductor, its impedance is 0 at zero frequency) is a straight line.

The Bode plot in Figure 6.10 shows the impedance of a 1µF capacitor. You can verify that this is the impedance of a 1µF cap by observing that the phase is flat at 90°, corresponding to capacitance; and the magnitude of the capacitance can be verified by

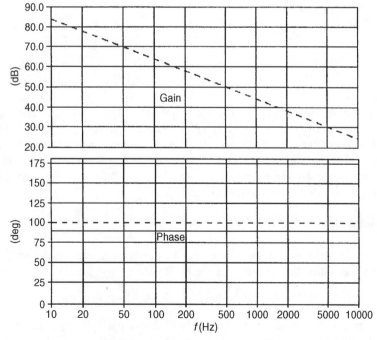

Figure 6.10   Impedance of a 1µF capacitor.

noting that, for example, at 10Hz, the magnitude is 84dBΩ = 15.9kΩ, which gives 1μF at 10 Hz ($10^{84/20} = 15{,}900\Omega$; $1/(2\pi\ 10\text{Hz}\ 15{,}900\Omega) = 10^{-6}$ F).

The next Bode plot (Figure 6.11) shows a 1kΩ resistor in series with the capacitor. This could represent a capacitor and its ESR, except of course that 1kΩ is much larger than the real ESRs of most caps. You can see that the magnitude levels off at 60dBΩ = 1000Ω, and the phase returns to 180°. Thus at low frequencies, the series combination looks like a capacitor, and as the frequency increases beyond $1/(2\pi RC)$, the combination looks just like the resistor, because the capacitor's impedance goes toward zero.

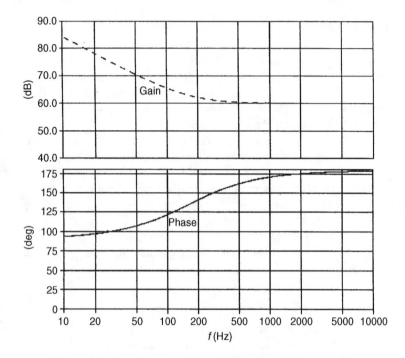

Figure 6.11   Impedance of a 1kΩ resistor in series with a 1μF capacitor.

Note: The phase goes to 180° at high frequency, not 0° as you might expect, because a 180° rotation on the complex plane corresponds to multiplication by −1 (start at the real number 1 and go counterclockwise half a rotation), and so doesn't affect the "mix" of real and imaginary parts. Indeed, many older machines for making Bode plots get confused (to anthropomorphize a design problem) about this 180° degree business, so you might as well get used to seeing such things.

Requirement for Stability

The requirement that the system be stable, stated above for the product $H(s) \times G(s)$, translates into a requirement on the Bode plot:

There must be positive phase when the gain = 1 (= 0dB)

To repeat, the amount of phase at 0dB gain is called the phase margin. Reworded again, the fundamental goal of the design of a feedback loop is to ensure that there is phase margin. 45°

Figure 6.12 shows a loop that is unstable: we see that there is 0dB at a frequency of 10kHz, and that at that frequency the phase is $-30°$; therefore, the loop oscillates, as shown in Figure 6.13.

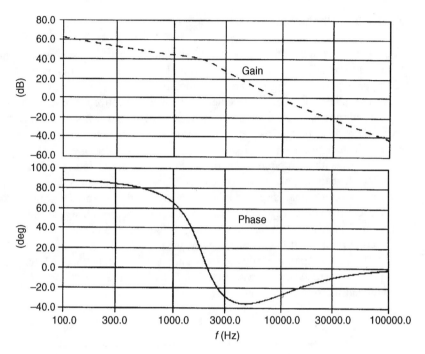

Figure 6.12   A Bode plot of an unstable loop.

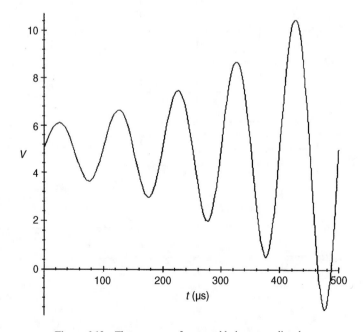

Figure 6.13   The response of an unstable loop to a disturbance.

In a stable loop (Figure 6.14), we see that there is again 0dB at a frequency of 10kHz, and that at that frequency the phase is $+30°$; therefore the loop damps oscillations, as shown in Figure 6.15. (The Bode plot shown is technically "metastable": see below.)

How Much Phase Margin Is Enough?

You sometimes hear arguments over how much phase margin is enough, and you frequently see differing requirements from spec to spec: 30° minimum, 45° minimum, 45° typical, an occasional 60° are all common.

To understand these disagreements, you need to realize that phase margin serves two separate purposes: it relates to the damping of output transients due to a step load on the converter; and it guarantees stability regardless of variations of component values (e.g., initial tolerance and temperature).

In the author's opinion, the first issue is not really relevant, because load steps invariably take the supply into the regime of "large-signal stability," whereas phase margin determines only "small-signal stability." (More on this soon.) Of course, you wouldn't want a supply to have, say, only 5° of phase margin, because it would ring for a very long time after a transient. But tiny phase margins like this are unrealistic anyway, because of the second purpose of having adequate phase margin.

Thus, phase margin really has to guarantee only that the loop will remain stable with component tolerances, load variations, and temperature variations. For this reason, I recommend the following design practice:

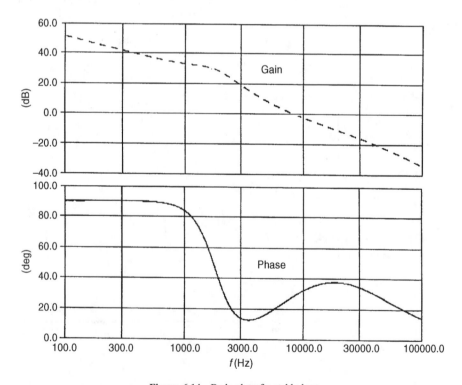

Figure 6.14 Bode plot of a stable loop.

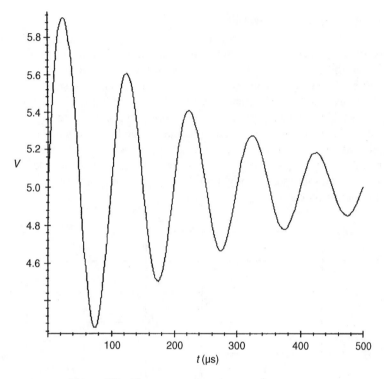

Figure 6.15   The response of a stable loop to a disturbance.

Practical Note Loops should have 45° of phase margin typical at room temperature, with nominal values and nominal load. This usually is enough to guarantee stability under all variations and tolerances. If the load swing or the input voltage range is exceptionally large, you might instead consider a specification for a loop having 30° minimum at all loads and all input voltages.

Gain Margin?   *gain.*   =7 *attenuation.*

Sometimes you also see gain margin specified. Gain margin is sort of the inverse of phase margin; it measures how much gain (actually attenuation) the system has when the phase reaches 0. The most important circumstance when this is relevant is in a system with a right-half-plane zero, such as a boost converter. (We'll be discussing RHP zeros below.) The magnitude part of the Bode plot in this circumstance may have an appearance similar to the *RC* impedance plot of Figure 6.11, with flat gain at higher frequencies; the phase however, continues to decrease. Although you may compensate this system to have adequate phase margin, changing the load may change the crossover frequency a great deal because of the flatness in the gain, resulting in a 0dB frequency at which there is no phase margin left. By specifying minimum gain margin (typically 12dB), you can avoid this situation. The author recommends that gain margin be specified only if a flyback converter is being designed; in other converters, naming a gain margin serves no practical purpose.

About Conditional Stability

Normally, in a closed loop system, both phase and gain decrease with increasing frequency (ignoring for now intentionally introduced phase boost, such as in the feedback systems we will be designing later in the chapter). Thus in a normal system, when gain is reduced, phase margin typically increases. But in a conditionally stable system (also called "metastable"), phase goes up again before going down (see Figure 6.16). So if gain were reduced for some reason, the phase might go below 0° while there is still some gain, proceeding to oscillate at this frequency, even though it is "stable" and "has adequate phase margin." Conditionally stable systems should thus be avoided when possible.

As an exercise, you might think about how you could word a specification to avoid this sort of problem.

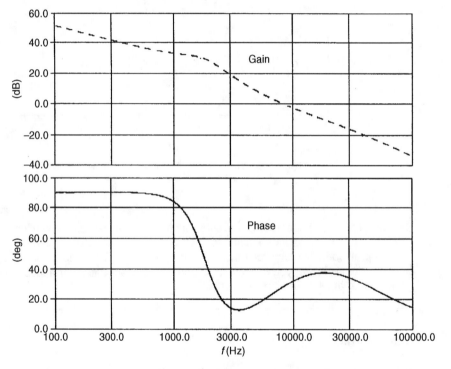

Figure 6.16   A stable loop exhibiting metastability.

Small- versus Large-Signal Stability

Bode plots relate to the response of a system to a small (ideally, infinitesimal) disturbance. But if a disturbance is large, the system response probably will not be determined not by the linear aspects of the feedback but by nonlinear aspects, such as op amp slew rate or rail voltages, or maximum and minimum achievable duty cycles, etc. When factors such as these enter into a system's response, the system is exhibiting a nonlinearity, and so the transform method doesn't apply. Thus, while small-signal stability is <u>necessary</u>, it is not <u>sufficient</u> to guarantee stable operation.

Practical Note If possible, a loop should be designed to avoid large-signal operation.

In any case, large-signal bandwidth of a converter is always less than or equal to small-signal bandwidth, because before the converter's loop can run into some nonlinearity, it first has to respond, and the response is set by the small-signal bandwidth. One way around this, which has been tried on occasion, is to have a completely separate nonlinear loop for large-signal response: but then, it must be decided when each loop should be active, how interference can be avoided between them, and so on.

EXAMPLE

A true story. A 1.2V power supply was designed to have very wide bandwidth, and measurement of its closed loop response showed 45° of phase margin. Unfortunately, when a load step was applied, the system began to oscillate: the op amp, which had insufficient gain bandwidth and slew rate, spent all its time trying to catch up with itself, first hitting its positive rail, then swinging down to ground, then back up again. This oscillation was eliminated by swapping the op amp for a pin-compatible one with higher gain bandwidth (and higher slew rate).

HOW TO STABILIZE A VOLTAGE MODE BUCK CONVERTER

With all these preliminaries out of the way, we can turn to the task of the practical design of a feedback compensation. We start by demonstrating the method for measuring and stabilizing a very simple converter, a voltage mode buck. The same methods demonstrated here are directly applicable to stabilizing other types of converter as well.

Initially, we have just the power stage (Figure 6.17). We have a power MOSFET controlled by a PWM switching at 250kHz; there is a freewheeling diode and an inductor and an output cap; and the PWM has an error amplifier but is otherwise just a block for the

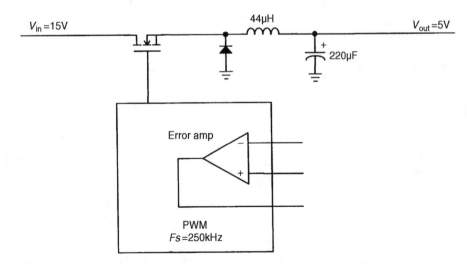

Figure 6.17 Power stage of the buck converter to be stabilized.

moment. The inductor is 44µH (at 0A—it's in fact just the DC inductor we designed in Chapter 5, the one that swings down to 35µH at 2A). The output capacitor is 220µF. The author has taught lab sessions on loop compensation with exactly this setup, so if you like, you can assemble the components as you go along and duplicate the measurements shown in the book.

Our overall strategy is going to be this. First we will measure the open loop response of the system, which can be done without using the error amp. From the data we collect, will be able to design a compensation that ensures stability. Finally, we measure the closed loop response, to verify that we did it right. It sounds easy, and it actually is; once you've done it a couple of times, the entire process of stabilizing a converter can be done in a morning—honest. No more two weeks wasted swapping components in and out. Stabilization can be successful on the first try!

How to Measure Open Loop Response

The open loop response of the converter is by definition the response of the power stage—that is, what does the output look like when you jiggle the duty cycle? To measure this open loop response, you need to have the converter operating more or less at its correct operational parameters: since the output is supposed to be 5V when the converter is working, you don't want to measure the open loop response when the output is 3V or 13V!

So the plan of action is going to be to find the DC operating point, and then add a small AC on top of it, as illustrated in Figure 6.18.

The error amplifier of the PWM is made unity gain; don't forget and leave anything attached to it, or you'll get crazy-looking results!

To make this measurement, add together (using a mixer, described below) an adjustable DC voltage and a swept sine wave from a network analyzer. Starting the adjustable DC voltage at zero, increase it very slowly until you get approximately 5V at the

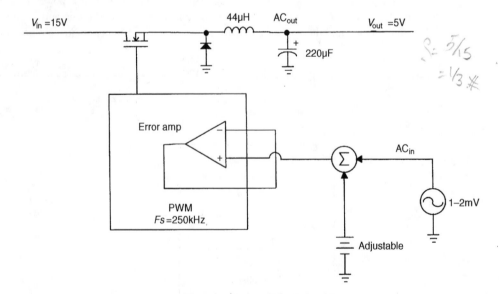

Figure 6.18 An open loop measurement will be taken by setting the DC operating point and adding an AC component.

output of the converter. Make sure that a resistive load (maximum specified load is preferable) is already attached to the output before you bring the adjustable DC voltage up from 0V. This is important because changing the load in this open loop mode can cause the output voltage to fluctuate wildly, potentially blowing up your output cap.

Practical Note Some PWMs have an offset voltage, so the duty cycle remains at zero until you reach a volt or so.

Practical Note Power stages with high gain will clearly be very sensitive to the adjustable DC voltage. With an ordinary lab supply, it may be frustratingly difficult to adjust the control voltage to get exactly the output voltage you want. In this case, you can probably settle for anything within 5% of the actual output. An alternative is to buy or build a precision voltage source that can be adjusted in millivolt steps. Better yet, see below for a method that avoids this measurment altogether.

Once you have the adjustable DC voltage set so that the output voltage is correct, measure the open loop transfer function by dividing AC_{out}/AC_{in}, at the points shown in the schematic (Figure 6.18), with the network analyzer which is generating the swept sine. (See Chapter 4, on instrumentation, for detailed operational information on how to run a network analyzer.)

Let's take a careful look at the actual measurement of the open loop response of the converter (Figure 6.19). At very low frequencies (below 10Hz nothing is happening in this circuit), the gain is 11.8dB, and the phase is $0°$. Zero phase is to be expected at very low frequencies, since when you increase the duty cycle on a buck, the output voltage increases (transfer function $=$ Out/In).

As for the low frequency gain, consider a hypothetical increase in the DC control voltage of, say, 100mV. The oscillator ramp for the PWM used (a UC2825) is $1.8V_{pp}$, so the 100mV causes a change in duty cycle of $100mV/1.8V = 5.6\%$. (Note that the ramp amplitude directly affects converter gain.) Now the PWM actually has two outputs, of which only one is being used. So increasing the duty cycle increases only the one output— the other is zero (as seen by the MOSFET) no matter what: that is, the MOSFET has a maximum duty cycle of 50%. So the real increase in duty cycle is only 2.8%. Now when the duty cycle increases, the effect is to increase the average voltage applied to the inductor, because the MOSFET is on longer; that is, the 15V input is applied longer. The output voltage thus increases by $15V \times 2.8\% = 420mV$. Since this was caused by a control voltage increase of 100mV, the gain at low frequency is $420mV/100mV = 4.2 = 12.4dB$, which is quite close to what we actually measure. (The 0.6dB error $= 7\%$, and is probably caused by finite rise and fall times of the MOSFET switching; it is unimportant for our loop measurements and can be eliminated by methods discussed further on.)

Looking again at the actual measurement, we see that as the frequency increases, the gain rises and the phase falls, which is caused by the LC tank resonance. As confirmation we may check that the resonant frequency should be

$$f = \frac{1}{2\pi\sqrt{LC}} = 1618\text{Hz}$$

in close agreement with the measurement.

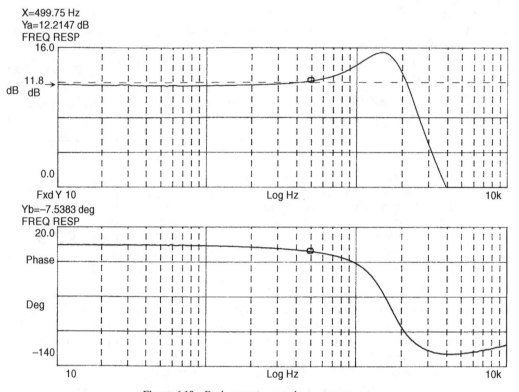

Figure 6.19 Buck converter open loop measurement.

Finally, at high frequencies, the gain rolls off at 12dB per octave (i.e., the gain at 4kHz is one-quarter the gain at 2kHz; an octave is a factor of 2 in frequency), corresponding to the two poles, the inductor and the capacitor. The phase at the topmost frequency in the measurement is starting to rise again, as a result of the ESR of the output capacitor. The measured ESR of the cap was 120mΩ, so the *RC* frequency is

$$f = \frac{1}{2\pi RC} = 6\text{kHz}$$

(The phase doesn't go all the way to $-180°$ because of this zero.) If the gain measurement had been continued to even higher frequencies, you would have seen the gain decreasing at only 6dB/octave, which is a single pole, because the capacitor had become resistive at these frequencies owing to its ESR, just as in the example earlier in the chapter of a series *R* and *C*.

Venable's *K*-Factor Paper

Now that we've measured the open loop, we can design a compensation network to make the converter stable in closed loop. We're going to choose a bandwidth of 500Hz, which is well below the resonant frequency of the output tank, because we are in voltage control mode. Although it is possible to compensate the loop so that it is stable with a bandwidth above the resonance, it is a better idea to go to current mode control for this. (Alternatively, it is possible to stabilize a voltage mode converter well above the RC frequency, because the phase is back to only $-90°$; we won't be demonstrating that here.)

The method described here, first demonstrated by Venable [1], amounts to computation of the amount of phase the error amplifier needs to give the desired phase margin ("phase boost"), followed by selection of one of three types of compensation based on this calculation. The actual component values are then computed based on the idea of placing zeros and poles symmetrically around the desired bandwidth frequency: zeros to cause the phase to rise below the bandwidth, poles to cause the gain to decrease above the bandwidth. The three amplifier types are shown in Figures 6.20, 6.21, and 6.22.

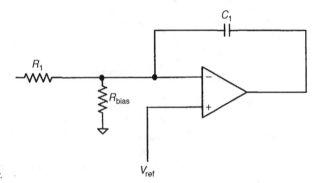

Figure 6.20 Type I amplifier.

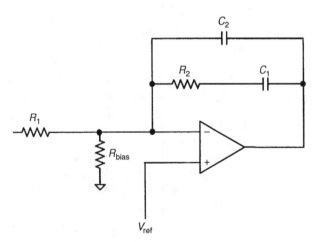

Figure 6.21 Type II amplifier.

Now the cursor of the network analyzer in our open loop measurement of the buck converter was set at our intended bandwidth of 500Hz (a convenient practice if you need to make presentations), so that we know the open loop gain there is 12dB, and the phase is $-7°$.

We've already done the first two steps of the K method, namely, making the measurement and choosing the cross over frequency (another name for the bandwidth.) The third step is to choose a phase margin; based on our earlier discussions, we will choose $45°$.

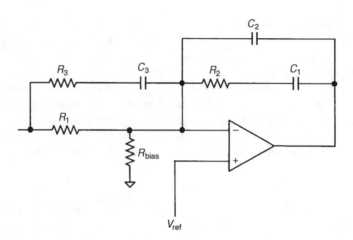

Figure 6.22 Type III amplifier.

The fourth step is to compute the gain necessary for the error amp. Since the open loop gain is 12dB, we have to <u>reduce</u> the gain by 12dB to get 0dB at 500Hz. So the error amplifier gain should be $G = -12\text{dB} = 0.25$ at 500Hz. Be careful in this step, don't leave the gain in decibels!

As a fifth preparatory step, we compute how much phase boost we need from the compensation:

$$\text{boost} = M - P - 90$$

where M is the desired phase margin and P is the measured open loop phase shift. For the case we are considering, we have boost $= 45 - (-7) - 90 = -38°$; since this is less than $0°$, no phase boost is required, and we can use a type I amplifier (see the discussion below).

One final preliminary step is to select R_1. Since this is a 5V output, and the UC2825 PWM IC has a 5V reference, no R_{bias} is required, and a good starting value for R_1 is 10kΩ. If the output voltage had been higher (or the reference voltage lower) an R_{bias} would have been used to divide down the output voltage. However, R_{bias} has no effect on the gain or phase of the error amplifier; as long as you leave R_1 alone, the output voltage can be adjusted by adjusting R_{bias} without affecting the error amp! (Note, however, that adjusting V_{out} <u>does</u> affect the open loop, and thus potentially loop stability. This is why the open loop measurement is done close to the actual operating point.)

Now, the compensation for our buck converter only requires C_1 to be computed. For the type I this is done as follows

$$C_1 = \frac{1}{2\pi f G R_1}$$

[Type I Amplifier]

For us, $C_1 = 1/(2\pi \times 500\text{Hz} \times 0.25 \times 10\text{k}\Omega) = 127\text{nF}$. Rather than trying to parallel capacitors, simply round this down to the nearest common value, 120nF—remember that the purpose of phase margin was to make it unnecessary to worry about component tolerances! In the lab, the value we actually measured on our 120nF capacitor was 135nF. (This was a CKR06 style cap, with a tolerance of 20%. Generally, it is better to use 10% NPO or C0G style capacitors in the feedback loop.)

Before getting back to our buck converter to verify performance, let's consider the other types of error amp. As long as the necessary boost computed is less than 0°, as in our buck converter, a type I amplifier is all that's required. However, if more than zero degrees of boost is required, one of the other error amps must be used. The type II amplifier theoretically can provide up to 90° of phase boost; practically, trying to get more than about 75° out of it results in component values that are either too large or too small to be practical. Above 75°, and less than about 160°, a type III can be used. If you need more than 160°, chances are you're measuring wrong!

Practical Note Limit the boost of a type II amplifier to 75°, and a type III to 160°.

For reference, the design equations for the other two types of amplifier are:

$$K = \tan\left(\frac{\text{boost}}{2} + 45\right)$$

$$C_2 = \frac{1}{2\pi f GKR_1}$$

$$C_1 = C_2(K^2 - 1)$$

$$R_2 = \frac{K}{2\pi f C_1}$$

[Type II Amplifier]

$$K = \left[\tan\left(\frac{\text{boost}}{2} + 45\right)\right]^2$$

$$C_2 = \frac{1}{2\pi f GR_1}$$

$$C_1 = C_2(K - 1)$$

$$R_2 = \frac{\sqrt{K}}{2\pi f C_1}$$

$$R_3 = \frac{R_1}{K - 1}$$

$$C_3 = \frac{1}{2\pi f \sqrt{K} R_3}$$

[Type III Amplifier]

Remember to use degrees in these equations, not radians!

Practical Considerations

Much of the time you will end up using a type II compensation. There should be something unusual about the power stage if you determine you need a type III—otherwise, either your measurement or your calculation may be wrong! A little bit of caution here will save quite a bit of aggravation later.

In any case, as stated above, you should never need more than 160° of phase boost. If >160° seems to be necessary, something's wrong for sure.

What happens if the values you calculate turn out to be very large (say, 10MΩ) or very small (say 7pF)?

Practical Note Avoid using resistors larger than 1MΩ, or capacitors smaller than 22pF. Strays will make them too inaccurate for loop compensation. If your calculations show a need for parts that are outside these bounds, a good plan will be to start over, using a different value for R_1, such as 1kΩ instead of 10kΩ.

Finally, what do you do when you calculate an oddball value, such as 900pF? Do you need to parallel caps?

Practical Note As long as you're not at the top end of the possible phase boost from the type of error amp compensation you're using, just round off the capacitor values to their nearest standard values; the compensation will still be good enough. For the question just asked, 1nF will be good enough instead of 900pF if you're trying to get 60° phase boost. If you're right at 80° phase boost with a type II, try going to a type III.

Other Comments

The comments above suggest that there is a practical limit on the maximum bandwidth you should try to give a converter. Of course, a voltage mode converter shouldn't be stabilized above its resonant tank frequency unless you are going to stabilize it above its output cap—ESR zero frequency; and of course no normal switch mode converter can be compensated to have a bandwidth close to its switching frequency. Beyond these limits, however, even current mode converters have limits, set by the compensation values that can be reliably attained. To get bandwidths of 100kHz or more not only will require very high switching frequencies, but probably, in addition, some sort of integrated or hybridized circuit, to control stray impedances. The typical practice is to give substantially more phase margin than is used with lower bandwidth converters, because the strays give increased variability to the values used.

One final comment on Venable's method. Symmetrical distribution of poles and zeros is enough to uniquely determine a type II (and, a fortiori, a type I) amplifier, but it doesn't uniquely determine the compensation values for a type III. There may be ways to adjust the position of the poles and zeros of a type III error amp for special purposes.

How to Measure Closed Loop Response

So now the buck converter circuit looks like Figure 6.23. In addition to adding the compensation on the schematic, a summer has been added (the circle with the Σ in it) showing injection of the swept sine wave, and the correct points to measure the closed loop response of the converter, AC_{out}/AC_{in}. Observe that the loop remains closed during this measurement, so that it automatically controls the output voltage to the 5V level; no external DC control is required.

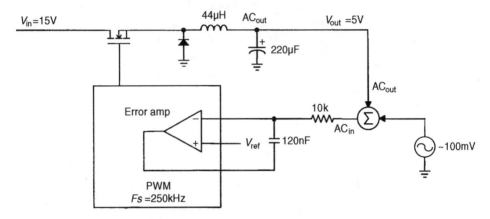

Figure 6.23 Loop with compensation added. Also shown is diagram for measuring closed loop response of converter.

For the astute reader, let's mention that what is being measured here is <u>not</u> the power supply transfer function, V_{out}/V_{in}. We're instead measuring a related quantity inside the loop. Relabeling our block diagram, we come up with Figure 6.24.

We are measuring the point labeled $GH(\text{In} - V')$ divided by the point labeled V'. Now the thing to notice is that the network analyzer measures only AC signals, using a bandpass filter centered at each frequency in its sweep. So the term $(GH \times \text{In})$ is filtered out before the division, because it is a constant, (i.e., DC). So the result from the analyzer is $-GHV'/V' = -GH$. So the design criterion that $GH \neq -1$ can be replaced by the criterion that what the network analyzer measures must not equal 1; that is, we have to avoid having gain $= 0$dB and phase $= 0°$ at the same time.

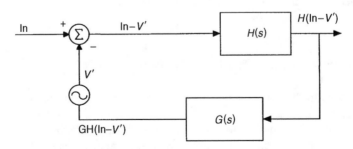

Figure 6.24 The closed loop measurement is really measuring GH.

How to Measure It : Transformer Method

Up to now the summing function used in measuring the loop has been shown as just that, a big Σ. In this section and the next, this omission will be remedied, showing the two popular methods for implementing this function, and pointing out practical aspects of their use. We start with the transformer method.

The transformer method (Figure 6.25) works just as you might suppose, by transforming the AC drive signal over into the loop. The 50Ω in parallel with the secondary is not strictly necessary, but accomplishes the following convenient function: the transformer can be soldered on top of the resistor, allowing you to measure the loop without having to desolder anything on the PC board. The 50Ω is small compared to the 10kΩ, and so does not affect the output voltage all that much.

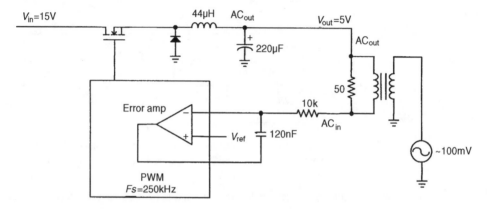

Figure 6.25   The transformer method of measuring the closed loop response of the converter.

The transformer method enjoys some popularity, and this ability to tack it in is its best feature. Of course, it also provides isolation between the network analyzer and the circuit, which can be important if you are measuring a high voltage output.

On the other hand, the transformer has to be carefully designed to be responsive over a very broad range of frequencies, both very low (where it mustn't saturate) and very high (where it mustn't have so much capacitance that the signal will be shorted out).

How to Measure It: The Mixer Method

A second method, and the one the author recommends, is using a mixer, which is just an op amp adder (see Figure 6.26).

The mixer (unlike the transformer) works at arbitrarily low frequencies, and with proper op amp selection can work at very high frequencies.

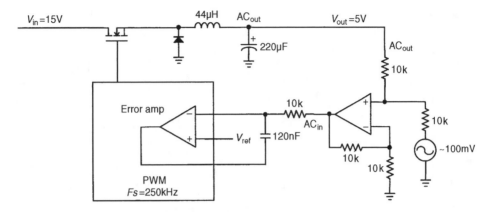

Figure 6.26   The mixer method of measuring closed loop converter response.

Practical Note Be careful! Before you use the mixer, measure its response, particularly its phase, with the network analyzer. Some high gain bandwidth op amps have lots of phase shift, and some don't; usually you can't tell from the data sheet. Don't forget 100nF bypass caps for the op amp's power lines. And for really high frequency measurements, you might want to make everything surface mount and use BNC connectors for inputs and output.

The major drawbacks of the mixer are as follows: (1) you have to desolder a component on the PCB to insert the mixer in the loop, and (2) you can't run it in a loop whose output is greater than the op amp's supply voltages. On the other hand, the only real requirement for the placement of the mixer is that it have low impedance inputs, and output to a high impedance node. So anywhere that is low impedance could go into the mixer— maybe even in the divider network, which will have to be present anyway for a high voltage output.

Converter Closed Loop

We used the mixer method to measure the response of the actual buck converter circuit in the lab (see Figure 6.27). Since we had targeted 500Hz as the crossover frequency, we expect to have 0dB at 500Hz, and a phase margin of $90 - 7 = 83°$. What we actually measure is -1.8dB and $83°$ exactly. The 1.8dB error ($= 23\%$) is explained in part by the 7% error in the capacitor value (135nF instead of 127nF), the remainder is due to a slight error in the output voltage when the open loop was measured. Below, we show how to avoid even this small error.

Let's examine the plotted measurement carefully. At low frequencies, the gain is higher as the frequency decreases, due to the pole at the origin (i.e., the capacitor in the feedback). At a very low frequency (not shown in this measurement), there is a maximum gain, set by the open loop gain of the error amp. The pole at the origin is desirable, and is standard in closed loop converters because it means that the DC output voltage will have

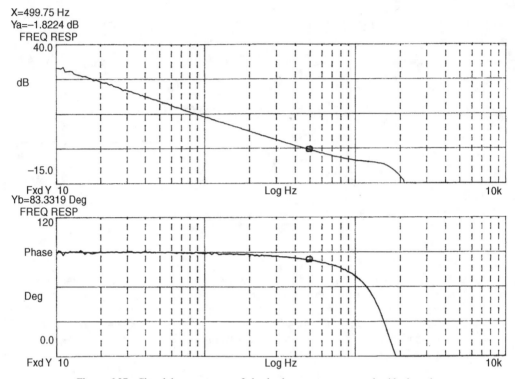

Figure 6.27 Closed loop response of the buck converter measured with the mixer method.

only a tiny error (with respect to the reference voltage); all three error amp configurations have a pole at the origin. For example, the gain of the error amp at very low frequencies might max out at 80dB. Since 80dB = 10,000, this forces the output voltage to match the reference voltage to 1 part in 10,000, 0.01%. This is of course much better than the accuracy of almost all references, and consequently the error in the output voltage is entirely due to the error in the reference.

At frequencies above the resonant tank frequency, the phase drops rapidly, but there is about 12dB of gain margin. Altogether, then, calculated performance and measurement match well.

Practical Note When doing your closed loop measurement, always make sure to hit all four corners: maximum and minimum input line voltage, and maximum and minimum output load. The open loop changes with these parameters, and thus so does the closed loop response; you need to be stable for all four conditions.

How NOT to Measure a Loop

Naturally, there are any number of ways of doing something wrong. Over the years, the author has encountered at least four incorrect approaches to measuring a loop. Here they are, with the reasons for inadequacy briefly noted.

1. Don't measure the "In" signal at the AC source rather than at the output of the mixer. This fails to take into account the feedback loop. It's more like measuring $H(s)[G(s) - 1]$ rather than $H(s)G(s)$.

2. Don't try to inject the AC at the reference pin instead of inside the loop. (Where would you measure the loop response then?)

3. Don't put the "In" and the "Out" probes at the same place (because the transformer's just a piece of wire, right?).

4. Don't try to stick the output of the network analyzer right into the loop directly, without an amplifier or transformer. Although this can be fine for a 5V input converter, generally it can be a good way to blow up the equipment.

A Better Method of Measuring the Open Loop

As we've seen in our buck converter, there can be some difficulty in measuring the open loop, both in the required equipment, as well as in achieving a desirable accuracy. And when the noninverting pin of the error amplifier isn't available (as in 8-pin PWM ICs), measuring the open loop can be rather problematic, since there's no straightforward way of making the error amp unity gain. Fortunately, there is a better way, devised by the author some years back. I now use this method to exclusion of all others because of its substantial superiority.

At low frequency, a power stage is always a fixed gain with 0° phase shift: you put in some duty cycle and get some voltage out, and increasing the duty cycle increases the output voltage. This implies that a converter can always be stabilized by picking a low enough bandwidth, and in particular, by using a type I amplifier. Following this thought, the preferred method for determining the open loop response is to use a large capacitor for compensation in a closed loop configuration, measure the closed loop, and then subtract the effect of the large capacitor. The compensation to be used in the actual circuit can then be derived as usual.

To illustrate the method, we perform a closed loop measurement on our buck converter with a 1μF capacitor as compensation, to determine the open loop characteristics (see Figure 6.28).

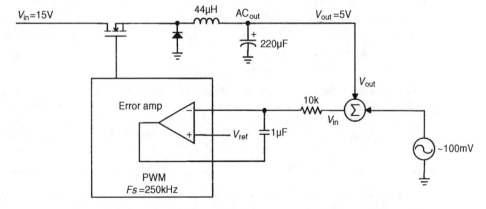

Figure 6.28   The best method of measuring the open loop characteristics of the converter is to compensate it at a low frequency.

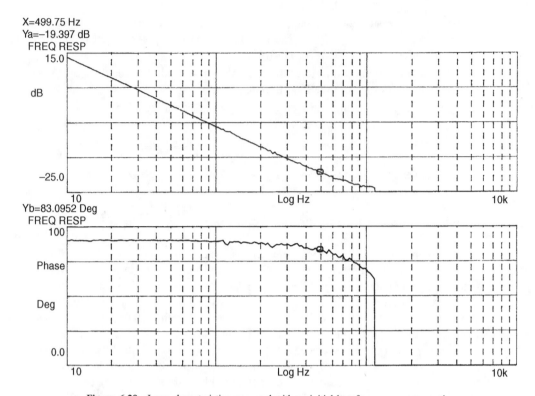

Figure 6.29 Loop characteristics measured with an initial low frequency compensation.

The measured response is shown in Figure 6.29. The bandwidth appears to be about 50Hz—but this is not what we're interested in. Closing the loop was just a stratagem for obtaining the open loop characteristics. At 500Hz, where we want to close the loop, the gain is measured to be −19.4dB, with a phase margin of 83°. This means we should select a capacitor smaller than the 1μF by −19.4dB = 0.107, which is to say 107nF, which will still give us 83° of phase margin, since it is still a type I amplifier. Using the 107nF instead of the 135nF actually selected would increase the measured gain by 135/107 = 1.26 = 2.0dB, which would bring the measured gain (−1.8dB) into agreement with calculation to within 0.2dB—dead on. Thus, this method can be expected to give almost perfect results, as seen here.

Practical Note Sometimes the gain of the power stage is low, and if you are trying to compensate the loop to a high frequency, the gain measured by this method at that frequency may be low enough to be in the noise (e.g., −60dB). In such a case, you should probably try decreasing the 1μF cap to 100nF, thus increasing the gain by 20dB.

If the phase margin we measured using this method had been too low, say only 20°, we would have selected a type II compensation, with a phase boost of 25° (because 20° + 25° = 45°) at 500Hz and a gain of −19.4dB at 500Hz, thus bringing us back to 45°

at a crossover frequency of 500Hz. Compensation with this method is thus almost trivially easy; you can astound your boss with how quickly you can stabilize a converter.

What If the Noninverting Pin of the Error Amp Isn't Available?

It's not uncommon to use an 8-pin PWM IC for a supply, in which case it is typical for the noninverting pin of the error amplifier to not be pinned out, but rather to be referenced internally to a reference voltage. As mentioned above, in this case it is quite hard to figure out how to measure the open loop gain directly, since there's no convenient way of making the error amp unity gain. If, however, you use the closed loop method described, such measurements are straightforward, and the inability to access the noninverting pin is no drawback. Figure 6.30 shows the measurement setup for determining the open loop characteristics of a converter using such a PWM.

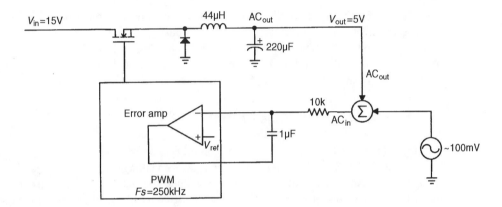

Figure 6.30   Using the low frequency compensation method to measure the open loop of a converter in which the noninverting pin of the error amplifier isn't accessible.

CURRENT MODE CONTROL

Theory

The difference between current mode control and voltage mode control is that current mode control has two feedback loops, one to control the inductor current, the other to control the capacitor (output) voltage.

   The control theory for this system can be worked out the same as for the voltage mode control system, though we're not going to. Let's note, however, that there are some subtleties involved with the high frequency response of current mode control converters that have been worked out only in recent years (notably by Ray Ridley).

   For practical purposes, the reason for having the second, inner loop (see Figure 6.31) is that controlling the inductor current acts to remove the effect of the inductor on the power stage's transfer function. This is because the transfer function of the power stage already includes the closed loop of the current loop, so that the effect of the inductor is

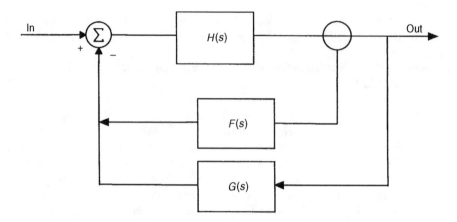

Figure 6.31   Control block diagram of a current mode converter.

entirely absorbed by the loop controlling it and doesn't appear in the response. Thus, there is no resonant tank to worry about, and at high frequencies there is only a single pole (the output cap), so that the phase shift goes to $-90°$ rather than $-180°$. These effects make it much easier to control current mode than voltage mode, and make it possible to give current mode controlled converters high bandwidth.

A Limitation of Current Mode Control

The usual implementation of current mode control is to sense a current with a resistor (or a current transformer going to a resistor, which is the same thing) and feed it into a PWM IC. However, as load current decreases, the magnitude of this signal must also naturally decrease. If the load is light enough, the current signal will be negligible, and the current feedback loop has no effect on the system; thus,

Current mode control becomes voltage mode control at light loads.

So if you give the converter a lot of bandwidth at maximum load, you need to carefully check that at minimum load the extra pole (the inductor) isn't cutting back in and causing instability. Counteracting this effect, though, is the fact that converters typically have less open loop gain in the power stage at light loads than at heavy loads.

> **Practical Note** From a practical standpoint, you won't have current mode control over the whole range of operation if your load range is more than 10:1.

Slope Compensation

When the duty cycle of a current-mode-controlled converter exceeds 50%, the converter will oscillate at a subharmonic of the switching frequency, actually half of the switching frequency, unless slope compensation is added. The origin of the problem can be understood thus. A current mode control loop works by turning off the switch when the current reaches a certain level (set by the error amp output). If the duty cycle exceeds 50%, the inductor current is being ramped up for more than 50% of the period. This means, obviously, that the inductor current is being ramped down for less than 50% of the period. This smaller time means that the inductor current has not yet returned to its steady-state initial value by the time the next period is getting started, so the current for the next period starts off too high. During this next period, therefore, the inductor current reaches the turn off level too soon, causing the duty cycle to be terminated early; in fact, it's terminated at less than 50% of the duty cycle. But now the off-time is too long (> 50%) and so the current at the start of the next cycle is too low, causing the duty cycle to again exceed 50%, and so on, oscillating between under- and overshooting the current every other cycle. There is a clear demonstration of this subharmonic oscillation happening in the literature [2].

Slope compensation fixes this problem basically by adding a fixed ramp to the current signal. Since this ramp has a constant value, the effects of variations in the current signal are better damped. In fact, the _real_ effect of slope compensation is to make the control loop somewhat more like a voltage mode control. This makes sense: if you think about it, a voltage mode controller works with a fixed ramp against which it compares the error amplifier's output. So adding more and more slope compensation brings the converter back closer and closer to voltage mode; if the ratio of slope compensation amplitude to current–signal amplitude went to infinity, you'd be back entirely at voltage mode. This explains the statement above that at low load power, your current mode control converter is back to voltage mode.

It is also to be observed that adding slope compensation puts the converter somewhere between voltage mode (with two poles) and current mode (with one pole); this means that when you take a loop measurement, and measure the slope of the Bode plot, you find that it is intermediate in value between one and two poles. Of course, it is the active circuitry that makes such a nonlinear transfer function possible.

As an aside, people sometimes tell me there's no such thing as a "subharmonic oscillation." I'm not sure what their reasoning is, but one need only try building a current mode power supply with duty cycle exceeding 50% and no slope compensation to see that there certainly is a subharmonic oscillation; the converter oscillates at exactly half of the switching frequency.

Adding slope compensation to a current-mode-controlled converter (see Figure 6.32) is as simple as adding in some amount of a fixed ramp to the current-sensing feedback. Without going into the technical details, it turns out that adding various amounts of fixed ramp accomplishes either perfect current mode control or perfect audio rejection of the

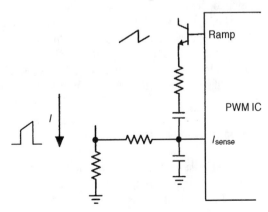

Figure 6.32 Adding slope compensation to a current mode control converter.

supply. But the reality is that tolerances in components and variations of the load make it impossible to attain either of these states.

> **Practical Note** If the duty cycle of a current-mode-controlled converter is going to exceed 50%, the converter needs to have slope compensation. The practical way to determine the right amount of slope compensation is to run the converter at maximum load current and add enough slope compensation to stabilize the converter against subharmonic oscillations. At lower loads the converter will then automatically be stable.

How to Compensate a Current Mode Controller

With one notable exception (discussed below), a current mode converter can be compensated in the same way as a voltage mode converter. Arrange the current-sense resistor to produce about the maximum signal the IC will take (typically, 1V) when the converter is at full load, and then forget about it. If you're going to have a duty cycle greater than 50%, remember to add in some slope compensation. Now you measure the open (voltage) loop exactly as you did for a voltage mode controller ($10k\Omega$ and $1\mu F$), design the compensation, and you're through! Don't forget to check the four corners!

Can I Measure the Current Loop?

The foregoing methods have proven so successful and easy at measuring the voltage loop, that I'm sometimes asked about the possibility of measuring the current loop as well.

As a first part of an answer, let's comment on the desirability of making such a measurement. In a general sort of way, the current loop is always stable, with (it turns out) lots of phase margin, at least as long as you remember to add the slope compensation when necessary. So with the notable exception of average current mode control (discussed below), there isn't any need to measure the current loop: you just use it and forget it.

Making the measurement turns out to be quite difficult, and in fact can't be done with a normal network analyzer. You'll recall that a PWM works by having a comparator that changes logic levels when the ramp signal (here, the current signal plus any slope compensation) is equal to the error amplifier output signal. The theoretical aspect of this digital operation is that instead of using Laplace transforms, the system needs to be described with a z transform, or else at least via an analog approximation to the dynamics of the comparator (worked out in recent years by Ridley) involving two RHP zeros.

Practically, because of this digital portion, ordinary swept sine wave analyzers can't be used. Instead, some sophisticated digital modulators have been devised. In any case, this sort of thing is done only in universities, never by practicing engineers. As stated above, the current loop is basically always stable in normal converters.

Average Current Mode Control

As noted in several places throughout this book, *average* current mode control, which is mainly used in off-line power factor correction converters, constitutes an exception to the general rules about current mode control.

The idea of average current mode control is that instead of using a comparator to compare the current signal with the output of the error amplifier, a second amplifier is used to provide some gain for the difference between the current signal and the output of the error amp. Thus, while the standard current mode control current loop has a bandwidth equal to the switching frequency of the converter, the average current mode control current loop can have a reduced bandwidth. In the author's original invention of average current mode control, the current error amplifier could be arbitrarily compensated to achieve any desired bandwidth and phase margin (using the same techniques used in compensating the voltage error amplifier). In the systems in common use today, the current loop is heavily filtered down to around line frequency. With a loop such as this, it is straightforward to measure the bandwidth and phase margin by means of the closed loop techniques described above.

A general requirement for stability is that the outer (voltage) loop have a smaller bandwidth than the inner (current) loop. Of course, this is a no-brainer for the usual current mode control, in as much as the current loop then has a bandwidth equal to the switching frequency.

NON-MINIMUM-PHASE SYSTEMS

Once in a while, you'll get a Bode plot that just doesn't make any sense, even though you're sure you've measured it correctly. For example, it will show the phase as being $-180°$ at low frequencies, crossing through zero degrees up to some maximum, and then coming back down again. This response is symptomatic of a non-minimum-phase system, for which a Bode plot is not sufficient to be able to determine stability.

A non-minimum-phase system is any system that has a right-half-plane zero in its open loop transfer function. What this means can be most easily understood by thinking about how a flyback converter works.

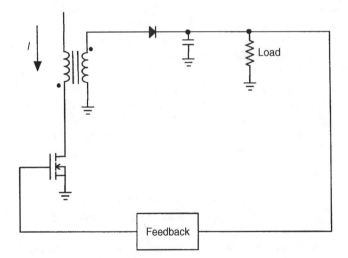

Figure 6.33   A flyback converter responds to a drop in voltage by turning on longer, causing the voltage to fall even further. This is what is meant by a right-half-plane zero.

Consider what happens when the load current increases (the load resistor value decreases) in the flyback converter shown in Figure 6.33. The output voltage begins instantaneously to drop. To supply more power, the feedback increases the duty cycle of the transistor, in order to store more energy in the primary inductance. Instantaneously, though, the transistor sees that it is turned on longer. This means that it doesn't deliver energy "on time" during that cycle, since it can't deliver energy until it's off again. But this causes the output voltage to drop even further; if the loop isn't designed to handle this, the voltage just keeps dropping. This, then, is a 180° phase shift, the essence of a RHP zero: *increasing* the duty cycle *decreases* the output voltage.

Remember from the earlier part of this chapter that an RHP zero causes the gain to go flat while the phase is still decreasing, making it difficult to guarantee stability. As a rule, the bandwidth of the converter will be designed to ensure that the RHP zeros occur at much higher frequencies than the bandwidth. But, caution! These zeros move with load. So, you need to check all four corners of the converter's operation to make sure you're not going to have problems with RHP zeros.

Nyquist Plots

Since the Bode plot of a non-minimum-phase system isn't enough to be able to determine stability, we need to use a different display of the information, called a Nyquist plot. Remember that the Bode plot consists of two graphs, one showing (the logarithm of) the root of the sum of the squares of the imaginary and real parts of the transfer function:

$$\text{magnitude} = \sqrt{\text{Im}^2 + \text{Re}^2}$$

and the other showing the phase:

$$\text{phase} = \arctan\left(\frac{\text{Re}}{\text{Im}}\right)$$

both as functions of frequency. Instead of this, the Nyquist plot plots the imaginary part on the y axis and the real part on the x axis, on a single graph (see Figure 6.34).

The important point on a Nyquist plot is "real part $= -1$, imaginary part $= 0$." Figure 6.34A shows the overall view of a Nyquist plot on a large scale (200 units per division). You can see that the graph goes around $(-1,0)$ once in the clockwise direction, but because of the scale of the axes, you can't make out details of what's happening close up to $(-1,0)$. The expanded picture, zoomed in to 1 unit per division (Figure 6.34B), reveals detail that isn't visible on the coarser graph: the graph goes once around $(-1,0)$ in the counterclockwise direction [it also contains another loop, but this doesn't matter because it doesn't enclose $(-1,0)$]. The net result is that $(-1,0)$ is encircled zero times: clockwise $+$ counterclockwise $= -1 + 1 = 0$. This guarantees that the system is stable:

**A Nyquist plot represents a stable system if
there are zero net encirclements of $(\underline{-1,0})$.**

As a practical matter, a measured Nyquist plot won't be closed the way this demonstration figure is because your measurement doesn't go down to 0Hz nor up to infinity hertz. Nevertheless, measuring the converter response over the normal frequency range, say 10Hz to 100kHz, is sufficient to determine the stability because the gain below

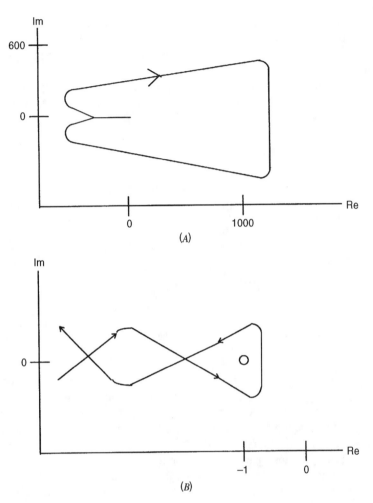

Figure 6.34 (*A*) Nyquist plot of a stable system. (*B*) Close-up of the area around (−1,0). (Modified from Ref. 3, p. 367.)

the low end is constant, and is less than 1 above the high end; encirclements of (−1,0) all occur in the same band of frequencies you would be using if you looked at the Bode plot instead.

SOME CONCEPTS OF SYSTEM STABILITY

Input and Output Impedance

As a final topic in practical feedback design, we're going to talk briefly about converter impedance and its relationship to system stability. Here "system stability" refers in particular to the stability of a group of converters interacting with each other. This is a situation frequently encountered in practical design work: for example, your 5V output converter is going to have a 3.3V output converter hung on its output; or your off-line power factor correction converter produces 300VDC, and you're going to use a second converter to step it down to ±12V. The key question for stability, it turns out, is what input and output impedance the converters must have to ensure that the system as a whole is stable.

Converter input impedance is a measure of how much the input voltage changes when the input current changes. As such, it is closely related to the transfer function of the converter. Figure 6.35 illustrates a generic method of measurement.

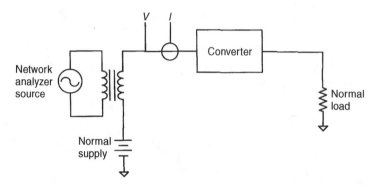

Figure 6.35 Block diagram of method of measuring converter input impedance: $Z_{in} = V/I$.

The idea is that the converter is run with a normal load and a normal input supply voltage. Superposed on top of the normal supply voltage, however, is a small AC signal, a swept sine from a network analyzer. As the frequency of this input voltage varies, the amplitude of the input current does also, and the ratio of these two is the input impedance, $Z_{in} = V/I$, as a function of frequency.

The only tricky part is remembering to use a scale factor: usually the output of a current probe is 10mV per division. So, for example, if you use a 1 : 1 probe for measuring the voltage, and the current probe is set to 1A/div, then $1\Omega = 1V/1A = 1V/(10mV/A) = 100 = 40dB$, that is, the 40dB mark on the network analyzer will be equal to 1Ω.

Practical Note For high power inputs, it may be necessary to use an amplifier to drive the transformer, rather than driving it directly from the network analyzer. You'll find that a good audio amp works well here; actually, one of the old linear (vacuum tube) amps is best because of its low harmonic distortion.

Exactly this measurement was performed on the buck converter we've designed in this chapter. Figure 6.36 shows the plot that was generated.

Let's take a close look at the results of this measurement. At low frequencies, we see that the impedance is approximately flat. Indeed, we expect that the input impedance at low frequencies will be a constant: it should be just the input voltage divided by the input current. For this buck, that is $15V/0.78A = 19.2\Omega = 25dB\text{-}\Omega$, which should show up as $(25 + 40) = 65dB$ on the graph, which is right on the money. (Actually 780mA is the measured input current, not calculated. As an aside, you might notice that input power is

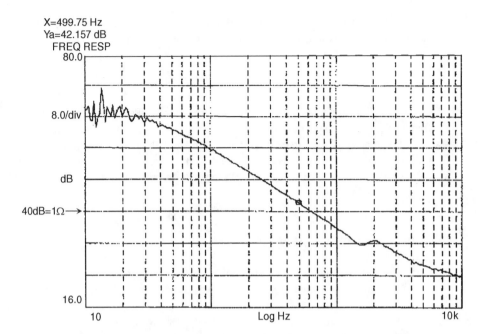

Figure 6.36 Input impedance of the buck converter.

$15V \times 780mA = 11.7W$, and output power is $5V \times 2A = 10W$, so this converter has an efficiency of 85%.)

Remember that the phase is $-180°$ at these low frequencies because a converter is a constant power load: if you <u>increase</u> the input voltage, the input current <u>decreases</u>! It is this effect that will cause problems when we consider system stability. (Phase is not shown in the measured plot. It's of no real importance unless you're cutting it very close when you get around to considering system stability; see below.)

As a further note, you hear people referring to the converter as a "negative impedance." In fact, they are referring to this 180° phase shift, and the statement is true only at low frequencies.

As the frequency starts increasing, the input capacitor becomes equal to the converter in magnitude of impedance:

$$f = \frac{1}{2\pi \times 19.2\Omega \times 220\mu F} = 38Hz$$

Above this frequency, the input is predominantly capacitive with a 90° phase shift. We can check this by looking at the cursor: 42dB scales to $2dB\Omega = 1.26\Omega$ at 500Hz, or

$$C = \frac{1}{2\pi \times 500Hz \times 1.26\Omega} = 253\mu F$$

which agrees reasonably well with the 220μF that was used.

At around the resonant tank frequency, we see a little bit of activity, but it is not nearly as pronounced as in the open loop case because the entire converter is in parallel with the input capacitance. Then at the top frequencies being measured, we see the gain starting to flatten as the ESR of the input capacitor cuts in:

$$C = \frac{1}{2\pi\ 0.12\Omega \times 250\mu F} = 5.2\text{kHz}$$

with the measured ESR of 120mΩ.

The input impedance of the converter thus looks like a "negative resistance" at low frequencies, like a capacitor at intermediate frequencies, and like a positive resistance at high frequencies. Of course, if you go high enough in frequency, you'll start seeing inductance as well, but at these frequencies, it may become necessary to consider also the cabling used in the system. System cabling can be very important to system stability in certain cases.

Converter Output Impedance

Converter output impedance is very similar in concept to input impedance: When I jiggle the load current, how much does the output voltage change? Ideally, of course, we would like this change to be zero, because we want an output voltage that is independent of load.

A circuit for measuring output impedance is shown in Figure 6.37. In this circuit, the network analyzer provides both a DC offset and a swept sine. It drives an electronically controllable load, which pulls both DC and AC current from the converter. (Make sure the amplitude of the AC current is small enough to ensure that the load is always pulling current—it can't source current!) The output impedance is $Z_{out} = V/I$ as a function of frequency.

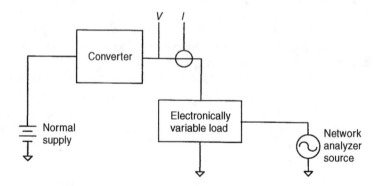

Figure 6.37 Block diagram of method of measuring converter output impedance: $Z_{out} = V/I$.

Practical Note You don't want to put a resistive load in parallel with the electronic load, since changing the output voltage changes the current through the resistor.

Using the buck converter once more, a measurement was made of the output impedance (remember the scale factor, again). Figure 6.38 is a typical-looking plot for output impedance. Take note that the scale is offset from the one in Figure 6.36 for input

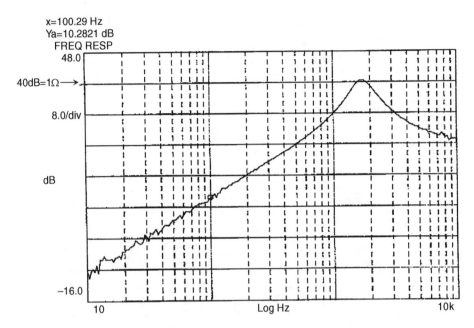

x=100.29 Hz
Ya=10.2821 dB
FREQ RESP

Figure 6.38 Output impedance of the buck converter.

impedance ($1\Omega = 40$dB is almost at the top of the graph). At low frequencies, the output is inductive. In fact, we have at 100Hz, from the cursor, that the impedance is 10.3dB, which is -29.7dB-$\Omega = 32.7$mΩ, so the inductance is

$$L = \frac{1}{2\pi \times 100\text{Hz} \times 32.7\text{m}\Omega} = 49\mu\text{H}$$

agreeing well with the actual value of 35μH. At the output tank resonant frequency, the output impedance peaks and thereafter is controlled by the output capacitor (you can again see the ESR at the top frequencies).

Two Stable Converters Can Make an Unstable System!

This rather shocking idea brings us to the forefront of today's research in power systems. It is quite possible (and indeed frequently happens) that you have two converters, each of which is stable with plenty of phase margin; but when the one is connected as a load to the other, the system, meaning here both their output voltages, oscillates! Figure 6.39 diagrams the problem.

Here is a rule of thumb to ensure that attaching two stable converters together in series won't cause oscillations:

Practical Note If possible, ensure that

1. The output impedance of the first converter is less than the input impedance of the second converter at all frequencies.
2. The bandwidth of the first converter is greater than the bandwidth of the second converter.

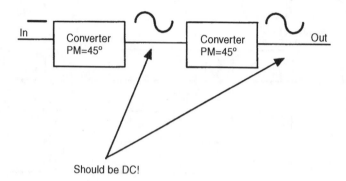

Figure 6.39   Two stable converters in series can form an unstable system.

This is merely a convenient way of ensuring stability; a system can be stable even if it doesn't meet this rule, although the question then becomes substantially more involved. When you are actually setting up such a system, of course, you need to verify that each individual converter is stable before attaching the set together!

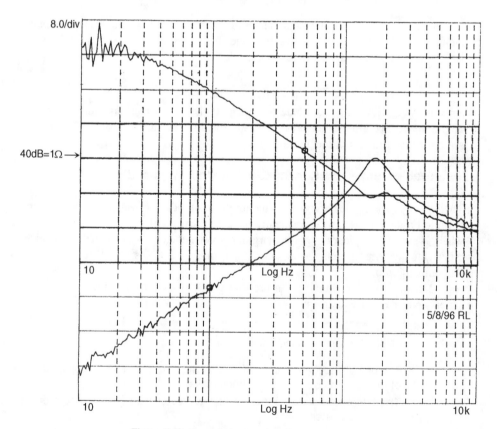

Figure 6.40   Input and output impedances superposed.

Example of an Unstable System

We have designed the compensation of our buck converter to produce a stable device. Let's suppose that for some (crazy) reason we connect two of these bucks in series. (That is, we would reset the first one to produce an output voltage of 15V so that it could run the second one. This could be accomplished by making the first converter run from $45V_{in}$, and tripling the switching frequency so that all the components retain their values; the loop and the impedances of the converter would then remain the same.)

How well does this system comply with the rules given above? Admittedly, rule 2 is marginally OK; at least the downstream converter doesn't have <u>more</u> bandwidth than the upstream one does. But rule 1 is definitely violated, as can be seen in Figure 6.40.

A look at the superposition of the input and output impedances shows that the source impedance (output impedance) is greater than the load impedance (input impedance) at frequencies greater than about 1.2kHz. This doesn't <u>guarantee</u> that the system will be unstable (you actually have to examine <u>system</u>, as opposed to converter, phase margin), but don't be surprised to see the 15V and the 5V outputs oscillating at about 1.2kHz!

SOME THOUGHTS ON THE ROLE OF SIMULATIONS

Although this book explicitly avoids talking about simulations, a few comments are in order here, because it is in the area of stabilizing converters that people most frequently turn to simulations.

For many years now, people (read managers) have been talking about the possibility of designing power supplies using just simulations, no breadboarding. Leaving aside the problematic existence of adequate computing power, one can see without going into the details that such a thing might be possible. To aid in this visualization, consider a simulation of the open loop of the buck converter we've been dealing with (Figure 6.41).

We're not going to discuss this simulation in any detail. Figure 6.41 shows a pseudodrawing of the blocks of an open loop buck, including a state-space-averaged switch model; the listing is part of a SABER listing, and the plots were generated using the SABER simulator. The names in circles are the node names, and the other names are the part names and values. Further information on simulations can be obtained from a number of books. At any rate, you can see that the simulation, shown in Figure 6.42, matches the measurements pretty well, certainly well enough to allow you to design the compensation, and that compensation would have the same values we came up with before. The trouble is, even assuming the data on ESR and so on are available from data books (which is only occasionally true), the model says nothing about switching. Thus you have to build either a much more complex model or a breadboard—in which case you've defeated the purpose of the simulation! Besides, unless you are *very* experienced (and even then), you need to measure a working unit to verify that you've built the simulation model correctly. It's so easy to type in incorrect numbers and assume that because the computer gave you an answer, this output corresponds to reality!

In the author's view, nothing is gained by using simulation to design a compensation, in part because doing it by real measurements is so easy. Simulation *is* useful in measuring worst case: it can be almost impossible in the lab to find components at their minimum or maximum values, whereas with a simulation it's easy. Simulation and breadboarding are

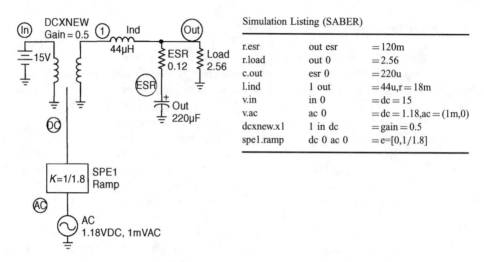

Simulation Listing (SABER)

r.esr	out esr	$=120m$
r.load	out 0	$=2.56$
c.out	esr 0	$=220u$
l.ind	1 out	$=44u, r=18m$
v.in	in 0	$=dc=15$
v.ac	ac 0	$=dc=1.18, ac=(1m,0)$
dcxnew.x1	1 in dc	$=gain=0.5$
spe1.ramp	dc 0 ac 0	$=e=[0,1/1.8]$

Figure 6.41 Simulation model of the buck converter open loop: circles enclose node names; see accompanying listing.

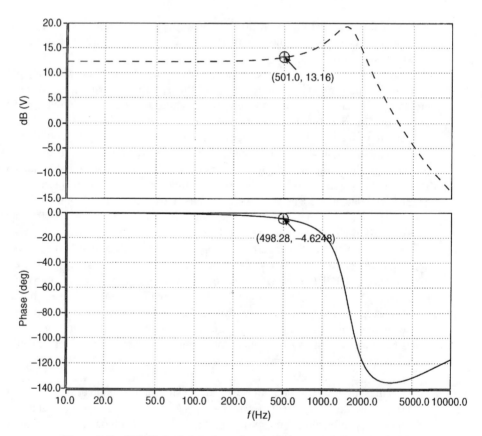

Figure 6.42 SABER simulation of open loop buck converter: both curves, OUT/AC.

thus complementary, not opposing: breadboarding is for doing the design, simulation is for worst-case analysis.

REFERENCES

1. H. Dean Venable, The *K* factor: A new mathematical tool for stability analysis and synthesis, *Powercon*, 10, H1–H12 (1983).
2. Thomas V. Papathomos, On the stability of peak current–controlled converters: Analysis, simulation, and experiments, *IEEE Transactions on Industrial Electronics*, IE-33(2), 176–184 (1986).
3. J. Kassakian, M. Schlecht, and G. Verghese, *Principles of Power Electronics*. Reading, MA: Addison Wesley, 1992.

Practical Design
of Control
and Monitoring Circuitry

CONTROL CIRCUITRY

Other chapters in this book have dealt with aspects of the power stage of a power supply. This chapter deals with the rest of the power supply, that is, the small-signal circuitry used to control the power stage and the circuitry used for monitoring the operation of the supply. (Except for the design of the error amplifier, which was covered in Chapter 6.) We start with some practical control circuitry.

Start-Up

It's always a problem: there's no power until the converter is running, but you need power to get the converter to run. The usual solution is to use a resistor and capacitor directly from the input power line to get things started, and then when the converter is running, provide power with a bootstrap winding from the main transformer (see Figure 7.1).

The way this works depends on the PWM having a UVLO (undervoltage lockout) with hysteresis. When V_{in} is applied, the capacitor is charged up through the resistor. When the UVLO threshold of the IC is reached, the circuit begins switching. It draws power out of the capacitor to run both itself and the switching transistor until the winding can supply enough power to run the IC. Figure 7.1 also shows a zener on the line, to prevent the voltage from rising so high that it damages the IC; this might be typically a 12–18V diode.

This circuit can require a quite large capacitor to store enough energy to keep things going until the converter is running. Consider a typical example: the PWM is a UC3825, which can require up to 33mA of supply current when running. Let's throw in an additional 10mA for gate drive, and a few milliamps for everything else, and we'll say it requires 50mA. Suppose the converter takes 10ms to come up to speed. (The winding on the transformer is voltage-limited by the other windings, and so typically won't provide

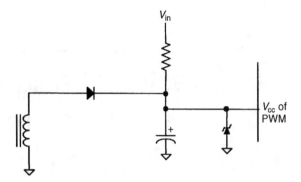

Figure 7.1 A bootstrap winding provides power after start-up.

any power until the main output is approximately in regulation.) The guaranteed hysteresis on the UC3825 is only 400mV, which means that if the voltage on the capacitor droops more than this, the PWM will go back into undervoltage lockout, cyclically hiccoughing. So we need to supply $50\text{mA} \times 10\text{ms} = 500\mu\text{C}$, with a voltage drop of only 400mV, needing a capacitance of $C = 500\mu\text{C}/400\text{mV} = 1.25\text{mF}\ (=1250\mu\text{F})$!

This particular problem can be solved by creating a larger hysteresis band for the PWM, as illustrated in Figure 7.2. This circuit has added in a PNP transistor that passes the current to the PWM (and any other loads). It works because the MOSFET isn't turned on until the capacitor voltage has reached a level set by its gate zener; once turned on, however, it stays on. The MOSFET in turn turns on the PNP, which passes current. By selecting, for example, a 12V zener, you can get approximately 5V of hysteresis (12V zener + 2V gate threshold for the MOSFET = 14V, and 14V − 9V UVLO = 5V hysteresis), so that the capacitor is reduced in size by a factor of 5V/400mV = 12.5, from 1250μF down to 100μF, a gigantic saving in size.

Of course in both these schemes the resistor continues to dissipate power as long as V_{in} is present: the winding provides the power to run things, but there is still voltage applied across the resistor. This problem is mitigated, however, by the consideration that

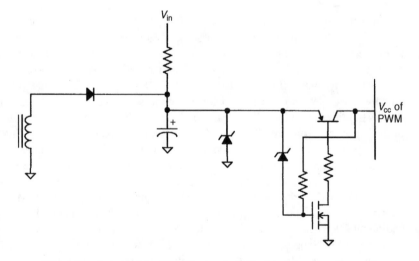

Figure 7.2 Increasing the UVLO hysteresis makes the start-up capacitor smaller.

the resistance value can be almost arbitrarily large. All a large resistance does is give a delay period between the time power is applied and the time the converter starts—it has no effect on the slow-start time of the converter. For example, with the second scheme, suppose that the resistor is 10kΩ, the input voltage V_{in} is 28VDC, and the normal output of the winding is 15V. Then the capacitor charges up to the required 14V, and the converter starts, in

$$14 = 28\left[1 - \exp\left(\frac{-t}{10\text{k}\Omega \times 100\mu\text{F}}\right)\right]$$

or $t = 700$ms. The steady-state power dissipated in this resistor will be only

$$P = \frac{(28\text{V} - 15\text{V})^2}{10\text{k}\Omega} = 17\text{mW}$$

If the converter has an output short, the winding will produce no power, and so the resistor might have to provide power continuously for extended times. But even in this case, it is dissipating only 78mW, which can be handled by a 100mW resistor.

There are other, more complex, schemes for start-up power—for example, using a MOSFET in series with the resistor to turn it off completely once the converter is running. This supposedly allows use of a smaller resistor value without impacting component size (relying on the pulse power rating of a wirewound) and allowing less turn-on delay. During an output short, however, there is still going to be dissipation in the resistor, and of course the smaller value resistor will dissipate more power, requiring a large component anyway. Thus, it seems that nothing is to be gained from more complex schemes, unless it is necessary to minimize turn-on delay (not slow-start speed, remember).

Soft Start

Soft start (or slow start) has been mentioned, but without specifying what was intended. The idea is straightforward. When a control IC first receives power, the output voltage the feedback senses is of course zero (or at any rate lower than it should be, in the case of a nonisolated flyback). This causes the duty cycle of the converter to want to go to its maximum value. Were it allowed to do so, very high and potentially destructive currents would be drawn from the input and through the power devices in an attempt to charge up the output capacitors. Instead, the duty cycle of the converter is limited to a maximum value that increases linearly with time, usually controlled by the charging of a capacitor. Once the capacitor is fully charged, the duty cycle will be whatever it needs to be to regulate the output voltage.

Practical Note Always use soft start to protect both the line and the converter.

Soft start is also frequently used for recovery from a fault such as overcurrent: when an overcurrent condition occurs, the soft-start cap is discharged, causing the duty cycle to come up slowly again while recovering from the fault. When this recovery is cyclical, it is known as hiccough mode. Since the soft-start cap is charged by a constant current source (whence the linear increase in voltage), this suggests a way of making the hiccough period different from the soft-start time: when an overcurrent is detected, switch on a transistor that pulls some current from the soft-start through a resistor, decreasing the speed at which the soft-start cap is charged.

On some older ICs, a soft-start pin may not be available. In this case, the same effect can be had by attaching an *RC* from the reference to the noninverting pin of the error amplifier: this causes the voltage to which the converter is attempting to regulate to slowly increase.

Sequencing

Related to start-up is a requirement, occasionally seen, that certain voltage(s) be up and stabilized before others come up, or that one output always have a higher voltage than another. For example, if a +5V supply runs some TTL that controls some +12V relays, the TTL may need to be operating before the relays are powered to ensure that the relays don't go into unwanted states.

Using a flyback converter can be a good choice to meet this requirement, because the output voltage on every winding is clamped by the other outputs. Therefore each output is proportional to its final output voltage: that is, if a +5V output is at 2.5V, a +12V output will be at 6V, etc.

Use of a converter with an inductor doesn't provide this scaling. Instead, output voltage depends on both the output capacitor and the load. Thus for this case, relative voltages for the various outputs during start-up can be controlled to some extent by how much capacitance is placed on the output: placing a large capacitance on the +12V can ensure that it comes up last.

Finally, if an output has to be completely up and stabilized before some other output is allowed up, there may be no choice but to use a switch such as a p-channel MOSFET. The MOSFET could be controlled by a comparator that detects that the first voltage is above minimum regulation.

Rather less commonly, there may be a requirement for turnoff sequencing when the converter is turned off: again with the example of the relays, it may be required that the +12V be entirely removed before the TTL goes down. In this case, neither the flyback (since the converter is not delivering power, the windings don't clamp each other) nor the amount of output capacitance (because of load current ranges) is really enough to guarantee sequencing; it is in practice mostly dependent on the loads. A switch seems to be the only way to perform this function.

Feedback

Chapter 6 on control theory discussed in great detail the design of a compensation network for the control loop, including selection of feedback resistors for the voltage being controlled. Frequently, though, the secondary voltage you're trying to regulate must be galvanically isolated from the primary where the error amplifier is. That is, no DC connection is allowed between the two. In such a case, a method of transferring the DC information across the boundary is required before the resistor feedback can be implemented.

There is no end of methods for accomplishing this isolated feedback. We mention a few that are popular ones:

1. Some people use an optocoupler, and perhaps attempt to linearize it with a second opto as feedback. (This approach has problems with optical gain affecting converter bandwidth if a single opto is used; it has problems if the two optos are not in the same package; and temperature and aging bring up additional problems.)

2. Other designers do a voltage-to-frequency conversion, send the frequency- (or pulsewidth-) modulated signal across the barrier with an opto or a transformer or just a capacitor, and then convert frequency back to voltage. (This approach is quite parts intensive.)

3. Still others use an instrumentation amplifier. (This is OK until you get a request for a 500VDC hi-pot test!)

The author's favorite method is shown schematically in Figure 7.3. It provides true high voltage isolation, uses few parts, has wide constant bandwidth, and can be made almost insensitive to temperature variation.

This method for isolating feedback works as a forward converter running from the (output) voltage to be measured. A BJT is switched by a secondary winding of the main power transformer. (If the freewheeling diode is not present, as in a flyback, the BJT is driven directly from the transformer, and it may be necessary to add a series base diode to prevent the BJT from emitter–base zenering during the on-time of the power FET.) When the BJT turns on, the output voltage is applied across the primary of a very small transformer. In a typical example, the voltage being sensed might be 5V. Then the transformer might be a step up of 5 : 1, so that the voltage applied on the schottky on the secondary side of the small transformer, which is grounded on the primary side of the converter, is 25V. The schottky and the capacitor then form a peak detector, and this

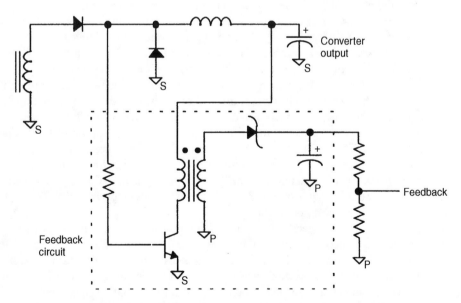

Figure 7.3 Isolated feedback using a small forward converter, driven by the main transformer.

voltage is divided down to get to a level suitable for the error amplifier. Note that the two grounds are denoted by "S" (for secondary) and "P" (for primary).

The inaccuracies of this method are due to the collector–emitter voltage of the BJT, which can be very low at low currents; the winding resistance of the transformer's primary, which can be very small because the current is only a couple milliamps; and the forward drop of the schottky, which is only a few tenths of a volt out of 25V. It is straightforward to achieve 2% accuracy with this method, surpassing all the other methods substantially. The bandwidth can also be made quite high—it basically depends on the time constant set by the peak detecting capacitor and the resistor divider network.

Current Limiting

A frequent requirement of power supplies is that they be current-limited; that is, they must be self-limiting in some fashion with respect to the amount of output current they can source. Such a requirement can be a little more complex than it seems at first blush, because "shorts", the generic term for output faults, can have differing impedances, ranging from levels that draw just slightly more current than they should to basically 0Ω. A short that has negligible impedance is usually called a "hard" short, and all others are referred to as "soft" shorts.

Despite users' frequent claims that the supply need be protected against hard shorts only, it is the author's firm belief that supplies should be protected against soft shorts as well. The goal here is not only to protect the user from experiencing currents that might damage the units, but also that the power supply should be able to protect *itself* from damage: not all shorts are 0Ω. The usual method of accomplishing this is routinely implemented inside typical PWMs with a two-stage current limit. The output of a current sense resistor (or a current sense transformer) in series with the switch is fed into a current limit pin of the PWM (this pin is frequently the same pin used for current feedback for current mode control). If the voltage on this pin exceeds a certain level, the PWM shuts off the current pulse going to the switch and doesn't restart it until the next cycle: this is called pulse-by-pulse current limiting. If the voltage on the current limit pin goes higher, and reaches a second level, the PWM terminates the pulse and re-soft-starts. This latter method is commonly called hiccough mode, burp mode, or various other names.

There is a major problem with relying on these methods if there is more than one output of the converter. The current limit sense on the primary has to be set up to prevent current limit from being reached under normal power (i.e., with all the power from every winding at maximum load summed up together). But now suppose that only one output gets a short. Then, if the other windings are at minimum power, almost the entire power rating of the converter has to go through that one output before current limit trips. The usual result of this situation is either a blown rectifier diode on that one output or an opened wire on the transformer (or inductor if the topology has one). In any case, the converter has failed to protect itself.

There doesn't seem to be a cheap solution hence. Assuming that you don't want to put current-limited postregulators on every output, the best that can be done is to sense each output current individually (with a sense resistor between the return of the output and secondary ground, so you don't need common mode rejection), let each one go into its own open collector comparator, and OR them all together. The ORed signal can then be used to control the current limit or shutdown pin of the PWM (if the converter is nonisolated), or it can control this pin through an optoisolator.

Switching Frequency

The switching frequency of a converter is defined as the number of times the convertor goes through the same set of states each second. Thus, for example, a flyback converter has a switching frequency of 200kHz if the switching transistor turns on and then turns off again 200,000 times per second.

It is necessary to be slightly wary when selecting the timing components for an IC to run at a certain switching frequency. Some ICs run an oscillator at one frequency and then use the first pulse of the oscillator to drive one output and a second pulse to drive a second output, or as a blanking signal to prevent duty cycles greater than 50%; the net result is that the actual converter frequency is half the oscillator frequency. Thus an IC that claims to be able to run at 1MHz may actually run a converter at only 500kHz.

There is also a practical limitation on maximum switching frequency. The problem is not with the controller ICs, some of which currently can run at 2MHz; the problem is with the gate charge of the MOSFETs. Gate current is proportional to frequency, so that as frequency goes up, so do losses in driving the gate; and of course, switching losses are also dependent on frequency. In very recent times, manufacturers of MOSFETs have started to come out with devices that have substantially reduced gate charge. For very high switching frequencies, this sort of MOSFET is a must.

Synchronization

A final topic of control circuitry is synchronization. It is sometimes required that the power supply switching frequency be synchronized with a master clock in a digital system, often with the idea that the noise spikes will have less effect on the digital parts' noise margin if the spikes occur at the exact time that the parts are undergoing state transitions. (The concept may well be flawed, since it ignores propagation delays inside the power supply.)

Anyway, data sheets never seem to explain what is required to synchronize a PWM, they just show an example. To rectify this oversight, here's a brief description. PWMs work by comparing the output of the error amplifier (approximately a constant compared with the switching frequency) with a ramp. As shown in Figure 7.4, they turn on a switch at a regular interval, and terminate the pulse when the ramp and the error amp output are equal. The next pulse then starts (a short time after) when the ramp reaches a certain level, internally set by the PWM. The idea of synchronization is to force the ramp to terminate prematurely by injecting a signal on top of it (Figure 7.5). The little pulse added "puts it over the top," and the next pulse begins sooner than it would have otherwise.

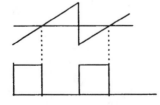

Figure 7.4 The gate drive turns on at a regular interval, and shuts off when the ramp is equal to the error amplifier's output.

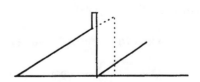

Figure 7.5 Synchronization occurs by adding a pulse to the ramp, starting the next cycle.

From this description, it is clear what needs to be done to synchronize a converter: (1) the free-running frequency of the PWM has to be lower than the synchronization frequency; (2) a short pulse, having the following characteristics, has to be added to the ramp: amplitude great enough to trip the PWM's comparator, and falling edge corresponding to the new period of the PWM. The pulse has to be short because the PWM is forced off while the pulse is present (i.e., the pulse acts like dead time).

Thus, a pulse can be generated by a TTL device, for example, and capacitively coupled into the timing capacitor (see Figure 7.6). The resistors R_1 and R_2 form a divider that can be used to scale the pulse. R_1 should be a low value (some tens of ohms maximum) to avoid disturbing the ramp, which will be integrated by the RC formed by R_1 and the timing cap. Additionally, the end of the synch circuit coming from the TTL signal should have a relatively high impedance to ground. One method of doing this is shown in Figure 7.6. This requirement exists because the coupling capacitor is quite large and is in parallel with the timing cap, and so would affect the free-running frequency, were it to be grounded.

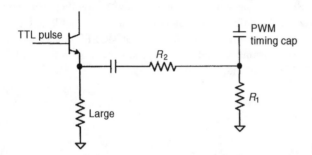

Figure 7.6   How to synchronize a PWM.

Let's mention one more little fact about synchronization. From our description of how synchronization works, it is clear that the peak-to-peak amplitude of the ramp is reduced by this process of premature termination. As we know from Chapter 6 on loop stability, the ramp amplitude is one of the factors directly determining the gain of the loop; by synchronizing a converter, therefore, you directly influence its bandwidth and phase margin. You should always set limits to the range of allowable frequencies for the synchronization, and check the power supply's loop at the maximum frequency (=minimum ramp amplitude) as well as when it is free-running.

Practical Note   A practical limit is to not let the synch frequency exceed 1.5 times the free-running frequency of the converter, if it can be avoided.

MONITORING CIRCUITRY

How to Monitor Voltage

One of the most frequent monitoring requirements is to produce a signal indicating when the output voltage(s) are valid. This means at least that the voltage is above a minimum value, and usually it must be below a maximum value as well. Both monitoring requirements can of course be met with a single comparator with hysteresis. Choosing the component values that accomplish the monitoring can be quite laborious, however; the author has found the use of a numerical or symbolic algebra computer program to be quite a time-saver in this regard. One just writes down the Kirchhoff equations and lets the computer find the values. (Assuming that a solution exists—it is possible to select a reference voltage for the comparison that forces some resistors to be less than 0Ω!) Generally, the reference voltage needs to be between the minimum and maximum trip points.

Voltage References

There is a need for a certain degree of caution when accepting a spec that calls for voltage regulation tighter than ±5%. Typical references on PWMs have several percent tolerance, and then the 5% may include monitoring tolerance, which means that a lot of your tolerance is eaten up by using 1% resistors—and since you probably can't get the exact resistor value you want, you always have to round off, adding another 0.5% or so. Finally, requesting better than 5% in an *isolated* feedback is really pushing it, because there are additional errors in crossing the isolation barrier. As indicated above, even quite good schemes have something like 1% error. If a spec calls for much better than 5% output regulation with isolation, it's best to plan on a postregulator on the secondary side.

As an example of what can be expected from a PWM reference, consider the UC3825, whose "features" section proudly announces a "trimmed bandgap reference (5.1V±1%)." The first thing to notice is that the 1% is for industrial and military grade parts only (the UC2825 and UC1825); the commercial part is 2%. This 2%, however, is at nominal conditions only; over line, load, and temperature, the commercial part is 3% (and the others 2%). Additionally, there is long-term drift: after 1000 hours, the parts may have changed an additional 0.5%. Thus, a typical off-the-shelf PWM claiming 1% reference voltage really gives 3.5%!

Furthermore, if you need a divider to bring the monitored voltage down to the reference voltage, there is an additional 1% error in the output voltage (assuming 1% resistors), and now you're up to 4.5%.

Of course, there are things that can be done to shave this percentage a bit. The most obvious (and the least costly) is to go to 0.1% resistors—2 cents a piece is all they cost. Then, you could eliminate line and load variations to the chip; but it's still going to be more than 2%. If you start checking through available zeners and other 2- and 3-pin devices, the story is much the same. The bottom line is, if a spec calls for much better than 5% tolerance on the regulated output (never mind the tertiaries), you're going to end up with a moderately expensive IC for a reference. (The REF01 is an excellent choice.) Perhaps a good plan is to carefully inquire *why* the user thinks such a tight tolerance is necessary. Is it just for the sake of a safety margin?

How to Monitor a Negative Supply Without a Negative Rail

Sometimes you'll have a negative output voltage in a nonisolated converter, and it sure would be nice not to have to stick in a transformer to monitor that rail. But since you are running all the control circuitry from +12V and ground, you can't just feed the negative supply into an IC somewhere. The solution, once seen, is obvious: the negative supply can be inverted (and divided, if necessary) by using the virtual ground of an op amp. It is clear from the circuit shown in Figure 7.7 that essentially any negative voltage can be monitored this way, even hundreds of volts below ground. There is only one caution: to keep the negative voltage from being applied directly to the IC pin, the power to the opamp should be present before the negative voltage is applied. If this condition can't be guaranteed, the IC can still be protected from damage by ensuring that the resistor from the inverting pin to the negative voltage is large enough to ensure that the current is limited to, say, 1mA or so. Then the diode (which needs to be a schottky) will prevent the IC from seeing voltages more than 0.3V below its negative rail.

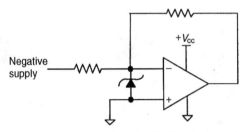

Figure 7.7   Monitoring a negative rail with a single supply: use a virtually grounded op amp. Also shown is a protection diode.

Why You Should Always Use Hysteresis on Comparators

A little hysteresis costs only one resistor, so don't think about saving 2 cents by dropping this component. Since a comparator has only finite gain, there will be a small range of voltages in which the comparator will try to operate in some sort of linear mode. The result is that the comparator may oscillate, slewing back and forth against its rails at its slew rate. This may be OK if it's driving a one-shot latch, but most of the time such oscillation gives oscillating failure signals, great for swamping a microcontroller's interrupt line. Worse yet (and the author has seen this), if the comparator is driving some sort of shutdown, you may have a closed loop system that sits at precisely the point where the comparator is oscillating and the system is just on the verge of shutdown, but doesn't quite get there. Surely one resistor isn't worth all this?

    Although it is obvious post facto, occasionally people don't realize that hysteresis can be used on a comparator regardless of whether it is inverting or noninverting. Just for reference, then, if the signal you want to monitor goes into the noninverting terminal of a comparator, do it as illustrated in Figure 7.8. On the other hand, if the signal goes into the inverting terminal, use the circuit arrangement shown in Figure 7.9.

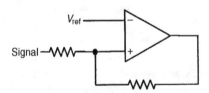

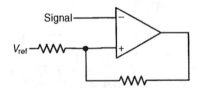

Figure 7.8   Comparator hysteresis when the signal is applied to the noninverting input.

Figure 7.9   Comparator hysteresis when the signal is applied to the inverting input.

The important thing to remember is that the hysteresis always goes back to the noninverting terminal, regardless of where the signal is. It should be noted in Figure 7.9 that some amount of current will be fed back from the output of the comparator to the reference voltage, so the reference needs to be stiff enough to prevent feedback from affecting its value.

Resistors and Shunts

Using a resistor to measure current is obvious, but a little thought shows that the resistor value has to be pretty small to avoid excessive power loss at moderate currents. Additionally, since resistors have inductance, if the current being measured has an AC component, the voltage across the resistor may be dominated by the AC current times the impedance of the inductance, rather than by the DC current times the resistance. (Don't even think of using a wirewound for such an application, unless it is noninductively wound.)

As discussed in the chapter on components, a shunt is a current-measuring resistor typically consisting of a wide, thin strip of manganin. Typical values range from 50mV at 5A ($=10m\Omega$) to 50mV at 500A ($=100\mu\Omega$) and less. The next section discusses how these small voltages can be measured. Here, it is to be observed that even shunts have some inductance. It might be tempting to try to compensate out the inductance, thus obtaining a high frequency, high current sensor, by paralleling the shunt with a capacitor, but only until you realize the size of the putative cap. Suppose the smallest one, a 5A shunt, has 20nH of inductance. Then the shunt's time constant is $L/R = 20nH/10m\Omega = 2\mu s$. To compensate this requires $C = t/R = 2\mu s/10m\Omega = 200\mu F$! A more practical method is shown in the next section.

Differential Amplifiers

To sense output current on the high side, a resistor (or shunt) is placed in series with the line (see Figure 7.10). This requires a somewhat difficult measurement to be made: that is, a small voltage difference has to be sensed on top of a large common mode voltage. For this purpose, a differential amplifier is used. ("Instrumentation amplifier" is another name for the same thing.)

It is certainly easier to measure current on the return side of a line rather than on the high side, because all you need is an op amp amplifier. Sometimes, though, a return side measurement is undesirable (see Figure 7.11): for example, there can be problems with

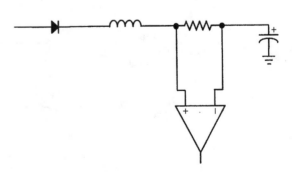

Figure 7.10 Measuring current on the high side requires a differential amplifier to eliminate the common mode signal.

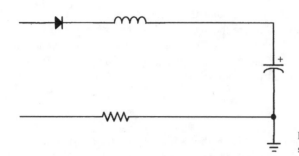

Figure 7.11 Monitoring current on the low side is not recommended.

having your load at some 50–100m VDC above "real" ground, and potentially (pun intended) much higher than that at AC. Furthermore, having a load at one ground and a power system at a different ground can have adverse effects on EMI control. So for various reasons, it may be necessary to monitor current on the high side.

> **Practical Note** Always do the current sensing in the power line, not the return line; don't use a ground elevated from the other grounds.

The simplest differential amplifier can be built with a single op amp as illustrated in Figure 7.12. In detail, this works as follows. Suppose a gain of 10, as in Figure 7.12. The more positive input gets divided by 10/11, which is the resistor divider value. Then the op amp works to force the inverting input to also be $(10/11)V_+$, where V_+ is the positive input voltage and V_- is the negative input voltage. The current through the 1kΩ to the inverting pin is thus

$$I = \frac{V_- - (10/11)V_+}{1\text{k}\Omega}$$

This same current flows through the 10kΩ, so that it has a voltage drop of

$$V = 10\left(V_- - \frac{10}{11}V_+\right)$$

The output voltage is then the voltage at the inverting pin minus this, or

$$V_{\text{out}} = \frac{10}{11}V_+ - 10\left(V_- - \frac{10}{11}V_+\right) = 10V_+ - 10V_-$$

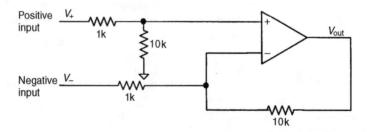

Figure 7.12 A single op amp differential amplifier.

which is to say, the voltage common to both inputs has been rejected, and only the difference between the two (with a gain of 10) is at the output.

As always, component tolerances produce limitations on this result. The tolerance of the resistors used is the dominant contributor to the error. Any error in the matching of the two ratios causes some portion of the common mode voltage to feed through to the output.

Practical Note A good estimate of the rejection of the differential amplifier is that the common mode voltage is rejected by the tolerance of the resistors. For example, if there is 5V of common mode, and the resistors are 1%, there will be approximately 50 mV of output even when there is no difference between the two inputs.

This in turn leads to a limitation on the signal size; assuming that 0.1% resistors are the best that can be obtained at a reasonable cost, the ratio of common mode to signal should be less than $1000:1$.

You also want to think very carefully before placing capacitive filters on the dividers to clean up noisy signals. Any imbalance in the capacitors will show up as reduced common mode rejection of AC. Even if you don't add capacitors, there will still be imbalances in stray capacitances, and unless your resistances are small, these strays can cause lack of adequate common mode rejection at moderately high frequencies.

There are also differential amplifier arrangements with two and three op amps (as well as IC versions). They are used in some applications because of their essentially infinite input impedance, which doesn't load the signal source. (The single op amp differential amplifier shown in Figure 7.12 loads it with $11k\Omega$.) For monitoring current, this is irrelevant, as the output line presumably has very low impedance anyway, and a single op amp amplifier is usually all that is required.

Compensating Shunt Inductance

Using a differential amplifier, it is possible to compensate out the inductance of a shunt with reasonable value capacitors, as illustrated in Figure 7.13. Using the same example as above, to get a $2\mu s$ time constant, a capacitor is required $C = t/R = 2\mu s/1k\Omega = 2nF$. Conceptually, what is happening is that the unwanted sudden rise in voltage across the shunt due to its inductance is integrated away by the RC filter, without affecting the DC response.

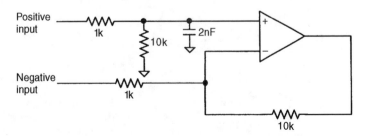

Figure 7.13 Compensating the inductance of a shunt.

Fail Should Be Low

Here's a practical tip that's obvious after reading—but surprisingly common to see violated. It is frequently required that a signal be provided indicating a problem with the converter in the event of failure. (Of course, this assumes that somehow whatever is monitoring this signal has a way of remaining powered—check that this assumption is warranted before acquiescing in a "converter fail" requirement!) Since the converter has failed, there is no guarantee that a signal can be pulled up to *indicate* failure, so:

> **Practical Note** Fail signals should always be low.

If sink capability is needed, a PNP with a base pull-down resistor provides a nice passive low signal; it has to be actively driven to be high.

Driving That Red LED

In multicard cages, there may be a requirement that a red LED be illuminated to indicate converter failure. This entails the same dilemma posed by a "converter fail" requirement: How can an LED be powered when the converter has failed? (This almost, but not quite, ranks up there with a requirement the author once saw that a signal be sent when the converter was about to fail!)

The solution diagrammed in Figure 7.14 may be acceptable. As long as the converter is active, the current to the LED is shunted away from the red LED by the BJT, so the red LED is off; and the other BJT pulls current through the green LED, and so the green LED is on. If the converter fails, the red LED turns on and the green LED turns off. If main input power fails, both the red LED and the green LED are off. Thus, the status of both the converter and the input power can be ascertained visually. This is probably the best that can be done to alert operators in the event of failure.

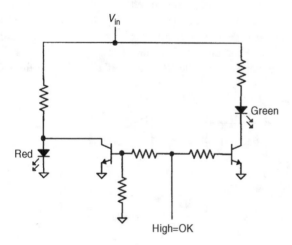

Figure 7.14 Driving signaling LEDs so that both converter failure and power input failure can be ascertained visually.

8

Practical Efficiency and Thermal Management

EFFICIENCY

Definition

Efficiency is <u>defined</u> to be the total output power of a converter divided by the total input power of the converter. So there's no possibility of confusion, we write it out:

$$\eta \equiv \frac{P_{out}}{P_{in}}$$

(η is pronounced "eight-uh," with the accent on the first syllable). The input power must include losses associated with preloads, EMI filters, fuses—everything. Occasionally you will hear talk of "power stage efficiency," which is supposed to refer to the conversion efficiency of just the components in the power path, such as the transistor and magnetics. It is best to stay away from such measures, as people outside the field will frequently misunderstand you to be talking of the converter's efficiency.

Why Is Efficiency Important?

There are a couple of reasons to be interested in efficiency, aside from merely a desire to meet a specification. The first is that a certain efficiency at a certain power level directly translates into losses in the converter, and, as discussed below in the section on thermal issues, these losses mean heat. Keeping the converter at a reasonable temperature is important for its MTBF, and so having a high efficiency translates to a good life expectancy.

Efficiency can be of paramount importance in battery-operated equipment. Here, the energy source is very limited, and so saving even one watt can greatly extend operational time before a recharge.

Efficiency can also be important for off-line converters. Since typical house circuits are limited to 20A, if a converter is very inefficient, it may not be possible to run its load from a normal outlet: so much power is wasted in the converter that not enough can be delivered to the load without tripping the breaker.

Modules

It is a sorry fact that one portion of the power supply industry routinely publishes figures that are misleading, at best. Modules (as opposed to VRMs, voltage regulation modules, which are used exclusively on computer motherboards) are small converters sold in a low profile housing, typically meant to be soldered into a PCB. Now while it is frequent practice in the power supply industry to cite efficiency at whatever output load maximizes efficiency (though vendors ought to state something like "efficiencies as high as . . . "), the module industry cites efficiencies for the module alone. That is, their literature fails to acknowledge that many applications, if not most, will require additional components to make a functional power conversion system—in particular EMI filters. Unless you are in the know, you will be sorely surprised when you buy a module, discover that additional pieces are needed, and then discover that these additional pieces cause a big drop in the wonderful efficiency you were promised. All module vendors cite efficiency in these misleading terms because any manufacturer who broke from the pack would be at a disadvantage relative to the others in the efficiency spec on the data sheet. Maybe an industry-wide standard could be set up to fix this problem?

90% Is Doing Great!

Although no general rules can be given, here are some ideas that will help you in deciding how hard it will be to meet a particular efficiency requirement.

1. As the output voltage of a converter goes below 5V, the losses in an output diode increase as a proportion of total power (because the forward drop of the diode is always about the same voltage); if you must have $> 80\%$ efficiency at $< 5V$ out, you're probably going to need synchronous rectification.

2. As discussed in more detail below, at low power (< 1–$2W$), losses in the IC supply current and gate drive current may dominate the efficiency. At this power level, 70% efficiency is doing a good job. For maximum efficiency, you will want to use a CMOS PWM, and a diode instead of a synchronous rectifier.

3. Higher efficiency almost always requires larger magnetics.

4. Very high efficiencies can be obtained in converters that have high voltage at both input and output, since the currents will be lower for a given power level; converter losses are proportional to either I or I^2.

5. Almost no converter in the low to medium power range is going to exceed about 95% efficiency. As a conceptual aid, let's suppose that you build a 100W input power converter. If this converter is 80% efficient, then its output power is 80W, and its internal losses are 20W. Increasing this efficiency by 2%, to 82%, involves getting 82W out—in other words, saving 2W out of 20W, which is 10%. On the other hand, suppose that the converter is already 90% efficient, so that its output power is 90W, and its internal losses are 10W. Now increasing the efficiency by

2%, to 92%, involves getting 92W out—or in other words saving 2W out of 10W, 20%. It is clear that saving 10% of the losses is much easier than saving 20% of the losses: increasing the efficiency by 2% becomes radically harder as the efficiency starts to climb over 90%. The moral of the story is that achieving a 90% efficient converter is doing great; if higher efficiency must be achieved, heroic efforts may be required.

Example Calculation 1

It is possible to get a pretty good estimate of the efficiency of a converter before you build it. Indeed, if a high efficiency is required, you certainly need to make such an estimate as part of the topology selection process; choosing the wrong topology may result in large costs (and headaches) later, when it becomes necessary to try to boost the efficiency. As an example, let's analyze the efficiency of a 10W output, discontinuous conduction mode, isolated flyback converter (Figure 8.1). In fact, we can use the one for which we designed the transformer in Chapter 5 on magnetics, since we already calculated the losses in the transformer there as 150mW.

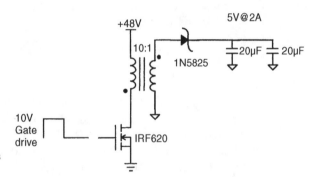

Figure 8.1 Power stage of a discontinuous isolated flyback converter.

The parameters assumed in Chapter 5 were as follows: input, 48VDC with no variation; duty cycle, 45% at this voltage; switching frequency, 250kHz. (When the forward drop of the diode is included, the duty cycle will turn out to be slightly higher than 45%; this difference has no significant effect on the transformer losses.) Recall that the design of the transformer didn't require us to specify the output voltage or the turns ratio; here we have set the output to 5V at 2A, which together with a turns ratio of 10:1 will ensure discontinuous conduction, as calculated below.

Let's start by recalculating the duty cycle, DC. At 2A, the forward drop of the schottky is about 300mV. This means that the power actually being delivered by the input is $(5V + 0.3V)2A = 10.6W$. Using the formula in Chapter 5, we write

$$DC = \frac{\sqrt{2LfP}}{V} = \frac{\sqrt{2 \times 93\mu H \times 250kHz \times 10.6W}}{48V} = 0.463$$

At this duty cycle, the peak current in the primary is

$$I_{pk} = \frac{V}{L} \times DC \times T = \frac{48V}{93\mu H} \times 0.463 \times 4\mu s = 0.956A$$

and the RMS current is

$$I_{RMS} = I_{pk} \times \sqrt{\frac{DC}{3}} = 0.956 \times \sqrt{\frac{0.463}{3}} = 0.376A$$

Since we already know the losses in the transformer, the first item to calculate is the losses in the MOSFET. These arise from three main sources, as discussed in Chapter 3: conduction losses, which are $P_c = I_{RMS}^2 R_{DS,on}$; switching losses, which are $P_{SW} = I_{pk}V_{pk}t_s f_s/2$; and gate charge losses, which are $P_g = Q_g V f_s$.

As discussed in Chapter 3, the $R_{DS,on}$ of a MOSFET is temperature dependent. Let's assume that through a self-consistent calculation of the thermal characteristics of the supply, we have found that the temperature of the MOSFET die is 60°C. The IRF620 MOSFET [1] has a guaranteed maximum $R_{DS,on}$ of 800mΩ at 10V gate drive voltage and 25°C. For this and other data, see Figure 8.2.

Practical Note A good approximation to the temperature dependence of the $R_{DS,on}$ of a MOSFET is:

$$R(T) = R(25°C) \times (1.007^{T-25°C})$$

Using this Practical Note, we find that at 60°C and with 10V of gate drive voltage, the MOSFET has an $R_{DS,on}$ of 800mΩ × 1.007^{35} = 1.0Ω. The MOSFET's conduction losses are thus $P_c = (0.376A)^2 \times 1Ω$ =141mW. Assuming that the drain switches in 50ns, switching losses are $P_{SW} = (0.956A \times 48V \times 50ns \times 250kHz)/2 = 287mW$. Typical gate charge at 10V and 48V drain–source voltage for the IRF620 from Figure 8.2 is about 9nC, so that gate charge losses are $P_g = 9nC \times 10V \times 250kHz = 22mW$. Total losses in the MOSFET are thus $P_{tot} = 141mW + 287mW + 22mW = 450mW$.

The diode losses [2] are set by the diode forward voltage and the diode current. We need to be just a little careful here—although the current in the calculation is the diode average current (2A, here), the forward voltage used should be the V_f at the average current during the conduction time (half of I_{pk}), *not* the V_f at the average current.

Now the diode current ramps down from $I_{pk,secondary} = I_{pk,primary} \times$ turns ratio = 0.956A × 10 = 9.56A to zero. The forward voltage in the schottky during its conduction time, following the approximation just mentioned, is given by the V_f at half its peak current of (9.56A/2) = 4.8A, for which, from Figure 8.3, $V_f = 0.32V$; and so the power in the schottky is approximately $P = I_{avg} \times V_f = 2.0A \times 0.32V = 640mW$. Note that this is by far the largest loss in the converter—the power lost in the diode is 50% more than that in the transistor! This is the problem with the discontinuous flyback topology—the currents are very high even for very moderate power levels. You should observe, though (as a slight mitigating factor) that for the discontinuous flyback, there is no reverse recovery loss in the diode, even if it weren't a schottky, because the diode current goes to zero before a reverse voltage is applied, as long as the reverse recovery time is fast enough (i.e., faster than the converter off-time, [4µs − transistor on-time − diode on-time]). Other topologies' losses may, however, strongly depend on diode reverse recovery time.

Electrical Characteristics @ T$_J$ = 25°C (unless otherwise specified)

	Parameter	Min.	Typ.	Max.	Units	Test Conditions
V$_{(BR)DSS}$	Drain-to-Source Breakdown Voltage	200	—	—	V	V$_{GS}$=0V, I$_D$= 250μA
ΔV$_{(BR)DSS}$/ΔT$_J$	Breakdown Voltage Temp. Coefficient	—	0.29	—	V/°C	Reference to 25°C, I$_D$= 1mA
R$_{DS(on)}$	Static Drain-to-Source On-Resistance	—	—	0.80	Ω	V$_{GS}$=10V, I$_D$=3.1A ④
V$_{GS(th)}$	Gate Threshold Voltage	2.0	—	4.0	V	V$_{DS}$=V$_{GS}$, I$_D$= 250μA
g$_{fs}$	Forward Transconductance	1.5	—	—	S	V$_{DS}$=50V, I$_D$=3.1A ④
I$_{DSS}$	Drain-to-Source Leakage Current	—	—	25	μA	V$_{DS}$=200V, V$_{GS}$=0V
		—	—	250		V$_{DS}$=160V, V$_{GS}$=0V, T$_J$=125°C
I$_{GSS}$	Gate-to-Source Forward Leakage	—	—	100	nA	V$_{GS}$=20V
	Gate-to-Source Reverse Leakage	—	—	-100		V$_{GS}$=-20V
Q$_g$	Total Gate Charge	—	—	14		I$_D$=4.8A
Q$_{gs}$	Gate-to-Source Charge	—	—	3.0	nC	V$_{DS}$=160V
Q$_{gd}$	Gate-to-Drain ("Miller") Charge	—	—	7.9		V$_{GS}$=10V See Fig. 6
t$_{d(on)}$	Turn-On Delay Time	—	7.2	—		V$_{DD}$=100V
t$_r$	Rise Time	—	22	—	ns	I$_D$=4.8A
t$_{d(off)}$	Turn-Off Delay Time	—	19	—		R$_G$=18Ω
t$_f$	Fall Time	—	13	—		R$_D$=20Ω ④
L$_D$	Internal Drain Inductance	—	4.5	—	nH	Between lead, 6 mm (0.25in.) from package and center of die contact
L$_S$	Internal Source Inductance	—	7.5	—		
C$_{iss}$	Input Capacitance	—	260	—		V$_{GS}$=0V
C$_{oss}$	Output Capacitance	—	100	—	pF	V$_{DS}$=25V
C$_{rss}$	Reverse Transfer Capacitance	—	30	—		f=1.0MHz See Figure 5

Source-Drain Ratings and Characteristics

	Parameter	Min.	Typ.	Max.	Units	Test Conditions
I$_S$	Continuous Source Current (Body Diode)	—	—	5.2	A	MOSFET symbol showing the integral reverse p-n junction diode.
I$_{SM}$	Pulsed Source Current (Body Diode) ①	—	—	18		
V$_{SD}$	Diode Forward Voltage	—	—	1.8	V	T$_J$=25°C, I$_S$=5.2A, V$_{GS}$=0V ④
t$_{rr}$	Reverse Recovery Time	—	150	300	ns	T$_J$=25°C, I$_F$=4.8A
Q$_{rr}$	Reverse Recovery Charge	—	0.91	1.8	μC	di/dt=100A/μs ④
t$_{on}$	Forward Turn-On Time	Intrinsic turn-on time is negligible (turn-on is dominated by L$_S$+L$_D$)				

Notes:

① Repetitive rating; pulse width limited by max. junction temperature

② V$_{DD}$=50V, starting T$_J$=25°C, L=6.1mH R$_G$=25Ω, I$_{AS}$=5.2A

③ I$_{SD}$≤5.2A, di/dt≤95A/μs, V$_{DD}$≤V$_{(BR)DSS}$, T$_J$≤150°C

④ Pulse width ≤ 300 μs; duty cycle ≤2%.

Figure 8.2 Data sheet for the IRF620. (From Ref. 1.)

The final loss to be considered in the power stage is that due to the ripple current in the output capacitor heating the ESR (for the sake of simplicity, this example calculation ignores losses in the input capacitor, EMI filter, fuse, etc.; these can be included by multiplying their RMS current squared times their resistance). In most converters, the loss in the output capacitor is negligible because an inductor smoothes the current before it gets to the cap. In a discontinuous mode flyback, however, we have a real mess: the peak currents are very high and go directly into the capacitor, and thus the losses can be substantial. The complete calculation is gone through in this example in order to provide a guideline for future calculations by the reader—because it is quite a mess!

First we have to know how long the diode is conducting. To calculate this, we must find how long the current in the primary of the transformer takes to return to zero (since

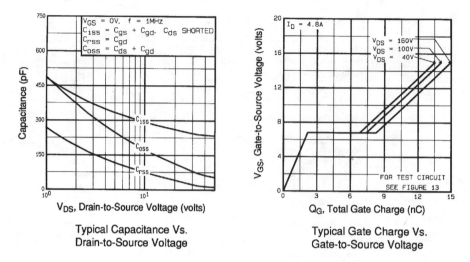

Figure 8.2 (*Continued*)

this current is reflected from the secondary current through the diode), which in turn is determined by the output voltage reflected back to the primary inductance by the turns ratio. In detail, the 5V output is actually about 5.3V on the anode side of the schottky. This reflects back to the primary as 53V in addition to the DC input (10 : 1 transformer). Since the voltage is across a transformer, it is AC; that is, the total voltage on the drain is not 53V, but rather $V_{DS} = AC + DC = 53V + 48V = 101V$. Thus the (reflected) inductor current ramps down at 53V/93μH = 570mA/μs. Starting from the peak primary current of 956mA, it then takes $t = 956mA/(570mA/μs) = 1.677μs$ for the current to return to zero. (What we have really done is to reset the flux in the core.) Incidentally, this tells us that the converter is indeed operating in discontinuous conduction mode: 1.677μs = 0.419 duty cycle, and the on-time of the transistor is 0.463, so both transistor and diode are nonconducting for $1 - (0.419 + 0.463) = 0.12$ of the period.

This rather roundabout method for calculating the diode conduction time is in fact the only way.

To calculate the losses in the capacitor, it must be remembered that only AC current goes through it. We already know the current in the diode, and the output current is 2ADC, so the capacitor current can be determined as shown in Figures 8.4 and 8.5, where current into the capacitor is defined to be positive. When the diode is conducting 9.56A, for example, 2A goes out to the load, the rest goes into the capacitor; when the diode is nonconducting, the 2A load comes from the capacitor. Since there is always 2A flowing out to the load, the 9.56A peak in the diode contributes only 7.56A into the capacitor, and progressively less as the diode current ramps down. We have already determined that the time when the diode current goes to zero corresponds to a duty cycle of 0.42. The capacitor current goes to zero at a time determined again by the reflection back to primary, as shown in Figure 8.5 and expressed in the following equation:

$$t = L\frac{I}{V} = 93μH\frac{7.56A/10}{53V} = 1.33μs = 0.33 \text{ of the period}$$

MOTOROLA
■ **SEMICONDUCTOR** ■
TECHNICAL DATA

**1N5823, 1N5824
1N5825**

■

1N5823 and 1N5825 are
Motorola Preferred Devices

Designer's Data Sheet
Power Rectifiers

. . . employing the Schottky Barrier principle in a large area metal-to-silicon power diode. State-of-the-art geometry features chrome barrier metal, epitaxial construction with oxide passivation and metal overlap contact. Ideally suited for use as rectifiers in low-voltage, high-frequency inverters, free-wheeling diodes, and polarity-protection diodes.

- Extremely Low v_F
- Low Power Loss/High Efficiency
- Low Stored Charge, Majority Carrier Conduction

Mechanical Characteristics:
- Case: Welded steel, hermetically sealed
- Weight: 2.4 grams (approximately)
- Finish: All External Surfaces Corrosion Resistant and Terminal Leads are Readily Solderable
- Polarity: Cathode to Case
- Shipped 50 units per tray
- Marking: 1N5823, 1N5824, 1N5825

**SCHOTTKY BARRIER
RECTIFIERS**

**5 AMPERE
20, 30, 40 VOLTS**

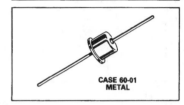

**CASE 60-01
METAL**

*MAXIMUM RATINGS

Rating	Symbol	1N5823	1N5824	1N5825	Unit
Peak Repetitive Reverse Voltage Working Peak Reverse Voltage DC Blocking Voltage	V_{RRM} V_{RWM} V_R	20	30	40	Volts
Non-Repetitive Peak Reverse Voltage	V_{RSM}	24	36	48	Volts
RMS Reverse Voltage	$V_{R(RMS)}$	14	21	28	Volts
Average Rectified Forward Current $V_{R(equiv)} \leqslant 0.2\ V_{R\ (dc)}$, $T_C = 75°C$ $V_{R(equiv)} \leqslant 0.2\ V_{R\ (dc)}$, $T_L = 80°C$ $R_{\theta JA} = 25°C/W$, P.C. Board Mounting,	I_O	←——————— 15 ———————→ ←——————— 5.0 ———————→			Amp
Ambient Temperature Rated $V_{R\ (dc)}$, $P_{F(AV)} = 0$ $R_{\theta JA} = 25°C/W$	T_A	65	60	55	°C
Non-Repetitive Peak Surge Current (Surge applied at rated load conditions, halfwave, single phase 60 Hz)	I_{FSM}	←———— 500 (for 1 cycle) ————→			Amp
Operating and Storage Junction Temperature Range (Reverse Voltage applied)	T_J, T_{stg}	←———— –65 to +125 ————→			°C
Peak Operating Junction Temperature (Forward Current Applied)	$T_{J(pk)}$	←———— 150 ————→			°C

*THERMAL CHARACTERISTICS

Characteristic	Symbol	Max	Unit
Thermal Resistance, Junction to Case	$R_{\theta JC}$	3.0	°C/W

*ELECTRICAL CHARACTERISTICS ($T_C = 25°C$ unless otherwise noted)

Characteristic	Symbol	1N5823	1N5824	1N5825	Unit
Maximum Instantaneous Forward Voltage (1) ($i_F = 3.0$ Amp) ($i_F = 5.0$ Amp) ($i_F = 15.7$ Amp)	v_F 	 0.330 0.360 0.470	 0.340 0.370 0.490	 0.350 0.380 0.520	Volts
Maximum Instantaneous Reverse Current @ rated dc Voltage $T_C = 25°C$ $T_C = 100°C$	i_R 	 10 100	 10 125	 10 150	mA

(1) Pulse Test: Pulse Width = 300 μs, Duty Cycle = 2.0%   *Indicates JEDEC Registered Data for 1N5823–1N5825

Figure 8.3   Data sheet for the 1N5825. (From Ref. 2.) (Copyright of Motorola, used by permission.)

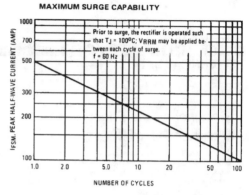

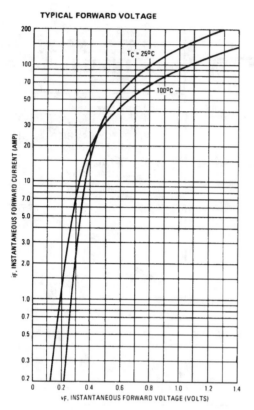

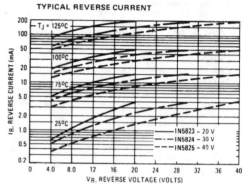

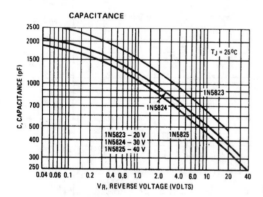

NOTE – HIGH FREQUENCY OPERATION

Since current flow in a Schottky rectifier is the result of majority carrier conduction, it is not subject to junction diode forward and reverse recovery transients due to minority carrier injection and stored charge. Satisfactory circuit analysis work may be performed by using a model consisting of an ideal diode in parallel with a variable capacitance. (See Figure 10).

Rectification efficiency measurements show that operation will be satisfactory up to several megahertz. For example, relative waveform rectification efficiency is approximately 70 per cent at 2.0 MHz, e.g., the ratio of dc power to RMS power in the load is 0.28 at this frequency, whereas perfect rectification would yield 0.406 for sine wave inputs. However, in contrast to ordinary junction diodes, the loss in waveform efficiency is not indicative of power loss; it is simply a result of reverse current flow through the diode capacitance, which lowers the dc output voltage.

Figure 8.3   (*Continued*)

As a check, we can verify that the average capacitor current is zero:

$$I_{\text{avg}} = \frac{7.56\text{A}}{2} \times 0.33 + \frac{-2\text{A}}{2} \times (0.42 - 0.33) + (-2\text{A}) \times (1 - 0.42) = 0$$

Now we are ready to calculate the RMS current. Remember that RMS is calculated by first squaring the current (RMS = root-mean-*square*), so that the AC current in Figure 8.6 is conceptually equivalent. This is true because squaring a negative is equal to squaring

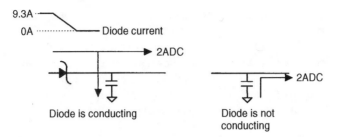

Figure 8.4 Currents in the secondary of a discontinuous mode flyback.

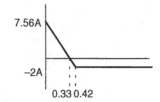

Figure 8.5 Capacitor currents are found by subtracting the load current from the diode current.

its absolute value. From this it is now straightforward to calculate the RMS current: it is the RMS of the individual RMS current pieces of this waveform. The first piece is

$$I_1 = 7.56\sqrt{\frac{0.33}{3}} = 2.51\text{A}$$

the second piece is

$$I_2 = 2.00\sqrt{\frac{0.42 - 0.33}{3}} = 0.35\text{A}$$

and the third piece is

$$I_3 = 2.00\sqrt{1 - 0.42} = 1.52\text{A}$$

so that the total RMS current is

$$I_{\text{rms}} = \sqrt{I_1^2 + I_2^2 + I_3^2} = 2.96\text{A}$$

Now at last we can calculate the losses. Suppose the output capacitor to consist of two paralleled 20µF, 10mΩ ESR MLC capacitors. (These are selected because 7.5A peak capacitor current times 5mΩ gives 38mV ripple, which is reasonable for a 5V output.) Losses in the caps are thus $(2.96\text{A})^2 \times 5\text{m}\Omega = 43\text{mW}$, or 21mW per package. Note that if

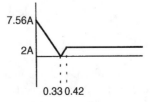

Figure 8.6 Equivalent currents for calculating RMS current.

a large aluminum had been chosen instead, with an ESR, say, of 25mΩ, not only would the ripple be up to 190mV, but the losses would be 215mW, possibly overheating it.

As a final source of loss in the converter, we suppose that the PWM is running from a 10V winding on the flyback (not shown in Figure 8.1), and that it draws 10mA of current (in addition to the gate current which has already been accounted for). If the rectifier on the winding drops 1V, the PWM uses $(10V + 1V)10mA = 110mW$.

We can now calculate the efficiency using Table 8.1.

TABLE 8.1 Losses for Example 1 Converter

Item	Losses (mW)
Magnetics	150
MOSFET $R_{DS,on}$	141
MOSFET switching	287
MOSFET gate charge	22
Diode	640
Capacitor	43
IC	110
Total	1393

Output power is 10W, so input power is 10W plus the losses, or

$$\eta = \frac{10W}{11.393W} = 88\%$$

which is quite good for this type of converter at this power level.

Before leaving this example, let's note a small inconsistency. We initially assumed that the power in the converter was 10.6W, accounting for the output power and the approximate losses in the rectifier. In the end, however, the actual power level was 11.4W, which is 800mW higher. To be fully consistent, we could now go back and redo the calculations at this higher power level. However, it is easy to see that the overall efficiency is going to remain close to 88%; since the difference was only 800mW, the additional losses calculated this second time through would be approximately 800mW × $(1 - 90\%) = 80mW$, which can be ignored for the level of approximation being used in this example.

Example Calculation 2

Let's now look at the same converter, but producing only 1W (5V at 200mA) instead of 10W. To make life easy, we'll assume that the magnetic core has been resized, but the inductance has remained the same, changing only the duty cycle appropriately, and that the magnetics' total losses are the same; all other items on the bill of materials will remain the same, as well. Repeating all the calculations yields the following results:

$$\eta = \frac{1W}{1.422W} = 70\%$$

The most significant thing to notice here (aside from the overall drop in efficiency, which always happens at lighter loads) is that the distribution of losses has changed (see

Table 8.2). Whereas in the first example the MOSFET losses were about two-thirds those of the diode (450mW < 640mW), so that it would make sense to consider synchronous rectification, in the second example, the MOSFET losses are double those of the diode's (116mW > 44mW), and so synchronous rectification would actually make the efficiency *worse*.

TABLE 8.2 Losses for Example 2 Converter

Item	Losses (mW)
Magnetics	150
MOSFET $R_{DS,on}$	4
MOSFET switching	90
MOSFET gate charge	22
Diode	44
Capacitor	2
IC	110
Total	422

Practical Note Rather than tediously calculating tables of losses, repeatedly trying to find an optimum, you can enter the various formulas into a spreadsheet, allowing easy parametric variation.

Improving Efficiency

From the two sample calculations above, it should be clear that achieving efficiency improvements is rather different for low power converters versus those in the medium and high ranges. For the latter cases, the most important way to increase efficiency is to lower the MOSFETs switching frequency, because this reduces the switching loss. This *does* make all the components physically larger, which is the usual trade-off. A second way of increasing the efficiency of medium and high power converters is to use synchronous rectification. Of course this is difficult if the supply is isolated, but whenever practical, replacing the diode, even a schottky, with a MOSFET will substantially reduce the loss, as is obvious from the first example. The underlying problem with the design in the first example is that it is a discontinuous mode flyback, so that the currents are high, generating high losses in both the transistor and the diode (and in the capacitor, had it not had very low ESR); selecting a different topology would generate substantially lower losses, though at the cost of additional components. It should also be clear that to maximize efficiency, extraneous losses should be avoided. That is, preloads either should not be used at all or turned off when not needed, the start-up circuit should be turned off after the converter is started, and so on.

  For the case of a low power converter, efficiency improvements are a little more difficult to come by. Reducing the switching frequency is still number one in importance, although now the savings may be due more to reductions in gate charge loss than in switching loss. Contrary to the case of higher power converters, synchronous rectification at low power may give *lower* efficiency than a diode. To repeat, this is because the losses due to increased gate charge losses may be greater than the savings due to the decreased conduction loss. To overcome this limitation, certain modern PWM ICs actually reduce their switching frequency when a light load is detected. Others go into "pulse frequency modulation" (PFM) in which the transistor is turned on only when the voltage has drooped to a certain level. Yet others turn off synchronous rectification at low power, running only on the paralleled schottky.

A final tactic that may yield efficiency improvement in low power converters is reducing IC current: some ICs take as much as 30mA of current to run, and at low power this can be a substantial hit on efficiency. In the second example, the loss due to IC current was one-fourth of the total losses!

THERMAL MANAGEMENT

Thermal management is an important part of many converter designs, and not only for the obvious reason that things burn up if they get too hot. The effect of temperature on component life, and thus power supply life, is explored immediately below. Besides, in consumer applications it may be undesirable to have a supply that is so hot that consumers can burn their fingers by touching it! Even if thermal management per se isn't necessary, your efficiency calculations have depended on knowing the temperature of the various components, and so being able to calculate temperatures is important to assuring that the desired efficiency is indeed achieved.

Component Life versus Temperature

The life expectancy of every component in a power supply depends on its temperature: if the temperature rises, the life expectancy decreases. This relationship directly affects the field failure rate of your converter, especially if any of the components are being run close to their maximum rated temperature.

> **Practical Note** As a rule of thumb, the life of a component approximately doubles for each 20°C drop in temperature. Thus, a capacitor rated at 2000 hours at 105°C will have a life of approximately
>
> $$2000\text{h} \times 2^{(105°C-25°C)/20°C} = 32{,}000\text{h} \approx 4\text{ years}$$
>
> at 25°C.

The most obvious example of this temperature dependence of operational life, and the most consistently and damagingly overlooked in power supply design, is the case of aluminum electrolytic capacitors. As mentioned in Chapter 3, and as the example in the Practical Note suggests, aluminums have very low life expectancy at their rated temperature, which rating is often 105°C or even 85°C—remember that 2000 hours is less than 3 months.

> **Practical Note** For most power supply applications that call for aluminum electro-lytics, you will be using 105°C parts; in most cases these parts should be rated 2000 hours or better yet 5000 hours. Give some serious thought to using tantalums instead!

As a mitigating factor, you should realize that supplies won't be operated 24 hours a day at their maximum temperature. If you can estimate the percentages of time spent at different temperatures, you will get a far more favorable estimate of the capacitor's life.

How does an aluminum electrolytic manifest that it has reached its end of life? The author ran a power supply using aluminums at high temperature for a year. Over that year, the ESR of the capacitors increased, at first slowly, and then rapidly. At the end of the year, the ESR was so high that the output ripple voltage of the supply was wildly beyond spec. Thus, running a capacitor beyond its rated life can be expected to result in a power supply failing spec, and possibly damaging the components it's supposed to be powering.

Another area of potential concern is the temperature rating of ICs. There are three temperature grades of ICs: commercial, which is rated from 0°C to 70°C; industrial, rated from −40°C to 85°C; and military, rated from −55°C to 125°C. Now of course the manufacturers of the parts don't make different dice for the differing temperature grades; the difference is in the packaging (plastic for commercial and industrial, ceramic for military) and the temperature over which the components are tested, that is, over which their operation is guaranteed. So operating a commercial part at 90°C probably won't cause any operational problem. Your worst-case analysis will be problematic, however, the MTBF will be bad (as indicated above), and if the part *does* fail, the manufacturer will be justified in claiming no responsibility.

A final topic deserving a mention is the temperature of MOSFETs. In the calculation of efficiency done earlier in this chapter, it was assumed that the MOSFET reached a stable operating temperature of 60°C, and the losses were calculated based on this temperature. However, it should be noted that the $R_{DS,on}$ of a MOSFET depends on its temperature, so that losses are temperature dependent, and of course temperature depends on losses. Thus a MOSFET can produce enough heat to make its temperature rise, which causes the resistance to rise, which causes losses to rise, which soon causes the device to exceed its rated temperature. The end result of such thermal runaway, of course, is failure.

Given all this, it is certainly highly desirable to use parts that are rated for the temperature they're going to see. On the other hand, there is a price differential between the temperature grades—moderate for a change from commercial to industrial temperatures, but extremely steep for industrial to military. Thus, holding down the overall temperature in the converter is imperative, not only for maintaining converter life, but also if cost is at all important.

Modules

Talking about component temperatures, we once again come to converter modules. The same reasons that drive manufacturers to quote unrealistic efficiencies result in the giving out of unrealistic estimates of the amount of output power the modules can produce. The limiting factor in output power is the amount of heat generated inside the module: the two are of course proportional. The problem is that if you just solder a module to a PC board and try to draw the rated power out, the module will burn up. Closer inspection of the module's data sheet reveals that the rated power is available only if there is attached to the module, *a heat sink that is larger than the module!* So the nice low profile power supply has suddenly doubled in height, or else you must buy a module that is (apparently) very overrated for the application, and therefore much more expensive.

MIL-HDBK-217

After all these dire warnings about the effects of temperature on converter life, how about a method for calculating MTBF, to see whether your design is going to meet its specified life? One standard way is to use MIL-HDBK-217 [3]. The U.S. military maintains an ongoing program on the failure rates of many common components, and the information gleaned is put into a useful form in this handbook, which is updated periodically (thus the F in MIL-HDBK-217F indicates the publication's sixth revision). We'll first do a quick sample calculation, and then discuss some of the possible concerns associated with using 217.

MIL-HDBK-217: Example

To give a simple example of the usage of MIL-HDBK-217, let's suppose that we are trying to establish the MTBF of a system of three paralleled aluminum electrolytic capacitors. The table of contents of 217F [3] shows two sections covering aluminums; one covers "non-established reliability" parts (i.e., commercial parts), and so we use this [3, pp. 10-24 to 10-25].

Examination of Figure 8.7 reveals that λ_p (in failures per million hours), of an aluminum electrolytic capacitor is the product of four factors. The first factor, λ_b, is the base failure rate, and it depends on the temperature rating of the capacitor. Let's suppose that this is 105°C, so we use the table for λ_b ($T = 105°C$ Max Rated) in Figure 8.7. Suppose the average temperature the capacitor is going to see during its life is 60°C. (Again, it is important to use *average* temperature, not maximum.) Our reference, 217F, also needs the "stress" on the capacitor, which it defines as the ratio of operating to rated voltage: suppose that the capacitor is rated at 5V, and we are applying in steady state 3.5V, so the stress $S = 0.7$. (Again, be sure to use *average* voltage, not maximum.) We then find that $\lambda_b = 0.14$.

The next factor is π_{CV}, the capacitance factor. Let's suppose each capacitor to be 1000µF. Now, 1000µF isn't listed in the table, so we can use the formula instead:

$$\pi_{CV} = 0.34C^{0.18} = 0.34(1000)^{0.18} = 1.18 \approx 1.2$$

Since all the factors in the table for π_{CV} are rounded off to two significant digits, the implication is that this is the accuracy of the formula.

The third factor, π_Q, is easy: this is a commercial capacitor, and so it is the lowest possible quality factor, 10.

Finally, the fourth factor, π_E, is for the environment. All commercial supplies operate in "ground, benign" conditions, and so $\pi_E = G_B = 1.0$.

We now find that the failure rate for a single capacitor under these conditions is

$$\lambda_p = \lambda_b \pi_{CV} \pi_Q \pi_E = 0.14 \times 1.2 \times 10 \times 1.0 = 1.68$$

MIL-HDBK-217F

10.14 CAPACITORS, FIXED, ELECTROLYTIC, ALUMINUM

SPECIFICATION
MIL-C-39018

STYLE
CUR and CU

DESCRIPTION
Electrolytic, Aluminum Oxide, Est. Rel. and Non-Est. Rel.

$$\lambda_p = \lambda_b \pi_{CV} \pi_Q \pi_E \text{ Failures/}10^6 \text{ Hours}$$

Base Failure Rate - λ_b
(T = 85°C Max Rated)
(MIL-C-39018 Style 71)

T_A (°C)	Stress				
	.1	.3	.5	.7	.9
0	.0095	.011	.019	.035	.064
10	.012	.015	.024	.046	.084
20	.017	.020	.033	.062	.11
30	.023	.028	.046	.087	.16
40	.034	.042	.068	.13	.23
50	.054	.065	.11	.20	.36
60	.089	.11	.18	.33	.60
70	.16	.19	.31	.58	1.1
80	.29	.35	.58	1.1	2.0

$$\lambda_b = .00254 \left[\left(\frac{S}{.5} \right)^3 + 1 \right] \exp\left(5.09 \left(\frac{T+273}{358} \right)^5 \right)$$

T = Ambient Temperature (°C)

S = Ratio of Operating to Rated Voltage

Operating voltage is the sum of applied D.C. voltage and peak A.C. voltage.

Base Failure Rate - λ_b
(T = 105°C Max Rated)
(MIL-C-39018 Styles 16 and 17)

T_A (°C)	Stress				
	.1	.3	.5	.7	.9
0	.0070	.0084	.014	.026	.047
10	.0085	.010	.017	.031	.057
20	.011	.013	.021	.040	.072
30	.014	.017	.027	.051	.094
40	.019	.022	.037	.069	.13
50	.026	.031	.052	.097	.18
60	.038	.046	.076	.14	.26
70	.059	.071	.12	.22	.40
80	.095	.11	.19	.35	.64
90	.16	.20	.32	.61	1.1
100	.30	.36	.59	1.1	2.0

$$\lambda_b = .00254 \left[\left(\frac{S}{.5} \right)^3 + 1 \right] \exp\left(5.09 \left(\frac{T+273}{378} \right)^5 \right)$$

T = Ambient Temperature (°C)

S = Ratio of Operating to Rated Voltage

Operating voltage is the sum of applied D.C. voltage and peak A.C. voltage.

Base Failure Rate - λ_b
(T = 125°C Max Rated)
(All MIL-C-39018 Styles Except 71, 16 and 17)

T_A (°C)	Stress				
	.1	.3	.5	.7	.9
0	.0055	.0067	.011	.021	.038
10	.0065	.0078	.013	.024	.044
20	.0077	.0093	.015	.029	.052
30	.0094	.011	.019	.035	.064
40	.012	.014	.023	.044	.080
50	.015	.019	.030	.057	.10
60	.021	.025	.041	.077	.14
70	.029	.035	.057	.11	.20
80	.042	.050	.083	.16	.28
90	.064	.077	.13	.24	.43
100	.10	.12	.20	.38	
110	.17	.21	.34	.63	
120	.30	.37	.60	1.1	

$$\lambda_b = .00254 \left[\left(\frac{S}{.5} \right)^3 + 1 \right] \exp\left(5.09 \left(\frac{T+273}{398} \right)^5 \right)$$

T = Ambient Temperature (°C)

S = Ratio of Operating to Rated Voltage

Operating voltage is the sum of applied D.C. voltage and peak A.C. voltage.

Figure 8.7 MIL-HDBK-217F reliability data for aluminum electrolytics.

failures per million hours (or 1680 FITs: one FIT = one failure per billion hours). As such things go, this is pretty high, showing that aluminums are poor components; many components will have only some tens of FITs. The predicted MTBF for this capacitor is

$$\text{MTBF} \equiv \frac{1}{\lambda} = \frac{1,000,000\text{h}}{1.68} = 600,000\text{h}$$

MIL-HDBK-217F

10.14 CAPACITORS, FIXED, ELECTROLYTIC, ALUMINUM

Capacitance Factor - π_{CV}

Capacitance, C (μF)	π_{CV}
2.5	.40
55	.70
400	1.0
1700	1.3
5500	1.6
14,000	1.9
32,000	2.2
65,000	2.5
120,000	2.8

$$\pi_{CV} = .34C^{0.18}$$

Environment Factor - π_E

Environment	π_E
G_B	1.0
G_F	2.0
G_M	12
N_S	6.0
N_U	17
A_{IC}	10
A_{IF}	12
A_{UC}	28
A_{UF}	35
A_{RW}	27
S_F	.50
M_F	14
M_L	38
C_L	690

Quality Factor - π_Q

Quality	π_Q
S	.030
R	.10
P	.30
M	1.0
Non-Est. Rel.	3.0
Lower	10

Figure 8.7   (*Continued*)

In our example, we have three of these capacitors in parallel. The total failure rate is the sum of the failure rates for each component (in a simple model) and so the total failure rate is 5040 FITs, for an MTBF of 200,000 hours.

What (besides using some other style of capacitor) can be done to improve this MTBF? The biggest factor in this case is voltage rating. In agreement with the rule of thumb given above, dropping the temperature from 60°C to 40°C reduces λ_b by a factor of 2, from 0.14 to 0.069. As a practical matter, however, it is much easier to go to a higher voltage capacitor: using a 10V cap reduces the stress from 0.7 to 0.35, reducing λ_b from 0.14 to 0.051, almost a factor of 3!

MIL-HDBK-217: Discussion

You should be aware of a potential problem in the use of MIL-HDBK-217. Since the handbook is designed for use on designs of military equipment, commercial parts are not always covered in the depth you could wish—practically, you sometimes have to guess which of the possible choices most closely matches the part you are actually using, as in the example above.

You sometimes hear people argue that the MTBFs derived from 217 are too pessimistic. These people sometimes cite a Bellcore reliability manual as giving far longer lifetimes. The author's experience is that 217 gives quite realistic estimates. Just be careful to verify that when a converter is advertised with an MTBF of such-and-such, the manufacturer used 217, not something else (such as imagination), and that the calculation was done using actual stresses, not the "parts count" method, which is based on a count of the number of components of a certain type that are likely to be used in a design. Parts count is supposed to be for preliminary estimates of reliability only, not for calculating MTBF of a finished design.

In line with the cautions elsewhere in this book, you might also want to be careful about the use of programs that calculate MTBF from 217 for you. This type of software can certainly save some drudgery, but how certain are you that the programmers typed in all the formulas correctly? Before using this software routinely, you would be well advised to check one calculation by hand for each type of component.

Temperature Calculation

After all this discussion of temperature, it's time to calculate the temperature of an actual component. Given a component's power dissipation and its thermal interfaces, this task is straightforward. It turns out there is an exact analogy between thermal and electrical characteristics, as shown in Table 8.3. (Mechanical engineers use many other units, also; the best plan for electrical engineers is to avoid confusion by converting these other units to the units shown here.) This analogy directly implies that if you have two thermal interfaces in series, their thermal resistances add.

EXAMPLE

The IRF620 used in the efficiency calculation in Example Calculation 1 was dissipating 450mW at 60°C. From its data sheet (Figure 8.2), we see that it has a thermal resistance from junction to case (i.e., from the actual die to the outside of the TO-220 package) of $\Theta_{JC} = 2.5°C/W$, and a thermal resistance from the case to sink (i.e., from the TO-220 package, through thermal compound, to a heat sink) of 0.5°C/W. Let's suppose the heat sink has a further thermal resistance of about 40°C/W to the point where the temperature is held fixed at 45°C. The electrical analogy is a current source of magnitude 450mA, attached through three series resistors, of resistance 2.5, 0.5, and 40Ω, respectively, to a voltage source of 45V. Clearly, the top of the resistor stack is $45V + 450mA(2.5Ω + 0.5Ω + 40Ω) = 64V$, or 64°C. In this example, the die is only a degree hotter than the case, but it does not always work out this way.

TABLE 8.3   Correspondence Between Thermal and Electrical Characteristics

Thermal	Units	Corresponds to	Electrical	Units
Temperature	°C		Voltage	volts
Heat source	watts		Current	amps
Thermal resistance	°C/Watt		Resistance	ohms
Thermal capacitance	joules/°C		Capacitance	farads
Thermal time constant	seconds		RC time constant	seconds

The analogy between thermal characteristics and electrical circuits also extends to thermal capacitance, although it is more usual to find the thermal time constant specified, or just a graph of thermal impedance as a function of time to be shown.

EXAMPLE

Let's suppose that the IRF620 was dissipating 10W. Clearly, the die temperature would rise so far that the device would fail, because $45V + 10A(2.5\Omega + 0.5\Omega + 40\Omega) = 475V$ or $475°C$! However, suppose instead that the 10W were dissipated for only 100µs, after which the power dissipation returned to 450mW. The curve for thermal response (Figure 8.2) indicates that a 100µs single pulse has a thermal impedance that is one-tenth its steady-state response; we'll suppose that the rest of the system has the same equivalent thermal time constant. Thus, at the end of this time, the temperature has risen to $64V + [10A(2.5\Omega + 0.5\Omega + 40\Omega)0.1] = 107V$ or $107°C$, which is entirely tolerable for the device. We can also find the thermal capacitance from this information, if we need to: since the thermal resistance is $2.5°C/W$, the thermal capacitance must be $C = t/R = 100µs/(2.5°C/W) = 40µJ/°C$.

It is for exactly this same reason, namely thermal capacitance, that the pulse power in a wirewound resistor can be much higher than its steady-state power dissipation, as discussed in Chapter 3.

Heat Sinks, etc.

The traditional method for getting extra heat out of a device (besides convection; radiation is usually negligible) is a heat sink (i.e., conduction). The heat sink provides a path in addition to convection for the heat, analogous to providing a second resistor in parallel with the first: since this reduces the total resistance, the temperature rise is similarly reduced.

The cheapest type of heat sink is just a piece of metal, frequently anodized, attached to the device being heat-sunk by a clip or screw selected from the huge variety of shapes and sizes available. (Screws are thermally better than clips, because clips have considerable variation in the amount of pressure they provide; but of course screw attachment requires an additional component and additional labor.) Because the device being heat-sunk and/or the heat sink may not be perfectly flat, it is common to apply thermal compound (grease) to the back of the device before attaching it to the heat sink. This fills in the voids, lowering the total thermal resistance. However, thermal compound is quite a mess, getting all over everything, and so its use in production lines tends to be frowned on.

> **Practical Note** If you turn too hard on the screw attaching the component to the heat sink, the metal may actually bow (form a shape like an arch), which leaves an air gap between the device and the heat sink, defeating the heat sink's purpose. Component packages usually specify the maximum torque to be applied, and special screwdrivers are available with calibrated torque, to stop turning the screw when the specified torque is reached.

The metallic heat sink may need to be electrically isolated from the circuit, since the heat sink may be connected to ground, for example, to the enclosure. The isolation can be accomplished by placing an insulator between the component and the heat sink. The most common insulator is a rubbery material called Silpad. Another possibility is the use of mica or beryllium oxide; the latter is often avoided, though, because of concerns about exposure to toxic beryllium dust if the heat sink were to become powdered. (As long as you don't grind the BeO, it will be just fine.)

Heat sinks can work well for applications such as a TO-220 package. However, there doesn't seem to be a good way to attach a heat sink to a surface mount component. This is a particular concern when one is using surface mount MOSFETs: the dominant form of heat transfer for these transistors is through their leads, which can seriously limit the usefulness of the devices in higher power converters. The situation can be somewhat improved by running a large trace underneath the body of the package; unfortunately, manufacturers often neglect to specify the thermal resistance from the die to the body of the package.

If the heat problem in a converter cannot be fixed by means of a heat sink, there are more complex possibilities, such as a fan or a heat pipe. Not only are such solutions expensive, however, their effects are often difficult to calculate as well. For example, knowing a fan's airflow doesn't necessarily tell you much about the amount of cooling a given component will see, because the airflow to that component probably will be partly blocked by other components. Generally, such possibilities should be left to a mechanical engineer who has specialized knowledge in this area.

FEA

A final comment can be made about computer programs for evaluating thermal performance of a converter. There are specialized programs for doing this, using FEA, finite element analysis. Essentially, such software (conceptually) breaks up the converter into small pieces and lets them all interact simultaneously to determine the temperature distribution in the supply, much as an electrical simulation would deal with a network of resistors. FEA programs can even do this on a dynamic basis, using thermal capacitances.

In fact, such a program could also be written using the electrical analogy to thermal properties to map the model into a SPICE model (or using SABER's mixed-mode capabilities directly). It might be interesting to investigate the computational (and economic) efficiency of such a routine versus the rather expensive thermal programs typically used.

REFERENCES

1. *HEXFET Power MOSFET Designer's Manual*, publication HDM-3, 1993. International Rectifier, 233 Kansas St., El Segundo, CA 90245.
2. *Rectifier Device Data*, publication DL151/D, rev. 2, 1995. Motorola, P.O. Box 20912, Phoenix AZ, 85036.
3. MIL-HDBK-217F, Notice 1, in *Military Handbook, Reliability Prediction of Electronic Equipment*, 1992. Rome Laboratory, Griffiss Air Force Base, Rome, NY.

9

Practical EMI Control

AN OVERVIEW

One of the nightmares of a power supply engineer is being assigned to design a supply to a specification that calls out some EMI limits. This is because a common timeline in such case is:

> Go ahead and design a supply to meet all the other specs.
>
> After the design has been breadboarded, measure the noise and find that it's way outside limits.
>
> Throw some inductors and caps in the front end of it, and find this doesn't help.
>
> Seek advice from other engineers, whose suggestions also don't pan out.
>
> Hire a consultant, who tells you to totally re-layout the board and the mechanical design that has already been through CAD.

Sound familiar? But whereas some books offer only generalities; this chapter gives some practical advice that will make compliance *really* easier.

The first step in the field of EMI is to straighten out some terminology. **EMI** (electromagnetic interference) refers to electrical noise from one device or system that causes malfunction in another device or system; but this term is now used generically to refer to noise regardless of whether it causes problems. The exact meaning of "noise" is discussed below. Other terms of related or overlapping significance are **EMC** (electromagnetic compatibility), which describes conditions under which two or more systems can work simultaneously in the presence of each other's noise; **susceptibility**, which is a measure of how much noise is required to upset a given system; and **EMV** (electromagnetic vulnerability), which is a new term that means the same as susceptibility.

There is no end of books about EMI, and it wouldn't be reasonable to try to cover the whole subject in one chapter. Instead, we're going to concentrate on EMI as it is generated by power supplies, and more particularly, on the practical aspects: where it comes from, how to measure it, and how to fix it—or, better, avoid it. Two topics we won't touch on except in passing are electromagnetic susceptibility (since the power supply is often the major source of system noise) and the response and protection of supplies to transients (since the same actions that are taken to prevent power supply noise from contaminating the environment to some extent protect the supply from damage by the environment). Where transients are larger, transient protection may well end up being a separate box from the power supply. While this chapter makes no claim to being comprehensive, if you follow the practical rules laid out here, you'll be far along on the road to meeting even the most stringent EMI requirements. Noise control need not be a black art!

Radiated and Conducted

Perhaps the most fundamental distinction in types of EMI is that between conducted and radiated noise: respectively, noise that is carried by conductors and noise that does not rely on conductors. Note that "radiated" noise is something of a misnomer. Measurements are usually taken at one or a few meters' distance from the supply, and at the lower frequencies this is actually near-field signal, meaning that you are measuring components of the field that do not propagate energy to infinity (propagating energy to infinity being the definition of radiation).

Not a lot can be done about radiated noise, and in fact you can do nothing at all about it once it's outside the system. So your goals are first to avoid generating it, and then to ensure that any unavoidable noise doesn't get outside. You avoid generating radiated noise by means of the same types of strategy we'll discuss in detail below to prevent the generation of excess conducted noise: attaching switching devices to grounded conductors, pairing cables that leave the box with their returns, and so on. The two tasks are related because radiated noise has to be radiated from an antenna (read: cables coming into or going out of the supply); so if there's no signal along the antenna (no conducted noise), there won't be any radiation either.

What to Do About Radiated Noise

What to do about radiated noise once you have it is an interesting problem. The very first thing to look for, both because it's the most common problem and because it's cheapest to fix, is whether each wire that comes out of the box (both power and signal) is matched with its return. "Matched" here means that the wire and its return are physically close together both as they exit the box and as they are routed to their destination or source out of the EMI chamber. Matching is important because the signal level (noise, in this case) is directly dependent on the loop area formed by the signal wires; putting them close together, or better, twisting them together, minimizes this area and thus the noise. What you *absolutely don't want* is a single signal wire that routes out to an instrument somewhere. Rather, give the wire its own ground return, even if the line has no high frequency signal on it or carries only DC: noise can be picked up on this wire while it's still in the box, and then you have a beautiful antenna.

The next cheapest thing to look at for fixing radiated noise is to see whether the box is adequately sealed. The supply should certainly have <u>some</u> type of metallic container around the box, if only to have a place to attach ground. No, plastic has no effect whatsoever (and won't serve as a ground, either). Remember that frequency (in hertz) and wavelength (in meters) are related by the speed of light:

$$\lambda = \frac{300,000,000}{f}$$

and considering quarter-wavelength antennas, it's clear that a 1cm hole will allow signals of frequency greater than about 600MHz free passage, and will probably allow some signal out at a tenth of that. The 1cm hole doesn't have to be round for this to be true, however; a 1cm slit (see Figure 9.1) can radiate pretty much the same frequencies as a 1cm diameter hole. The only holes in the box ought to be those where lines are entering or exiting.

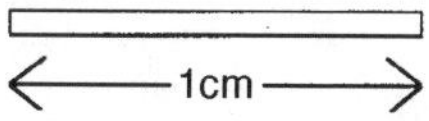

Figure 9.1 A 1cm slit will allow passage of signals as low as 60MHz.

$$\longleftarrow \text{---} 1\text{cm} \text{---} \longrightarrow$$

Once you have achieved control of the radiation from the system by enclosing it in an EMI-tight box, the only source of radiation will be the signal and power lines entering and exiting the box. Since you're going to be controlling the conducted noise on the power lines anyway, this design feature will control their radiation of noise. This leaves only the signal lines. You may want to consider putting filter pins on the signal lines, starting with those that carry high speed signals, such as digital clocks. But even static lines may potentially cause a radiation problem because of pickup onto them inside the box: that is, as the static lines go through the box toward their exit (or entry) point, various devices irradiate them, so that they carry noise; then once they exit the box, they are antennas, and radiate the noise to the outside world. So in many cases, it is advisable to simply save the hassle by getting a complete filter pin connector.

What Kind of Box Material?

From a practical standpoint, as long as the enclosure around the supply is metal, it doesn't matter too much what the material is; because of cost, then, it will almost certainly be aluminum. When people get into trouble with EMI, sometimes they try something like a mu metal enclosure. Mu metal shields low frequency magnetic fields; the material is very expensive and difficult to shape mechanically. Although this approach can be made to work (for best results, the enclosure should be sandwiched between layers of grounded aluminum), it shouldn't be necessary if you pay attention to the signal and power lines.

> **Practical Note** Get the conducted noise under control first, as this will solve 80% of your radiated noise problem. Pay attention to signal lines. If a consultant recommends mu metal, don't even think about it; get a new consultant.

Common Mode versus Normal Mode

Concentrating from now on on conducted noise, there are two basic types, common mode and normal mode (also called differential mode). It's easy to explain the difference: Normal mode (see Figure 9.2) is noise that flows in on one power line and returns on the other (neutral), whereas common mode (see Figure 9.3) is noise that flows on both the power lines simultaneously and returns on the ground line.

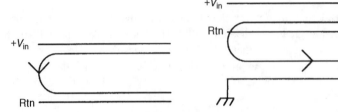

Figure 9.2 Normal mode noise flows in on one power line and returns on the other.

Figure 9.3 Common mode noise flows in on both power lines and returns on ground.

Return versus Ground

"But I thought return and ground were the same thing—the black wire going back to my power supply."

Even for your lab supply, return and ground aren't the same. Every good lab supply will have a third terminal which is the ground. The supply will have its output isolated from the AC line, as in Figure 9.4, and ground will be attached to the metallic box in which the supply is housed. You *may* then strap the ground and return together at the posts. This isn't necessary, though, and it's not always desirable.

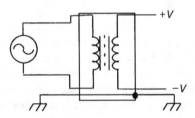

Figure 9.4 A lab supply should have its return separate from ground.

In an AC system, ground and return are the same only at DC: the national wiring code requires that they be attached together where power enters the building, which can be a long way away from your system. When this is the case, ground and return are effectively isolated from each other at AC frequencies of concern for EMI. Thus it makes sense to talk about common mode noise as flowing back from the power and neutral to ground. Let's be explicit again:

Normal mode current is current flowing from $+V$ to $-V$ in Figure 9.4; it is what is normally thought of as delivering power.

Common mode current flows simultaneously through both $+V$ and $-V$ and returns on chassis ground; it does not normally deliver power.

Military versus Commercial Measurements

The final major distinction to address before getting down to practice is what EMI tests you're trying to meet, which is to say, what kinds of measurements you're required to make.

The goal of all measurements of EMI is to ensure that the noise generated by the supply doesn't cause malfunction in anybody else's equipment (radio, garage door, helicopter navigation system). But military and commercial regulations have ended up with measurement techniques, and thus noise specifications, that are diametrically opposite, and this to some extent influences the corrective actions open to you if you are a noise generator.

To start with military measurements, the controlling document, MIL-STD-461, requires that the power and return lines be (AC) coupled together with a very high quality (meaning low ESR) 10µF capacitor for the measurement. You then measure the current flowing in each line, and the limits are set by the amount of current allowed at each frequency.

In a completely opposite way, commercial measurements [domestic (FCC), European (VDE), and others] require that the power and return lines be independently isolated from the power source with a 50Ω impedance that is more or less constant with frequency. (The impedance box is called a line impedance stabilization network, or LISN.) You then measure the voltage on each line, and the limits are set by the amount of voltage allowed at each frequency.

Even though these standards seem completely different, with military requirements measuring current and commercial requirements measuring voltage, they are related, as they must be: the current the military will measure flows through the impedance of the commercial system to generate the voltage the commercial system will measure. However, the techniques used for meeting these requirements will also, in a certain sense, be mirror images, as explained below.

HOW CAN I SEPARATE CM FROM NM?

No doubt you noticed that neither the commercial nor the military measurements said anything about measuring the ground wire. This is because it is assumed that currents in the ground are of no practical concern to any system. But since you measure only one line at a time, the common mode and normal mode noise get mixed together: referring to Figures 9.2 and 9.3 and considering the power line for a moment, you can see that a measurement of the noise on this line includes both common mode, which is returning via ground, and normal mode, which is returning via the return. It is this "partial measurement" that is responsible for EMI's annoying habit of disappearing at one frequency but then re-appearing at another. Adding a normal mode filter to reduce normal mode noise can seemingly increase common mode noise, and vice versa. (A technician once told the author that EMI resembles a balloon—when you push down in one place it pops up in another.) Of course, in reality common mode and normal mode are independent, and to meet specifications, you must be able to control them both.

What's needed, then, is a way to separately measure common mode and normal mode, so that adequate filtering can be done for each, independently. This is fortunately very easy, especially in a military measurement. To measure common mode current as in Figure 9.5, you want to measure the current that is flowing simultaneously (in phase) through both wires. Thus all you need do is place the current probe around both wires with no twist. To measure normal mode current, you want to measure the current flowing in the power wire that is flowing out of phase with that flowing in the return, as in Figure 9.6. Thus you put a foldback in the return wire and measure the current while it's pointing in the same direction as the power. [The broken line in Figure 9.6 signifies that that part of the return line isn't inside the current probe.]

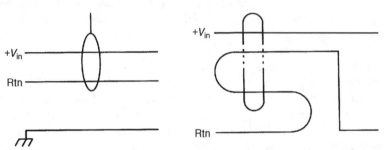

Figure 9.5 Measuring the common mode current.

Figure 9.6 Measuring the normal mode current is done with a loop in the wire to eliminate the common mode component.

When you're doing commercial measurements, there's no such convenient method, although recently Lee et al. [1] proposed doing something equivalent with transformers that couple the wires together appropriately. But as indicated above, the current and the voltage are certainly related to each other, so you can use a method like the one shown for military limits. Measure the normal and common mode currents with a current probe, just as presented above. The ratio of common mode to normal mode currents will reflect the ratio of common mode to normal mode voltage; so by measuring the noise voltages the commercial way, you will then be able to partition the noise between common and normal mode, and design filters appropriately.

SIMPLISTIC EXAMPLE

The current for the common mode is measured to be 300µA at 100kHz, and the current for the normal mode is 3mA at the same frequency. This ratio of normal to common mode is 10 : 1. The total noise voltage is measured on the power line at 100kHz to be 101dBµV = 110,000µV = 110mV. Presumably, then, 100mV of this comes from normal mode noise, and 10mV from common mode, because 100mV/10mV = 10 : 1, and 100mV + 10mV = 110mV, the total.

WHERE DOES THE NOISE COME FROM?

The first step in controlling noise emissions is to understand where the noise comes from: that is, what generates it and how it gets to the lines being measured. Given knowledge of the origins of the noise, the first and best control technique will be arranging the circuitry to prevent noise from escaping to the measurement lines at all; filtering the noise that does get there is decidedly second best.

Switching Waveforms

The major source of conducted (and radiated) noise from a switching power supply is, not surprisingly, the switching. This is not surprising because the switching involves the highest power in the circuit (and thus highest currents) and highest dV/dt, and also has the highest frequency components in the supply: for example, a MOSFET being switched from on to off in 50ns has a fundamental at something like $1/50\text{ns} = 20\text{MHz}$, and also odd harmonics (at 60MHz, 100MHz, etc.). A diode has similar types of spectrum because we want it to turn on and off as fast as possible also, and for the same reason: fast switching minimizes power loss.

And in fact, one need only trace through the power path of a converter to see which elements are likely to be serious noise offenders: the switching transistors and the rectifying diodes (or synchronous rectifiers). If there is an inductance on the secondary, the high frequency, high power components of the spectrum won't conduct through it (though it will still radiate), so everything after the diodes is less noisy. Moreover, if the power transformer is designed well, its core material will form a partial shield and so it won't generate too much noise either.

Capacitive Coupling

Having identified the major noise sources (see Figure 9.7), let's think about what can be done to reduce their generation of noise. We said that the high speed switching is desirable because it keeps down losses, and we don't want to do anything that might hurt the converter's efficiency.

The realization that the noise mechanism is the high speed switching of power perhaps brings to mind the idea of resonant conversion, since the switching in such a supply is by definition done at low power. (The current or voltage across either the FET or diode or both is zero when the switching occurs.) The possibility may seem tempting, but overall the disadvantages of resonant converters outlined in Chapter 2 outweigh the noise reduction benefit gained. Many types of resonant converter also change switching frequency with line and load, causing changes in the noise spectrum. This can make it harder to filter these converters than it would have been if you had stuck to a fixed-

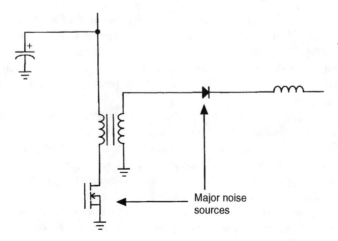

Figure 9.7   Major noise sources in a switching power supply.

frequency, hard-switching converter. The practical aspect remains the same: avoid resonant converters. However, the same arguments show that the best of both worlds may be attainable by using a quasi-resonant converter, which retains zero switching, but with a fixed harmonic spectrum.

Nonetheless, acceptable noise performance can be achieved even with very high speed hard switching by considering the mechanisms whereby the switching noise gets out to the world and its measurement lines. The most obvious is that the current is pulled from the input line by the converter at the switching frequency. Aside from choosing a topology that has continuous conduction rather than discontinuous (which decreases edge amplitudes), filtering is the only option, as discussed shortly. A less obvious, but still potentially very serious mechanism for noise conduction is capacitive coupling of the switching waveforms onto ground. The conduction paths are shown in Figure 9.8.

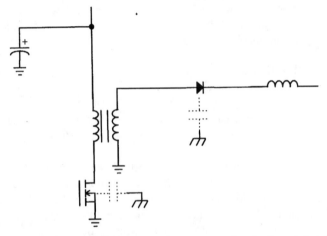

Figure 9.8 Transistors and diodes can couple common mode noise through their body capacitance.

Power switching devices are typically mounted to the case of the power supply for heat sinking; this case is grounded. Since there is a small distance (e.g., the thickness of the MOSFETs case) between the actual die and the case, and a large area, there is a significant capacitance between the two, which will conduct high frequency signals to ground. The signals then return through the power and return lines, which is to say it is common mode noise.

Instead of filtering this signal, a better tactic is to reduce the coupling—that is, reduce the capacitance to ground. The area of this capacitance is fixed by package size, but the distance can be increased. The trick is to use a thermally conductive insulator between the case of the device and the power supply case, preferably one with a low dielectric constant. Typical choices are silicone-based plastics and beryllium oxide. This reduction in capacitance can mean very substantial benefits in reduced common mode noise filtering. In addition, for isolated supplies, it can cut down on noise transmitted between secondary and primary through the two series capacitors, the path in question being diode to case, then case to FET.

CONCEPTS OF LAYOUT

Having been discussing the origin of conducted noise on the power lines, let's turn to another aspect of noise generation control, namely, the placement and routing of components and traces to prevent noise from upsetting the operation of the circuitry in the power supply. Such an upset can be a very serious problem; in the worst case, supplies won't work at all because of noise. We'll get to filtering shortly.

Signal Ground versus Power Ground

A signal ground is, by definition, a ground trace that carries low currents; a power ground is a trace that carries high currents. This isn't exactly what you'd call a quantitative pair of definitions, but in practice the concepts usually are clear enough: the ground from the resistor that generates the timing signal from a PWM IC is a signal, the source of a power MOSFET is attached to power ground, and so on.

Maintaining separate signal and power grounds is essential to good operation of a power supply at all stages of the design. It will save endless trouble in your breadboards, and will make the difference between a good PC board and one that requires endless troubleshooting with noise filtering of signals. The reason becomes clear from a consideration of Figure 9.9.

Any trace (or wire, or even ground plane) has some resistance and inductance.

Practical Note The resistance of a trace is approximately given by the formula:

$$R = 0.5\text{m}\Omega \frac{\text{length}}{\text{width}} \quad \text{1oz. copper}$$

at room temperature. Two-ounce copper is half this, etc.

If a high current passes through the trace, there is a voltage drop across it because of its resistance; if the current is high frequency, there is additional voltage due to the inductance. If this high current passes through the same trace that is being used to ground a signal component, the signal component doesn't see the proper ground; rather, it is

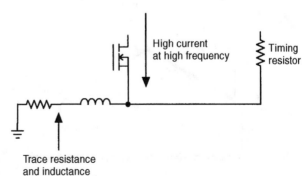

Figure 9.9 Power paths can upset signal grounds because of trace impedance.

elevated off ground by $IR + L(dI/dt)$. Potentially even worse, the high frequency component elevates the signal component's ground periodically, and quite possibly even *synchronously* with the signal that the component is supposed to be processing! This is a prescription for disaster. The solution is to create separate grounds for signals and power and attach them together at a single point, preferably at a bypass capacitor at the power entry point (see Figure 9.10). This configuration is known as a star ground.

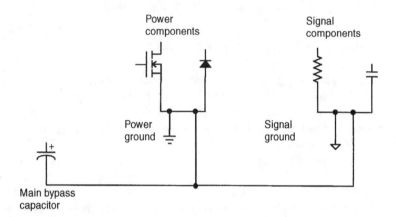

Figure 9.10 Power ground must be separate from signal ground; only at the power entryway can the two grounds be tied together.

Practical Note Create these separate grounds on both breadboards and PC boards. Do it religiously! As a practical matter, anything above about 100mA can be considered to be power. It is re-emphasized that the two grounds are to be attached together only at a *single point*. Otherwise there can be ground loops, which defeat the whole purpose.

Figure 9.11 is a picture of how <u>not</u> to lay out physical traces (i.e., with multiple paths for the ground currents).

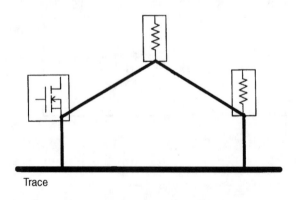

Trace

Figure 9.11 DON'T lay out a PCB like this. Return currents have more than one way of returning to the point on the left. In this physical picture, bold lines are traces.

If you feel the need for additional copper for the power ground, thicken the traces instead of trying to run multiple traces all over the place. The correct way corresponding to our bad example is shown in Figure 9.12, where the bypass capacitors are located at the junction at the far left.

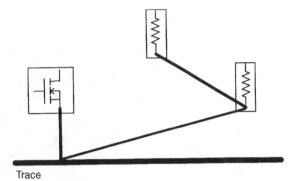

Figure 9.12 The right way to lay out a PCB: connect all the power returns together before attaching them to the main return trace. Return currents have only a single path to return to the point on the left.

Trace

In the (presently unusual) case in which there is substantial high speed digital circuitry on the power supply, it would certainly be worthwhile to consider a third, digital, ground system separate from analog signal and power ground, again attached to the others only at one point.

Grounding a High Current Driver; Ground Islands

A special case of needing a separate ground is nevertheless so common that it warrants mention here: the MOSFET gate driver. A gate driver works by pulling from its bypass caps current that it then delivers to the gate–source capacitance of a MOSFET. When the MOSFET is turned off, that gate capacitance is discharged, and the charge returned to ground. In the full cycle, there are two very fast pulses of high current (as high as 6A on some devices). The object of the layout is to ensure that these fast pulses are not seen by the rest of the board, which should only see the (much lower) average current. Figure 9.13 shows a highly recommended layout for this type of device. You can think of this as creating a little "island" of ground just for this current path. The current from the FET's gate is returned preferentially to the capacitors, preventing the high fast currents from flowing into the rest of the ground plane, which would cause upsets. Of course the drain current passes through to the source and then to the main ground trace. This arrangement

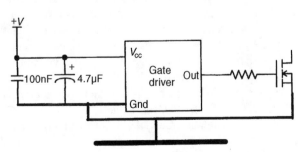

Figure 9.13 Creating a ground island for a gate driver ensures that gate currents won't upset the ground.

is called an "island" because on a PC board these grounds are all large traces connected by a thin neck to the rest of the ground plane: (see Figure 9.14).

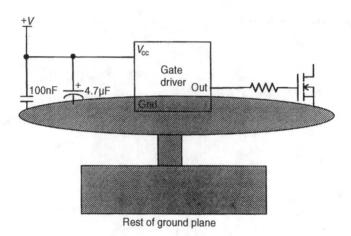

Figure 9.14   How to lay out a ground island on a PCB ground plane.

What If the Device Has a Signal Input But No Signal Ground?

Some of the best gate drivers have multiple pins for power ground (which is good) but neglect to have a separate pin for the ground of the signal that is driving the device (which is bad). In this case, it is still desirable to use both ground pins for the power ground, and let the signal take its chances with ground bounce (it usually has TTL noise margin). As long as the connection to the rest of the ground plane isn't too far away, this arrangement seems to work. If ground bounce becomes a real problem, you may have to select a different gate driver. (The qualifier "best" above is to be understood in the sense of gate drivers having the highest drive current.)

Where to Put the Current Transformer

As long as we're talking about gate currents, it is useful to point out that the high current also may affect the current transformer if positioned improperly. Based on the analogy with a current sense resistor, the natural place to put a current sense transformer is in the source of a MOSFET (see Figure 9.15). However, this means that the gate turn-on current (which, remember, can be as much as 6A) also passes through the current sense transformer. Even for high power converters, this can be a significant fraction of the switching current you are trying to measure; for lower power converters, it can be the largest component of the signal. As a result, either the signal is corrupted by this irrelevant current pulse from the gate or it has to be so heavily filtered that the signal you want to measure gets filtered out as well. Whether the signal is then used for current mode control, or just a pulse-by-pulse current limit, the result is bad.

The way around this set of problems is to put the current sense transformer's primary in the drain of the FET, where it sees only the MOSFET's drain–source current, not the

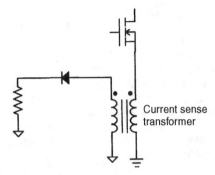

Figure 9.15 It seems natural to put a current sense transformer in the source of the power MOSFET.

gate–source current associated with the gate capacitance (see Figure 9.16). This design has no deleterious effects, either on the current signal (since it is after all transformer-isolated), or on the operation of the converter (since the primary inductance, which is usually single turn, is negligible). The current sense transformer could even go between the main transformer primary and the power bus, as long as it comes after the main input cap.

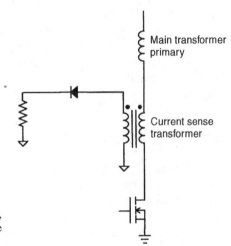

Figure 9.16 To avoid measuring gate current, place a current sense transformer in the MOSFET's drain.

Feedback Lines

While we're on the subject of positioning components, a few practical tips on feedback layout are in order. The two usual feedbacks are those for voltage and current, and the practical tips here apply to both.

When you build a breadboard, there are usually components every which way, and a mess of wires all over, quite possibly mixing power and signal lines. And while the converter has been compensated to have 45° of phase margin, if the noise pickup is too great onto either the current feedback or the voltage feedback, there may still be, if not instability, at least considerable duty cycle jitter.

Practical Note When one is building a breadboard, it can be helpful to use a twisted pair of wires for the feedback lines, to reduce the noise pickup onto these critical lines. Shielding the twisted pair is rarely necessary, but if shielding is required, ground the shield on the signal end only; leave the power end floating. (The power end for a voltage feedback line refers to the output voltage node. For a current feedback line, it refers to the secondary of the current sense transformer.) It is also desirable to have any small-signal components close to the PWM rather than located at the output. For example, if there is a voltage divider for feeding back the output voltage, locate these resistors close to the PWM, not the output, and run the twisted pair from the output voltage; don't try to put the divider close to the output, and *then* use the twisted pair.

The reason for the injunction with respect to voltage divider placement is that a low impedance source, such as the converter output, is more noise resistant than a high impedance source such as a $10k\Omega$ resistor.

When you go to a PC board, of course you can't use twisted pair anymore, but you can still try to run the trace containing the feedback signal in parallel (i.e., on top or bottom) with a ground trace, or even better, with a ground trace both on top and on bottom (in a multilayer PCB).

One more trick works for both breadboards and PCBs. Try terminating the twisted pair or trace for a voltage sense line with a 100nF capacitor. Yes, from a schematic viewpoint the capacitor is just in parallel with the output caps already present. From a noise viewpoint though, those output caps don't help: they're in the wrong place. A cap right at the termination filters noise very nicely, on the other hand, and obviously has no effect on the loop.

Further Layout Tips

All the foregoing layout tips have been variations on the same theme: power and signal must be kept separate! In line with this restriction, a few additional specifics may be in order. When laying out the power stage of a converter, it is important to keep all the power components physically as close together as possible. Not only is this good for efficiency (by reducing trace resistance), it also minimizes loop area for radiating noise onto signal lines.

This rule is of the greatest importance in designing the conection between the gate driver and the MOSFET gate. Specifically, make the connection as short as possible. It is probably worthwhile to orient the IC so that its output pin faces the transistor's gate pin. And DO NOT connect the two together through any vias—this shortcut risks contamination of other planes!

LOW FREQUENCY FILTERING

The Basics

Now we're ready to find out what to do with the noise that's still there after you've done your best with layout and the physical aspect of design. The subject of filtering divides itself rather naturally into two parts, low frequency filtering and high frequency filtering.

Low frequency filtering is what can be done with discrete, lumped components, such as discrete capacitors and inductors; high frequency filtering is everything else, and into which we lump filter beads, feedthrough caps, etc.

Filtering consists basically of presenting a high impedance to the signal in the path you want to keep free of noise, and a low impedance on the path you do want the noise to travel.

Normal Mode Filters

Low frequency filtering comes in two parts, normal mode filtering and common mode filtering. Following the discussion above, normal mode filtering tries to reduce noise on the power line that returns on the return line. Remember that this means noise on the power line *that exits the box* and returns on the return line. So the tactic for filtering is to shunt the noise on the power line to the return line *before it leaves the box*, thus ensuring that it will return without having been measured. This amounts to putting an inductance in line with the power line, to block it from getting out, and at the same time providing a capacitor from the power to the return line to provide a low impedance path for the noise to go through instead.

Commercial versus Military

Now although the preceding discussion on commercial versus military filtering indicated that the two conventions are closely related, their difference shows up here, when a low frequency normal mode filter has to be designed. The question is whether (looking from the power supply out toward the power source) to design a filter that first has a capacitor and then an inductor, or one that has first an inductor and then a capacitor. The commercial measurement has a (relatively) high impedance source (50Ω) and measures voltage; thus we can use this source as a block for the noise, and it is advantageous to use first an inductor and then a cap, as illustrated in Figure 9.17.

In some situations, the noise may be so low that the inductor is unnecessary; the capacitor forms a voltage divider with the 50Ω that is small enough to divert away most of the noise. Remember, though, that for this circuit to work, the ESR of the capacitor is critical. Either a multilayer ceramic or a metallized plastic capacitor might be tried for this application.

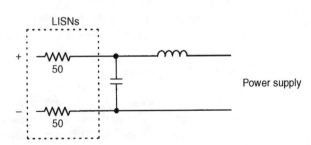

Figure 9.17 A commercial supply should be filtered with a two-pole filter's capacitor facing the LISNs.

For a military measurement, conversely, the source is a low impedance source (10μF) and measures current; we thus need to block current from getting to this low impedance, and the filter should be first a cap and then an inductor (see Figure 9.18).

In this case (unlike the commercial case) the capacitor is doubtless already there in the form of a large electrolytic. With this bulk cap, however, it is advisable to parallel a ceramic 1μF or 100nF cap (or both—a 1μF capacitor loses its effectiveness around 1MHz, whereas a 100nF device continues working up to about 10MHz). This measure is advised to counter the effects of the poor high frequency characteristics of the large cap.

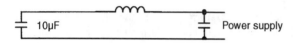

Figure 9.18 A military supply should be filtered with the two pole filter's inductor facing the source cap.

Selecting the Values

Selecting the values for the L and C is relatively straightforward. You already know from measurement the unfiltered spectrum, and we know that the two-pole filter we are designing is going to roll off the noise at 40dB/decade. So here is the procedure for deciding the position for the filter to start rolling off.

Practical Note Find the lowest frequency component that is out of spec (preferably of the normal mode measurement, rather than the specification measurement that combines normal and common mode, as discussed above). Suppose, for example, that it is out of spec by 20dB = 10 at 100kHz. The filter that would bring this into spec would start at a freuqency of 100kHz/$\sqrt{10}$ = 30kHz (square root because it's two poles). Now, on top of (a copy of) the noise measurement, draw a straight line, starting at this frequency (30kHz here) and rolling off 40dB/decade. If none of the other peaks are above this line (and frequently they won't be), you're done: you need a filter with an LC resonant frequency of 30kHz. If one or more of the other peaks *are* above the line, repeat the whole calculation with the lowest frequency peak until you have a frequency that guarantees that all the noise peaks are below it. [It is interesting to observe that the noise specifications typically roll off at 30dB/decade, which is between one and two poles.]

With the frequency for the LC filter determined, one more parameter still needs to be determined to calculate the magnitudes of the components. In a general sort of way, inductors are more expensive than capacitors, both in cost and in power loss (since they have series resistance). So the preference is to use more capacitance and less inductance. A practical recommendation is given in the section below entitled Optimal Filtering.

Common Mode Filters

Common mode filters are easier to design than the normal mode variety because the former have fewer available choices. A common mode filter consists of common mode capacitors (called "Y caps" in the commercial world; "X caps" are normal mode) and a balun (the word comes from "balanced–unbalanced transformer") or a common mode inductor: see Figure 9.19. The common mode caps shunt current on both lines to ground, and the balun (note the polarity dots) presents a balanced impedance—that is, the same impedance on both the power and return lines, which constitutes a high impedance path for common mode noise. (The Z shape shown on the balun is standard, as is the set of two dots, although you will generally see just one or the other.)

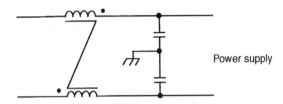

Figure 9.19   A common mode filter consists of a balun and capacitors to ground.

Selecting the Values

The common mode case is quite the opposite of the normal mode case with respect to selecting components: here, the capacitors are more expensive than the inductor. The reason is twofold. First, the capacitors go to ground and must be rated to take a transient that may be 3kV or even 6kV, making them quite large. Furthermore, there are strict safety limits on the amount of current allowed to flow to ground, which limits the maximum size of common mode capacitance that can be used, typically to a few nanofarads. Thus, you select the maximum allowable capacitance and then use the same technique sketched above to determine where the *LC* needs to be; this procedure uniquely determines the balun's inductance value.

> **Practical Note** Don't panic if you calculate that a large value is required for the common mode inductance. Baluns carry the same current in both windings, and so, ideally, see no net current. They can thus have a large number of turns without saturating the core.

Furthermore, when calculating the inductance required, remember that the two capacitors are in parallel (doubling the net value) for purposes of common mode noise; and the individual windings of the balun are in series. Thus you have double the number of turns, which is four times the inductance. This gives you an extra factor of 8 noise suppression for free (see Figure 9.20). The capacitance in Figure 9.20 equals 9.4nF, and the inductance is 4mH, giving a cutoff frequency of 26kHz!

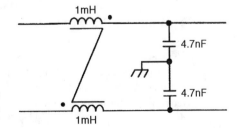

Figure 9.20   The windings of the balun are in series and the capacitances are in parallel for the common mode noise.

Caps and Inductors and Their Limits

Capacitors have limitations in their frequency response, and this translates into limitations on their usefulness for EMI filtering. Electrolytic capacitors have relatively large ESR, which means that above the *RC* frequency, they look resistive and no longer are a pole. For example, a 100μF cap with 100mΩ ESR becomes resistive at about 16kHz. It is thus of no use for EMI control.

In practice, ceramic or plastic capacitors are always used for EMI. Even these have their limitations, though, because of lead inductance.

Practical Note 1μF caps are good only up to about 1MHz. Above this, use a 100nF cap, which in turn is good only up to about 10MHz. It may thus actually make sense to have a 1μF, a 100nF, and a 10nF all in parallel for noise suppression.

Inductors have limitations too. (Their winding resistance, though bad for power consumption, is too small to be significant at noise frequencies.) The most important limitation is distributed capacitance, which may be thought of as occurring in parallel with the inductor. Above a certain frequency, the capacitance is lower impedance that the inductance, and so the inductor no longer blocks noise above this frequency in the way that might be naively expected.

EXAMPLE

Suppose that a 1mH inductor has a capacitance of 100pF. Then its impedance will stop increasing above 500kHz, and will actually start decreasing. Of course, a smaller inductance also has a lower capacitance, and thus a higher frequency.

It might thus make sense to have two inductors in series, rather than a single larger inductor, which would put the inductances in series (increasing inductance) and the capacitances in series (decreasing capacitance). Inductors are so expensive, however, that this is never done in practice.

MOVs Have Capacitance

Here's a freebie! Many, if not most, designs will require an MOV on the power lines to deal with transients. An MOV has a small capacitance and so can be used as part of the filter. This is also a caution to those who put MOVs from power and return to ground: the MOVs capacitance adds to the leakage current, so the size of the Y caps must be suitably reduced.

Two for the Price of One

Now here's a good idea. You can build both a normal mode inductor and a balun into a single magnetic device, saving the price and space of an extra device. This is done in a way that is straightforward to describe but requires care in design. You wind up a balun, using, let's say, 47 turns on each side; then on the power line side, you *add one extra turn*. The device is still a balun, but now it also has a series inductance, equal in magnitude to

$(48^2 - 47^2)A_L$, far larger than a single turn on the same core. The catch is that now the core has to support a flux density, and you have to check to be sure that it won't saturate at maximum current.

You Can't Get 100dB Attenuation!

You've no doubt noticed that the discussion of low frequency filters only talked about two-pole filters, not higher order filters with more than one capacitor or inductor or both. There are reasons for this. First, such filters are much harder to design; indeed, there are people who make a career of designing them. Another reason, at least for commercial designs, is that a higher order filter requires another inductor, and this often means unaffordability.

The most basic reason, though, is that except in special circumstances, such filters shouldn't be necessary. Four-pole roll-off is pretty fast already, and if you require six poles, something is probably wrong.

> **Practical Note** If your calculations indicate a need for more than about 60–80dB of attenuation in the low frequency regime, you had better go back and work on your layout. Another possible way to reduce the filter requirements is to increase the switching frequency.

Here's another point along the same lines. We've already mentioned that components have imperfections which limit their performance. Additionally, layout on real boards entails leakage paths and cross talk between traces. The bottom line is the same as in the practical tip above: you can't get 100dB of attenuation. If you think you need it, try again.

It's possible to get somewhat more attenuation using a commercially available filter than building your own, primarily because the commercial device has paid very close attention to avoiding cross talk in the layout, and typically has enclosed the filter in a metallic box. Of course, you can achieve the same results by building your own with the same techniques, and at far less cost.

HIGH FREQUENCY FILTERING

High frequency filtering comes into play at frequencies where lumped components start having imperfections that make them poor filters. A "high" frequency might start at 10MHz. From this frequency up to maybe a couple of hundred megahertz, there are still components that can be added to help the spectrum; above this frequency, all you can do is seal the power supply enclosure better.

Where Should I Use Beads?

Ferrite beads have excellent high frequency characteristics, with impedance continuing to increase even above 100MHz. Unfortunately, they are also very easy to saturate with just a little DC current—a parameter some manufacturers don't even bother to specify. So for the most part, a bead is pretty useless for input noise filtering.

As a sidelight, you may see a design that uses a bead on the gate (or drain) of a MOSFET. On the gate, this is a really bad idea: the reduction in noise is caused by a reduction in the FET switching speed, which directly translates into power loss. On the drain, it is typically ineffective, again because it saturates at a low current. If the idea is to block current flow for a few tens of nanoseconds (such as in synchronous rectification) and then let it saturate so that it doesn't add inductance to the power path, however, a bead on the drain may have a use. Even then, though, the power stored in the bead has to be dissipated or otherwise dealt with each cycle, just like leakage inductance in the main power transformer.

Feedthroughs

Feedthrough caps and filter pins are roughly the same, though pins are typically used for signals and feedthrough caps for power. They are very high quality capacitors, effective out to hundreds of megahertz, occasionally with tiny inductances that can take as much as 10A, depending on size. They begin providing filtering at about 10MHz, unless you get a large one, which may have some modest attenuation as low as 1MHz. Note, though, that their attenuation is typically rated in a 50Ω system, which gives almost no clue to what it might do in a military measurement.

In many cases you can get by without a great deal of feedthrough capacitance. This is because at the high frequencies at which the feedthroughs work, the power cable leading up to the power supply box has very significant impedance: about 1μH, which at 10MHz is 60Ω, for a meter of wire. Since all these numbers are quite dependent on details of physical layout, there are no rules for how to filter the high frequencies: you try a filter, and if it doesn't work, you try a bigger one. Sorry.

SOME OTHER TOPICS

Noise Estimation

The amount of noise a converter will generate can be estimated before the device is built. For example, a buck converter draws current in rectangular pulses. This pulse train can be decomposed into its spectral (frequency) components. Each such component can then be divided up between the input capacitors and the source impedance. The resultant currents in the source (for military; multiply by the impedance to get the voltages for commercial) can then be compared with the spec limits to design a filter as detailed above.

EXAMPLE

Suppose you have a buck converter with 5V input and 2.5V output, so that it conveniently has 50% duty cycle. Suppose the input current is conveniently 0.5A. Since the input is a square wave, the peak current is 1A. We can easily look up in a math book [2] that a square wave has spectral components at odd multiples of the fundamental, with amplitude inversely proportional to the multiple. For our case, let's suppose the switching frequency is 100kHz, so we have $4/\pi$ amps at 100kHz, $4/3\pi$ at 300kHz, $4/5\pi$ at 500kHz, etc. If we have an input cap of 1000μF, the 10μF source-impedance cap for the military measurement will source about 1/100 of the current, that is, $4/100\pi$ amps at 100kHz, $4/300\pi$ at 300kHz, etc. For the higher frequencies, the rise and fall times of the current waveform dominate. Suppose that the rise and fall times are both 100ns. These will generate spectral components at odd multiples of 1/100ns, (i.e., 10MHz, 30MHz, etc.) and the resultant currents can be estimated if some knowledge is available about trace inductances. A filter can now be designed using these various estimates.

The trouble with this procedure, despite its seeming utility, is that in practice it is common to add 20dB to the estimates to ensure that the filter produced will really work. This doesn't seem like much until you remember we are talking about *10 times the size of the inductor or the capacitor*! The trouble is that even for the low frequency components, there are numerous "sneak paths" that add in to the actually measured current. The high frequency components have so many capacitively coupled paths (and radiated paths, too) that your estimate is likely to be wildly wrong. Estimating using a simulator has, of course, exactly the same problems.

Practical Note Estimating noise is unlikely to get you to a reasonable filter design. The only thing that works is a measurement on real hardware.

Optimal Filtering

The question of how to select the L and C values of a low frequency filter was not fully answered above, in that the pole frequency was found in terms of the required attenuation but actual values were not determined. Subject to stability criteria, though (discussed in the next subsection), the best possible selection of component values can be based on optimizing the cost, or volume, or some other parameter of the filter. This is covered in an article by the author, which, as it is now hard to get, is reproduced here.

OPTIMAL MILITARY EMI-FILTER DESIGN*

Military power supplies must comply with conducted emi limits specified in MIL-STD-461. This standard calls for measuring, across a wide band of frequencies, the noise current flowing into a 10μF capacitor. This is often done by installing a filter, measuring the current, installing another filter of similar design, remeasuring the current, installing still another filter and repeating the process until the emi limits are met. This method is not only inefficient, but can also result in a filter that is substantially larger, heavier, and more costly than it need be. By making suitable measurements of the noise source, however, it is possible to design a filter that works the first time and that occupies the minimum possible volume.

A DC input power supply with a single ground (nonisolated secondary) typically has two main sources of conducted noise: the switching transistor(s) and the output rectifiers. These two sources are, in turn, associated with two main frequencies: the basic switching frequency of the converter and the inverse of the transition times. The transition times for the switching transistors are the rise or fall times; for the diodes, the reverse recovery

* *This article appeared originally in Powertechnics Magazine* (April 1989, pp. 47–48).

times. There is also some noise generated as the result of ringing in various parasitic circuit elements, but the contributions from these sources is minimal.

A Thevenin source is characterized by its open-circuit voltage and short-circuit current, the two being divided to yield the Thevenin impedance. The Thevenin equivalent open-circuit voltage of the power supply [$V_{oc}(\omega)$] is a function of frequency. It can be measured using a high impedance connected in series with either the high or low power line, as shown in Figure 1. A spectrum analyzer is used to measure the frequency spectrum of the voltage existing betwen the line and chassis ground. Note that the voltage measurement is referenced to the chassis and not the return line. This is because MIL-STD-461 requires that the $10\mu F$ capacitor in which the noise current is measured be referenced to the chassis, as shown in Figure 2.

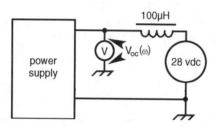

Figure 1 Measurement of open-circuit noise voltage.

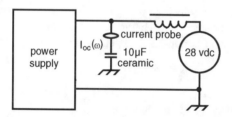

Figure 2 Measurement of open-circuit noise current.

The capacitor used to measure short-circuit noise current [$I_{sc}(\omega)$] should exhibit a very low impedance at the noise frequencies of interest. A multilayer ceramic (MLC) capacitor is well suited to this application. This capacitor must be connected as close to the supply as possible, since even a few inches of wire presents significant inductive reactance at the frequencies being measured. With the capacitor in place, the short-circuit current can be measured with a spectrum analyzer using a current probe enveloping the wire lead to the capacitor. The Thevenin equivalent impedance at any frequency can then be calculated by dividing the equivalent open-circuit voltage by short-circuit current at the frequency of interest.

With the noise source characterized, the filter can be modeled. As shown in Figure 3, the basis of the filter is a discrete two-pole LC ladder (C and U), the values of which are such that the filter provides the required attenuation in the minimum volume. Also present in the filter model are an additional capacitance and inductance ($C1$ and L) representing a high frequency filter that attenuates noise in the spectrum at which the parasitic elements of the discrete filter give it poor performance. In addition, there is an inductance ($L1$) representing the one-meter wire required by MIL-STD-461 to connect the power supply to

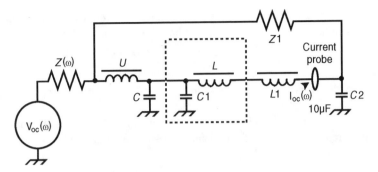

Figure 3 Model of complete emi filter

the 10μF capacitor ($C2$). This wire has an inductance of about 1μH. In parallel with the filter is an impedance ($Z1$) representing all other paths for the noise.

Calculating Attenuation The calculation of how much current will be measured by the probe [($I_0(\omega)$)] is straightforward. For example, if the shunt impedance is infinite and the 10μF MLC capacitor approximates a short circuit, the current will be:

$$I_0(\omega) = \frac{V_{oc}(\omega)}{a + b + Z + c + \omega U} \tag{1}$$

where $\omega = 2\pi f$
  $a = \omega(L + L1)$
  $b = Z\omega^2(L + L1)(C + C1)$
  $c = \omega^2(L + L1)(C + C1)U$

A filter slug has already been chosen on the basis of current-carrying capability and high frequency rejection; thus L and $C1$ are approximately known. The inductance of the one-meter wire represented by $L1$ can be measured directly. The value of $C2$ is set by MIL-STD-461 to be 10μF. MIL-STD-461 also sets the maximum value of $I_0(\omega)$ that can be allowed to flow at each frequency within emi spectrum. This means that the value of $I_0(\omega)$ is known at the switching frequency and its harmonics, the frequencies at which the greatest attenuation will be required. Similarly, $V(\omega)$ and $Z(\omega)$ are also known at these frequencies. Note that if $Z1$ is not infinite, it can be measured. Consequently, the equation can be solved for U and C at these frequencies.

Minimizing Volume Clearly, there will be one frequency at which the equations relating U and C represent the worst-case condition; that is, the condition at which maximum filtering is required to bring the value of $I_0(\omega)$ within the limit set by MIL-STD-461. Depending on the topology, this is typically the fundamental or one of the first harmonics.

A second equation is required to determine the total volume of the filter. The inductors' size roughly tracks the maximum energy that can be stored. Typically the inductor in a DC bus filter is wound on a molypermalloy-powder (MPP) toroid, which permits high currents to be carried before the core saturates. Allowing inductance to fall by a maximum of 20%, the volume can be roughly estimated as:

$$\text{Vol}_L \approx \frac{200 \text{ in.}^3}{\text{H} \cdot \text{A}^2} \tag{2}$$

where the current is the maximum current the inductor must carry and still provide filtering.

Similarly, a ceramic capacitor's size also roughly tracks the maximum energy that can stored. The volume of, for example, a 1μF, 50V type CKR06 ceramic capacitor can be approximated as:

$$\text{Vol}_C \approx \frac{3 \text{ in.}^3}{\text{F} \cdot \text{V}^2} \tag{3}$$

where the voltage is the maximum voltage the capacitor will have to withstand. These calculations are, however, fairly rough because of the discrete nature of the components; one cannot get an arbitrary-voltage capacitor, not an arbitrary-size core. Because of this, the component values yielded by the calculations must be rounded up to the values of the real-world components.

The total volume occupied by the filter is essentially equal to the sum of the volumes of the capacitor C and the inductor U. Equation 1 provides a relationship between U and C and, as a result, total volume can be expressed in terms of just one variable. Thus, total volume can be determined by taking the derivative of the volume with respect to this variable and setting it equal to zero. This yields a quadratic equation that can be solved for the variable selected with the result then being used to solve equation 1 for the other variable. Once the optimal filter component values have been determined, the inductor can be designed using standard practices with the capacitor value rounded up to the nearest available standard value.

A simulation of the filter is highly recommended to make sure there are no resonances at frequencies close to the switching frequency or its harmonics. This is important because the reactances involved have relatively high Qs, which can boost the noise at the resonance above the maximum allowable level. If resonances are close to critical frequencies, they can be shifted by increasing the value of the offending component(s). This not only moves the resonance to a spectral region of background noise where it does no harm, it also maintains the quality of the filter at other frequencies by increasing attentuation.

Converter Stability versus EMI Filtering

In filter design there are limits (though usually not *practical* limits) to how large the inductor can be, and how small the capacitor. As follows from the discussion in Chapter 6, on stability, if the source impedance the converter sees is too high, the system may oscillate, and this is true whether the source is a filter or another converter. *Middlebrook's criterion* is the plan that the output impedance of the filter should be at least 20dB lower than the input impedance of the converter. Clearly this satisfies the rule of thumb given in Chapter 6 about stability; but it is not a necessary condition, only a sufficient one. The real criterion for system stability is the same as that given in Chapter 6:

**The phase margins of the system consisting of the filter
and the converter must be positive.**

REFERENCES

1. T. Guo, D. Y. Chen, and F. C. Lee, Separation of common-mode- and differential-mode-conducted EMI noise, *IEEE Transactions on Power Electronics*, PE-11(3), 480 (1996).

2. *CRC Standard Mathematical Tables*, 24th edn, W. Beyer, Ed. CRC Press, Cleveland, OH, 1976, p. 406.

10

Practical Worst-Case Analysis

INTRODUCTION

The Purpose of Worst-Case Analysis

If all you had to do was build a single supply that would operate on your lab bench for a couple of hours, you could get a system running and forget it. In reality, of course, your breadboard is a prototype for hundreds or thousands or even millions of supplies, every one of which ideally would operate over a range of temperatures and power sources and loads, would meet the specifications regardless of component tolerances, and would continue doing so for many years. The purpose of worst-case analysis (WCA) is to ensure that your design is robust—that is, even if all the varying conditions mentioned above occur in a single supply, the supply would operate within specifications over its lifetime.

Given this statement of purpose, it is obvious that WCA is an essential step in design, and time and budget must be allocated for each design that is intended to reach production. Since this step is often ignored, it purpose must be explained to management, and it must be repeatedly stressed to management that WCA is *essential* for creating a reliable product.

How Do You Do WCA?

The general idea of WCA is to take each and every component of the design, find its worst possible value(s) for the function or functions it is intended to perform, and verify, either mathematically or through simulations, that the function is correctly performed even when all these worst-case values occur simultaneously. "Mathematically" here refers to some combination of analytical solutions and numerical approximation; "analytical" means real, old-fashioned algebra (calculus, differential equations, etc.); simulations are tests of operation using a computer model, but *not* Monte Carlo methods, for reasons explained below. The preferred method is analytical because it *proves* what you are trying to show; numerical work is next in line, with simulation being the least desirable. The problem with simulations, as discussed below, is not that the computer might make a mistake (although this has been known to happen!), but rather that you are at the mercy of whoever wrote the simulation software, and whoever made the simulation models; if the model wasn't tested the way you use it, there's no way of telling whether its results are valid for your application, and typically the model is unavailable to the person doing the simulation.

The author has developed a systematic method for doing WCA that reduces what is at first blush an overwhelming task into a manageable, if somewhat tedious set of procedures. Indeed, once you have done WCA a few times, you'll notice that many of the circuits you analyze repeat themselves from design to design, and so the analyses done for the one supply apply to the next. Eventually you learn to *design* things in such a way that they will pass WCA.

The first step is natural. Simply break up the circuit into function blocks: this block is a timer, this block is overcurrent shutdown, etc. Each block is then going to be the subject of its own WCA. Of course there will be some inputs from other blocks, but since you're going to be doing a WCA on the other blocks also, you can assume that those other blocks meet the spec requirements.

Having identified a block, the next step is to assemble a table indicating the maximum and minimum value of each (relevant) parameter of each component. Of course, you can't know exactly which parameters are going to be needed up front, but with some experience you can make some good guesses. (See the example below for details on table entries.) Other parameters can be calculated and entered into the table as the work progresses.

The first page of a WCA is an overall description of the function of the circuit block, stating the conditions of operation, listing each parameter that is to be analyzed, and providing a conclusion that the block works as it's supposed to (the presumption being that the design is changed until it *does* work—WCA will make it clear which components need to be changed). The following pages constitute the analyses of each parameter, preferably organized as one analysis per document to make revision easy; then there is a page showing a stress analysis (see below); and the last page is the completed parameter table. This then constitutes a complete analysis of the function block, which can be assembled with other such analyses to form a book documenting the validity of the power supply design.

When doing the analysis, don't forget that some circuits may have their worst case during start-up rather than during steady-state operation. Many converter designs have been known to fail exclusively at start-up!

The Purpose of Stress Analysis

Just to be clear, a stress analysis is different from a worst-case analysis. The purpose of a WCA is to determine that the circuitry functions according to specification; the purpose of a stress analysis is to verify that none of the components is exceeding its ratings (or derating guidelines).

Whether you use the manufacturer's ratings for the stress analysis (after all, they have some margins built into their specs, too) or one of the common derating guidelines (the author typically uses military derating guidelines) is of course a matter of company policy. It is something you have to know up front, however. Be sure to find out before getting started. You don't want to do these analyses repeatedly if you can possibly avoid it!

RMS versus Worst Case

Some readers may have noticed a certain vagueness in the statement of exactly what a WCA is going to analyze. Does the statement that the correct functioning of the circuit must be established in the case that all the components and conditions are at their worst value mean that everything is "worst" *simultaneously* and *on the same unit*? The usual argument against this interpretation (which the author refers to as "worst-case") is that it is impossibly rare for all the worst conditions and components to conspire in such a way as to all end up on a single supply. Given this presumption, it is argued, it is more reasonable to do an "RMS" analysis, in which the effect of each component going to its worst-case value is orthogonal to the effect of every other component. For example, if the effect of a worst-case value of R_1 is to increase some condition's value by 10%, and the effect of a worst-case value of R_2 is also to increase the same condition's value by 10%, the effect in RMS is only $(1.10^2 + 1.10^2)^{1/2} = 1.14 = 14\%$ versus $1.10 \times 1.10 = 1.21 = 21\%$ in worst-case.

> **Practical Note** You spare yourself little effort by doing RMS instead of worst-case WCA. There is usually not much circuitry difference either. The practical approach is to use worst-case unless you're sure that so few units will be built that statistics won't be too important. So for everything except small runs of manufacturing (say 100 pieces or less), it makes sense to go ahead and verify the circuitry with worst-case rather than RMS WCA. Of course, for small runs of critical designs (e.g., on a satellite), worst-case needs to be done instead of RMS. In any case, make sure your management understands the issue and has made a decision regarding the appropriate goal before you get started.

Mathematics versus Simulation

Here is a tempting possibility: throw the whole circuit on the computer, and let *it* figure out the answer, instead of you hurting your head. You'll see in the example below that the author never does this (with one exception, noted in the next paragraph). The reason is that a user just doesn't know whether the authors of the simulation's model were thorough enough to capture all the parameters of interest to the analysis at hand. Of course the device works like a comparator, but does it correctly model input bias current? Input offset voltage with temperature? Output saturation voltage with current and temperature and die lot variations? The author once found a simulation model, in an expensive simulation program, of an open collector comparator whose output would go to $+15\text{V}$ without a pull-up resistor! Your lack of knowledge about the model makes relying on a simulation a bad idea.

There is a single exception to the foregoing proscription against use of a computer for WCA, however: determining phase margin of a converter is so complicated that you really don't want to do it by hand (although it *could* be done with a symbolic mathematics program). Fortunately, all the important parameters (inductance and resistance of the inductor, capacitance and ESR of the output cap, etc.) can be entered into the computer directly; you don't have to rely on models. The only IC parameters of interest are the open loop gain of the error amp and the ramp amplitude of the PWM. So WCA of phase margin can be safely done by computer, simply varying each component individually to see whether it should be a maximum or minimum to get minimum phase margin, and then setting all the components to their respective minima or maxima simultaneously (at least for a minimum-phase system).

Monte Carlo? Sensitivity Analysis?

Monte Carlo analysis goes computer-based WCA one step worse: it not only relies on models of unknown validity, it also implicitly assumes something akin to RMS analysis. The trouble is in the great number of cases you need to simulate to get a certain level of confidence that a parameter is OK.

EXAMPLE

We need to be 99% certain that six parameters varying simultaneously won't cause a problem in some circuitry. How many Monte Carlo analyses do we need? If you guessed something like $2^6 = 64$, you're way off. Let's assume that the probabilities are lumped at the two ends—that is, each parameter is either a minimum or a maximum (a bimodal distribution). There are thus a total of $2^6 = 64$ possible value sets (i.e., component 1 is low, 2 is high, etc., constitutes a single value set). Each time you do an analysis you get one of these 64, so your chances of hitting the worst one are 1 in 64 each time. The chances of not getting it are clearly one minus this, $1 - (1/64)$. The chances of not hitting the worst one after N trials is $[1 - (1/64)]^N$, and this number has to equal $1 - 99\% = 0.01$. We have

$$\left(1 - \frac{1}{64}\right)^N = 0.01$$

which yields $N = 292$! And clearly this number gets larger very fast, as either the number of parameters grows or the certainty required grows. And since the end result is that even after 292 trials you're *still* not certain (you can't be sure that you got the worst case no matter how many trials you made), it just isn't a good idea to do WCA with Monte Carlo analysis.

As for sensitivity analysis, again you don't know whether the computer has the right models. This mode of analysis may be useful for knowing which parameters to concentrate most attention on, but ultimately, you still need to look at them all, because otherwise you won't know what level of sensitivity is low enough to be ignored. It is also to be observed that sensitivity analysis is a linearization of the models around a particular operating point—if the operating point varies, the results of the sensitivity analysis do too.

AN EXHAUSTING EXAMPLE

The purpose of this section is to give a sample WCA of a common circuit block in full detail. This will then serve as a template for the reader to do his or her own analyses. Take the time to read this example through carefully; there are many helpful techniques to be gleaned from it. The author feels confident that after reading through this detailed example, you will be in agreement with the title of this section, but you will be ready to analyze your own circuits.

The Circuit

The circuit block to be analyzed (see Figure 10.1) can be described fairly simply and is pretty common in practice. When a comparator that is sensing some function (let's say the current from a low impedance resistor) detects that this current has gone too high, it turns on a BJT that discharges a cap; the cap is attached to the soft-start pin on a PWM IC, in this case a UC3825, and turns the IC off.

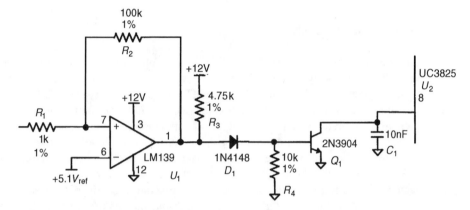

Figure 10.1   The circuit to be worst-case-analyzed is an overcurrent limit that shuts down the PWM.

You may observe that the output of the comparator does not go directly into the base of the BJT; rather, it passes through a dropping diode, which then requires a base turnoff resistor for the BJT. This is a necessary addition that will become clear as the WCA is performed; it was added to the schematic based on prior experience so that in the example, we won't have to go back, add it in, and re-analyze the system.

Properties to Be Analyzed

Having decided on the circuit function to be analyzed, we must consider what properties to analyze. Generically, we want to analyze the circuitry that responds to the input, that which generates the output, and any other circuits that interface between the two; some engineering judgment is necessary to select the important functions in a circuit. For this example:

1. We'll want to know the level at which the comparator trips on in response to an overcurrent, both minimum and maximum (but not where it comes back off, at least not for this example analysis).
2. We'll want to verify that the transistor is indeed normally off (if the output saturation voltage of the comparator is too high, the BJT might be always on).
3. We'll want to know how long the BJT will take to discharge the capacitor, turning off the PWM, given the transistor's limited beta.

In a more complete analysis, we might also want to check the maximum collector current on the BJT, to verify that it isn't going to be overstressed when discharging the cap, since it has no limiting resistor and may have a high beta.

We also need to know the conditions under which the circuit is going to operate: assume minimum temperature of $-40°C$ and a maximum of $+85°C$.

The next step is to develop a table listing the worst-case values of all the relevant parameters. In practice, you'd take a guess at the parameters needed, adding more items as the analysis progressed, or occasionally deleting some that proved to be unnecessary. Table 10.1 displays the final product.

Table Evaluation Techniques

Let's examine Table 10.1 closely. The first thing to observe is the column headings. Of course there is a part type column to identify each component's nominal value. Next is a column for a reference designator; there might be more than one type of 1kΩ resistor (e.g., to accommodate different temperature coefficients). The next column defines the parameters to be examined, such as the output saturation voltage of a comparator, the limit in which it's to be examined (minimum or maximum), and the conditions under which the limit is to be taken, such as the collector current at which the voltage is measured. Next come columns for the initial value (meaning nominal value at room temperature), initial tolerance (i.e., manufacturing tolerance), and temperature coefficient. In some circumstances, additional columns might be needed to display factors for age or radiation effects. Wedged in between are two columns labeled "Scale type" and "Scale factor." These are for additional factors that allow us to work around the limitations of data sheets. Thus if we need to know the output saturation voltage of the comparator at 2.5mA but the data sheet has a printed *value* only at 4mA and then a *curve* showing a scaling factor, we would go to the scale type column for an explanation of the scaling factor; we would put an evaluation in the scale factor column. Finally, there are columns for the two temperature extremes, since the results of the calculation are not symmetrically distributed around 25°C: $-\Delta T = (25°C) - (-40°C) = 65°C$, while $+\Delta T = (85°C) - (25°C) = 60°C$.

The actual evaluation of some of the entries in Table 10.1 can require specialized techniques. To start with, observe that the entries are all done in worst-case: the minimum resistance is found by *multiplying* the 1% tolerance and the $(50ppm/°C \times 65°C) = 0.325\%$ temperature coefficient, not adding them. Specifically, *don't* take 10kΩ $\times 99\% = 9900Ω$, and then 10kΩ $\times 99.675\% = 9967.5Ω$, with the total then assumed somehow to be a combination of these two. Rather, take 10kΩ $\times 99\% = 9900Ω$, and then 9900Ω $\times 99.675\% = 9867.8Ω$ (rounded off here to 9868Ω).

Observe also the way the temperature coefficients are handled. The resistor specification says only that the tempco of the resistor is $\pm50ppm/°C$, not whether it is positive or negative with temperature. Thus we must assume that the tempco is going to conspire to be either positive for minimum resistance at temperatures below ambient (i.e., as it gets colder the resistance decreases further, making the minimum smaller) or negative at temperatures above ambient (i.e., as it gets hotter, the resistance also decreases further, again making the minimum smaller), and oppositely for maximum resistance. Of course, chances are this coefficient is either positive or negative, not both; but lacking additional information, you have to assume the worst. Generally, an analysis will simply take the

TABLE 10.1 Listing of Worst-Case Values for Example Circuit

Part	Reference designator	Parameter	Initial value	Initial tolerance	Scale type	Scale factor	Temperature coefficient	At $-40°C$	At $+85°C$
1kΩ	R1	R, min	1,000Ω	1%			±50ppm/°C	986Ω	987Ω
1kΩ	R1	R, max	1,000Ω	1%			±50ppm/°C	1,013Ω	1,013Ω
4.75kΩ	R3	R, min	4,750Ω	1%			±50ppm/°C	4,687Ω	4,688Ω
4.75kΩ	R3	R, max	4,750Ω	1%			±50ppm/°C	4,813Ω	4,812Ω
10kΩ	R4	R, min	10,000Ω	1%			±50ppm/°C	9,868Ω	9,870Ω
10kΩ	R4	R, max	10,000Ω	1%			±50ppm/°C	10,133Ω	10,130Ω
100kΩ	R2	R, min	100,000Ω	1%			±50ppm/°C	98,680Ω	98,700Ω
100kΩ	R2	R, max	100,000Ω	1%			±50ppm/°C	101,330Ω	101,300Ω
10nF	C1	C, max	10nF	20%			+15%, −25%	13.8nF	13.8nF
1N4148	D1	V_f, max at 2mA	1V	0.87	$I=10mA \to 2mA$	0.88	1.28, 0.73	1.13V	642mV
2N3904	Q1	V_{be}, min at $I_c=1mA$	650mV				−2mV/°C	696mV	446mV
2N3904	Q1	V_{be}, max at $I_c=50mA$	950mV				−1, −1.1mV/°C	1.07V	940mV
2N3904	Q1	h_{fe}, min at $I_c=50mA$	60				0.56, 1	34	60
LM139	U1	V_{ios}	5mV				4mV	4mV	9mV
LM139	U1	I_{ios}	25nA				75nA	100nA	100nA
LM139	U1	I_{ib}	100nA				200nA	300nA	300nA
LM139	U1	V_o, max at $I_c=2.5mA$	400mV		$I_o=4mA \to 2.5mA$	0.62	300mA	430mV	430mV
UC2825	U2	V_{ref}, min	5.10V	50mV	Long term	25mV	0.4mV/°C	4.999V	5.049V
UC2825	U2	V_{ref}, max	5.10V	50mV	Long term	25mV	0.4mV/°C	5.249V	5.299V
UC2825	U2	I_{chrg}, max	9µA				11µA	20µA	20µA

worst value for each component, blithely ignoring whether the worst case occurs at cold temperatures for some components and at high temperature for others. Such inconsistencies usually turn out to be unimportant. In the rare case of an analysis that shows the circuit right on the borderline between meeting its requirements and not meeting them, one option is to do two worst-case analyses: one in which all values are taken at cold, and another taking all values at hot.

Dealing with scale factors is another interesting problem. Generally, the data sheet contains a curve of a parameter for *typical* data, not maximum (nor minimum). The proper method is to use the scale factor for the typical data *applied* to the worst-case data. For example, it will turn out that we will need to know the maximum output saturation voltage of the LM139 when it is drawing a current of 2.5mA. The data sheet gives a guaranteed maximum output saturation voltage at a current of 4mA of 400mV, so we need to scale the data to the lower current. A data sheet curve shows that the typical output voltage changes by a factor of 0.62 in going from 4mA to 2.5mA, and so the worst-case number is also scaled by the same factor. That is, the worst-case is 400mV × 0.62 = 248mV (for this factor). Making this table de novo, you might originally have simply used 4mA for the worst-case current. As the calculation progressed, you'd find through an iteration that the current is actually 2.5mA, and the table then could be adjusted as indicated.

It frequently happens that you are using a device with a temperature range wider than the one your device actually sees. Thus, the LM139 has data for −55°C and +125°C, even though we want only −40°C and +85°C. It is clearly reasonable to use the wider temperature data limits, since they certainly provide a bound on the actual temperature limits. In case of problems, it might be possible to look at a device in the same family with reduced temperature range—but this choice introduces some uncertainty (is it *really* the same?). Moreover, you'll often find no change in the data. The manufacturer is simply taking batches of devices and labeling them according to what tests they pass!

One more thing to pay attention to is the format used when the data sheet directly provides the worst-case number over temperature. For example, the LM139 I_{ib}, which is specified at room temperature as a maximum of 100nA, is specified over the temperature range considered as a maximum of 300nA. Rather than leaving the tempco column confusingly blank, it is better to pretend there is a temperature delta of 200nA, and use this in the data presentation to show why the answer is 300nA.

Finally, the part you are using may be underspecified. For example, an output electrolytic capacitor might not specify ESR at all, or specify it only at 60Hz.

Practical Note The best plan is to stay away from parts that are underspecified. Just because one sample worked in the lab, what makes you think the next one will be satisfactory? If you have to use such a part, it is safe to assume that the under-specified parameter is zero, or limited by another factor (e.g., power supply voltage). For the example of the electrolytic capacitor at the output of a power supply, assuming the ESR is zero will minimize the phase margin, clearly giving the worst case.

Worst-Case Analysis: Comparator Trip Levels

With the data tabulated, it is now possible to do the analyses, the first of which is to determine the voltage level at which the comparator will go from a low state to a high, both the minimum value and the maximum value. This information directly tells you, for example, the minimum current at which the circuit being monitored will function (so you know that it won't trip during normal operation) and the maximum current at which this circuit will start to function (so you don't pull so much current that something blows up). If the analysis reveals values that turn out to be unacceptable, you can go back and change the values and tolerances of the resistors, or possibly the type of comparator being used; the WCA of course shows which changes would be most effective.

Starting then with the minimum trip level, the minimum will occur for the minimum reference voltage from the PWM, which Table 10.1 lists as occurring at $-40°C$, 4.999V. Thus the comparator will certainly trip high or will have tripped high when the voltage at its noninverting terminal is 4.999V. Let's consider the factors that influence the voltage at this terminal. Foremost of course is the two resistors: the 1kΩ resistor forms a divider network for the input voltage with the 100kΩ, which goes to the output of the comparator. (Remember that comparator output is assumed to be low because the comparator hasn't yet tripped.) This output is not ground, though, because the comparator is sinking current from the 4.75kΩ resistor and thus has a saturation voltage. Additional factors are a potential offset voltage for the comparator, and its input bias and offset currents. Let's tote all these factors up into an equation:

$$\frac{V_{trip} + V_{os} - 4.999V}{1k\Omega} + I_{ib} + I_{ios} = \frac{4.999V - V_{sat}}{100k\Omega}$$

Here, V_{trip} is the voltage that is causing the transition; the other notations are obvious. This is just Kirchhoff's law, that all the currents into the node at the noninverting input of the comparator must sum to zero. Since we want to find the *minimum* trip level, the offsets are added on to the trip voltage; that is, they are subtracted from the amount of current that the tripping voltage has to supply. Exactly the opposite will be done when we calculate the maximum trip level. Remember that offsets don't have a sign: they can be either positive or negative. Here we are choosing the positive (maximum) because it makes for the minimum trip level. As for the resistor values, we can at once see that making the 1kΩ as small as possible makes V_{trip} small; and therefore making the 100kΩ large makes V_{trip} small, because it multiplies the other side. Substituting values from Table 10.1, we write

$$\frac{V_{trip} + 9mV - 4.999V}{986\Omega} + 300nA + 100nA = \frac{4.999V - 430mV}{101,330\Omega}$$

and solving, V_{trip}, min = 5.052V. These equations show what is meant by solving the problem "mathematically": setting up an equation that determines the parameter, determining which parameters should be minimized and which maximized, substituting values from a table of worst-case values, and then solving numerically, either with a calculator (in this simple case of one equation) or with a computer program (if there are several equations in several unknowns, as sometimes happens).

With this solution in hand, it is straightforward to see that the equation for the maximum trip level is the same, except with all the factors that were minima now maxima, and vice versa:

$$\frac{V_{\text{trip}} + 9\text{mV} - 5.299\text{V}}{1013\Omega} - 300\text{nA} - 100\text{nA} = \frac{5.299\text{V} - 0\text{V}}{98,680\Omega}$$

The only other differences involve the various offsets, which now have a polarity that hinders the tripping rather than helping, and the saturation voltage, which is now assumed to be 0V rather than maximum. (It can't be less than zero because the comparator has ground for its negative rail.) Solving, we have V_{trip}, max $= 5.363$V.

Conclusion. The trip level will certainly be between 5.052V and 5.363V. If this were the voltage across a current sense resistor, you could divide by the resistor's value (including its worst-case!) and come up with the current levels at which this comparator circuit would trip. Note that you certainly could not have guessed this answer, say by adding 2% tolerance to a 5.1V reference, and adding 1% for the resistors.

Worst-Case Analysis: The BJT Is Normally Off

The second analysis for the block of circuitry shown in Figure 10.1 is to verify that the BJT is off when the comparator is low. The (potential) problem is the comparator's output saturation voltage: after dropping through the diode, and sinking current into the 10kΩ base resistor, the voltage left should not be sufficient to turn on the BJT—otherwise, the converter could never start because the soft-start pin of the PWM was being held permanently low! In fact, precisely this can happen if the diode is not included in this circuit.

To make the calculations manageable (the actual characteristics of both the diode and the base–emitter junction are exponential, making complete equations transcendental), we can start by considering that the BJT is supposed to be off and verifying that this is a self-consistent solution. This means verifying that all the other components of the circuit, under the assumption that the BJT is off, in fact work in a way guaranteeing that it *is* off. This is a frequently used technique for dealing with discrete semiconductors. Although the results are the same as those found for writing out the full transcendental equation set, and then solving them numerically, the results are more humanly understandable—and therefore easier for a human to check. The author has seen commercially available numerical software that does not converge to the correct solution for problems of this sort.

To summarize the procedure before starting: we're going to find the maximum base–emitter voltage of the BJT when it's still off by putting the minimum listed collector current into the transistor, finding the corresponding base current by looking at the beta, and then observing that the V_{be} doesn't change as the collector current is decreased beyond this point, even to 0A. To get this V_{be} requires current through the base resistor; but this current comes through the diode, which has a forward voltage to conduct that much resistor current. The sum of the base–emitter drop and the V_{f} of the diode will be greater than the comparator's saturation voltage. Again: even to get "zero" collector current calls for some base–emitter voltage. But this requires current into the base resistor, and getting this current requires a diode drop, since the saturation voltage of the comparator isn't high enough to provide the base resistor with enough current to turn the transistor on.

The BJT's base current must thus by assumption be tiny. The smallest listed V_{be} in the data book is for $I_c = 1$mA, at which in worst-case $V_{be} = 446$mV. We can estimate the beta: guaranteed minimum at 25°C is 70; according to the data curves, 1mA corresponds to a normalized factor of 0.8. At -55°C, the normalization is 0.4, so the minimum $\beta = (70 \times 0.4/0.8) = 35$. The 1mA of collector current then corresponds to a base current of 1mA$/35 = 29\mu$A. Furthermore, the curve for V_{be} versus I_c appears flat below $I_c = 1$mA, so as long as we're below the 446mV on the base, the transistor can be assumed to be off.

Now, to get 446mV on the base, we need a minimum current through the base resistor of 446mV/10kΩ, which is minimum when the 10kΩ is maximum: $I = 446$mV$/10,133$Ω $= 44\mu$A. This current has to come through the diode. Now no manufacturer provides data specifying *minimum* forward voltage of a diode. Instead, the best we can do is to estimate a bound on the minimum V_f. Looking at the curves (which go down only to 100μA), at 100°C the $V_f = 300$mV. Since we are actually dealing with lower temperatures (and V_f increases with decreasing temperature), this is a good curve to choose for a minimum; tracing out the curve, it is clear that the V_f must be at least 200mV. So for the transistor to turn on, we need at least 446mV + 200mV = 646mV. But since we already know that the maximum output saturation voltage of the comparator is 430mV, we know also that there is more than 200mV of margin to ensure that the transistor is off.

You can see what happens if the diode is not there: the margin is only 446mV − 430mV = 16mV, and there might be enough inaccuracy in the base–emitter calculations to cause the BJT to turn on. This certainly would be the case if the 4.75kΩ pull-up were any smaller. So the diode and the base resistor do need to be there; in general, you just design all your "comparator driving base" circuits with the diode and base resistor. Then it's not necessary to repeat this calculation each time.

The conclusion is that the BJT stays off during normal operation.

Worst-Case Analysis: How Long Until the PWM Is Turned Off?

The final analysis done in this example is to determine the maximum amount of time the BJT might take to discharge the soft-start cap. Since this circuit is being used as a current limit, you don't want much delay till shutdown, when the overcurrent condition occurs. The result of this analysis might pass on to a worst-case thermal analysis, say, of the switching transistor, to ensure that it can take the overcurrent for the calculated time without blowing up. The BJT has limited drive current, and finite beta, so it will pull current from the capacitor at some maximum rate, which then will determine when the PWM is off: pin 8 has to be pulled down from its initial 5V to 0.5V to shut down.

We're going to start by ignoring the propagation delay of the comparator (typically, 300ns) and look only at the capacitor discharging current; at the end, the delay will be added in. Now we need to get the minimum base current. The current is set by the 12V supply (which we'll assume is ±5% from another WCA not presented here), the 4.75kΩ resistor, and the forward drops of the diode and the base–emitter junction:

$$I_{base} = \frac{12V - V_f - V_{be}}{4.75k\Omega} - \frac{V_{be}}{10k\Omega}$$

This is again Kirchhoff's law. Here, the current into the base resistor lessens the current available for the base. To find minimum base current, we take minimum 12V supply, maximum diode drop and base–emitter drop, maximum limiting resistance, and minimum 10kΩ (choosing the 10kΩ to pull as much current away from the base as possible). Conveniently, maximizing V_{be} works in the correct direction for both terms, both increasing the current shunted away from the base and decreasing the current passing through the 10kΩ. If this had not been the case, we would have had to take the derivative of I_{base} with respect to V_{be}, and found out whether minimum or maximum V_{be} minimized I_{base}. (Here, $dI_{base}/dV_{be} < 0$, so we need maximum V_{be}.) We are assuming in Table 10.1 that the collector current will be approximately 50mA; this is just an estimate, but it will be justified a posteriori by the calculation; that is, we assume this value, and at the end that value will be derived, showing that it was a self-consistent assumption. Substituting values, we write

$$I_{base} = \frac{11.4\text{V} - 1.13\text{V} - 1.07\text{V}}{4813\Omega} - \frac{1.07\text{V}}{9868\Omega}$$

or I_{base}, min $= 1.80$mA.

Having the minimum base current, we can find minimum collector current by determining minimum h_{fe}. At 50mA of collector current, minimum beta is 34, which requires a base current of 50mA/34 $= 1.47$mA, quite close to the actual calculated minimum base current; this then justifies the assumption we made in estimating V_{be}.

So with a minimum beta of 34, the minimum collector current will be 1.80mA $\times$ 34 $= 61$mA. Now the capacitor is originally charged to the 5V reference and has to pull down to 0.5V. In equations, since $I = C(dV/dt)$ and $t = C(\Delta V/I)$, discharge time t will be maximum for maximum capacitance and minimum collector current, as we already know. One additional factor is that pin 8 is still sourcing current, and so this factor should also be maximum. The whole equation is:

$$t = \frac{C\Delta V}{I_C - I_{pin8}}$$

Substituting numbers, we have

$$t = \frac{13.8\text{nF}(5.299\text{V} - 0.5\text{V})}{61\text{mA} - 20\mu\text{A}}$$

and of course the pin 8 current is negligible. We end up with $t_{max} = 1.1\mu$s, surely fast enough. Adding the propagation delay gives 1.4µs, so this value doesn't affect the matter. The conclusion is that when the input pin to this circuit exceeds the limit, the PWM IC will be turned off quite quickly.

Stress Analysis

Having done all of the worst-case analysis, for completeness we'll now do a stress analysis. The goal of a stress analysis is to guarantee that in operation, no component will be overstressed; or better, that no component will have applied to it stresses that are too close to its ratings. If a part is operated right at its maximum rating, not only is it more likely to occasionally have its rating exceeded during a transient, but also its MTBF is greatly increased. A stress analysis reveals which parts are likely to have a large influence on the reliability of the design.

The stress analysis itself simply is a table listing the stresses each part in the circuit sees, compared with the rated limits for the part. The comparison is done as a percentage, that is, stress = actual/rating. Some companies provide derating guidelines (e.g., "resistors shall dissipate no more than 70% of their rated power"). If such a list is not available, it is probably acceptable to take the following as a rule:

Practical Note Steady-state stresses should not exceed 90% of the manufacturer's ratings, and transient stresses should not exceed 100% of the manufacturer's ratings.

The end result is a column in a table like Table 10.2, showing that each part passes.

The stresses to be analyzed can be taken to be those that affect the reliability of the part, such as in MIL-STD-217. You would naturally expect to see data on power in a resistor, voltage on a capacitor, forward current and reverse voltage for a diode, and so on. Not every parameter a manufacturer specifies needs to be analyzed, only those that relate to the survival of the part.

Let's examine Table 10.2. The first column lists the components, each repeated as many times as there are stresses. Thus the LM139 is repeated three times, once each for its supply voltage, differential voltage, and common mode voltage. Normally, there would also be a column to list reference designators (since, e.g., a block could have several 1kΩ resistors), but we haven't bothered to assign references in this example. The parameter examined is in the next column, followed by the rating of the part, from the manufacturer's data sheet.

The actual stress is calculated in column 4. For most parts in a design, it is adequate to estimate the stress, since this value will be far less than its rating. For example, it's not necessary to think very hard to see that since the circuit has a maximum of 12V, the power dissipated in the 100kΩ resistor can't be more than $(12V)^2/100k\Omega = 1.5mW$, which is far less than the part's rated 100mW; we therefore don't care about its actual operation. Similarly, the 10kΩ resistor can have only about 1V on it, since it is clamped by the base–emitter junction; we don't even bother to list microwatts—just call it 0 watt. On the other hand, for the 1kΩ resistor, we calculate that the maximum voltage on the comparator side is 5.299V, and since the other side can be 0V, the power in the resistor could be as high as $(5.299V)^2/986\Omega = 28mW$, where we have used the minimum resistance value to get maximum power. As already stated, stress = actual/rated, and every cell in the Pass

TABLE 10.2 Example Stress Analysis Table

Part value	Parameter	Rating	Actual stress	Stress (%)	Pass
1kΩ	P	100mW	28mW	28	Y
4.75kΩ	P	100mW	34mW	34	Y
10kΩ	P	100mW	0mW	0	Y
100kΩ	P	100mW	1.5mW	2	Y
10nF	V	50V	5V	10	Y
1N4148	I_f	200mA	3mA	1	Y
1N4148	V_r	100V	0V	0	Y
2N3904	V_{ceo}	40V	5V	12	Y
2N3904	I_{ce}	200mA			
LM139	V_{cc}	36V	12V	33	Y
LM139	$V_{differential}$	V_{cc}	5V	42	Y
LM139	V_{cm}	V_{cc}	5V	42	Y

column should have a Yes. In some rare instancès, a part doesn't in fact pass; this should be taken as a strong recommendation to substitute a part with a larger rating in the design, or give a satisfactory explanation for the failure.

The row for the maximum collector–emitter current in Table 10.2 hasn't been filled in because the analysis wasn't performed; we leave it to the reader to do this analysis, and decide whether the collector should in fact have a resistor to limit the current. In reaching this decision, it is probably acceptable to have an I_{ce} up to 400mA, since the 200mA is a DC rating, and BJTs can safely take double their rated current in a pulse (cf. Chapter 3). If this rule is adopted, an explanatory note at the end of the table would be needed.

Conclusions

The conclusions of the overall analysis of the circuit block are the results of each individual analysis: the comparator will trip between 5.052V and 5.363V; the BJT stays off when it's supposed to; the trip on overcurrent occurs in less than 2µs; and all parts are properly derated. Presumably these results could be checked against specifications, or, as indicated, passed on to the next WCA as input data.

SOME CONCLUDING THOUGHTS

As is evident from our detailed example, a fairly substantial amount of work goes into creating a WCA. However, there are no mysteries involved, just a lot of slogging through messy algebra. At the end of such an analysis, you can feel assured that the circuitry will work every time in production.

In general, given a good design at the start, very little circuitry has to be added to guarantee worst-case operation. By far the most common problems found in WCA entail values that must be be slightly adjusted. Occasionally a circuit will need some redesign, but experience in WCA will guide you in avoiding such designs from the beginning. There is thus usually not too much cost to production in assuring the circuit's good performance; the cost rather is up front in the designer's time, where it should be. WCA should be made a part of every design intended for production.

List of Acronyms Used in the Book and Some Symbols

BJT	Bipolar junction transistor, now commonly used only in small-signal applications.
BNC	A type of circular connector used for coax.
c.m.	Circular mils; 1 c.m. $= 5.07 \times 10^{-6}$ cm^2.
C0G	("cee zero gee") A type of capacitor with essentially zero temperature coefficient.
CAD	Computer-aided design, a common design step in which software is used to lay out traces on a PCB.
CGS	Centimeter-gram-second; one of the standard systems of units.
CM	Common mode; noise current that is in both the power and return lines relative to ground.
DMM	Digital multimeter.
DVM	Digital voltmeter.
EEPROM	Electrically erasable programmable read-only memory.
EMC	Electromagnetic compatibility; ability of two or more systems to work together in the presence of each others' electronic noise.
EMI	Electromagnetic interference; electronic noise causing problems in another system.
EMV	Electromagnetic vulnerability; susceptibility to electronic noise.
ESD	Electrostatic discharge; the little spark you get when shuffling your feet across the carpet.
ESR	Equivalent series resistance (of a capacitor).
FEA	Finite element analysis.
FET	Field effect transistor, see MOSFET.
IGBT	Insulated gate bipolar transistor; the type of power device commonly used in off-line converters.
I_{ib}	Input bias current; the average leakage current into the inverting and noninverting terminals of a comparator or op amp.
I_{ios}	Input offset current; the difference between the leakage currents into the inverting and noninverting terminals of a comparator or op amp.
JFET	Junction field effect transistor (not commonly used in converters).
LED	Light-emitting diode; frequently used for a status display of the health of a converter.
LISN	Line impedance stabilization network; a 50Ω impedance used for EMI measurements.
MKS	Meter-kilogram-second; one of the standard systems of units.
MLC	Multilayer ceramic; a very low ESR capacitor.
MOSFET	Metal oxide semiconductor field effect transistor; the most common power device used in converters.
MOV	Metal oxide varistor; a type of voltage clamping device used for high power transients.
MPP	Molypermalloy powder; a type of magnetic material used for DC inductors.

MTBF	Mean time between failures.
NiCd	Nickel–cadmium; a type of rechargeable cell.
NiH	Nickel–hydrogen, a type of rechargeable cell.
NiMH	Nickel–metal hydride; a type of rechargeable cell.
NM	Normal mode; noise current that flows in the power line relative to return.
NPN	One of the two types of BJT.
NPO	A type of capacitor with essentially zero temperature coefficient.
PCB	Printed circuit board.
PFM	Pulse frequency modulation.
PNP	One of the two types of BJT.
PWM	Pulse width modulation.
$R_{DS,on}$	On resistance, drain to source; the resistance of a fully on MOSFET.
rf	Radio frequency, electromagnetic radiation, used in this book as it pertains to EMI.
RHP(Z)	Right-half-plane (zero); position of a zero that can cause instability in a system.
RMS	Root-mean-square; one method of doing worst-case analysis.
TTL	Transistor–transistor logic; a standard type of logic gate.
UVLO	Under–voltage lockout; a type of circuit that keeps an integrated circuit off until the supply voltage is high enough.
VDE	A standards group in Europe responsible for safety and EMC; also refers to standards from this group.
VRM	Voltage regulation module.
V_f	Forward voltage; the voltage drop from anode to cathode of a diode.
V_{os}	Offset voltage; the equivalent input voltage to a comparator or op amp even when both inputs are tied together.
WCA	Worst-case analysis.

Data Sheets for
Worst-Case Analysis

The figures in this Appendix provide the datasheets used to extract parameters for the worst-case analysis of Chapter 10.

COMPUTER DIODE
General Purpose
Switching

1N914; JAN, JANTX 1N914
1N4148; JAN, JANTX, JANTXV 1N4148
JAN, JANTX, JANTXV 1N4148-1
1N4531; JAN, JANTX, JANTXV 1N4531

FEATURES
• Metallurgical Bond
• Qualified to MIL-S-19500/116
• Planar Passivated Chip
• DO-34 or DO-35 Package
• Non-JAN Available

DESCRIPTION
This series is very popular for general purpose switching applications in electronic equipment.

ABSOLUTE MAXIMUM RATINGS, AT 25°C
Reverse Breakdown Voltage 100V
Peak Working Voltage 75V
Average Output Current, 1N914 ....75mAdc
                         1N4148 .... 200mAdc
                         1N4148-1 .... 200mAdc
                         1N4531 .... 125mAdc
Surge Current, 8.3ms 500mA
Operating Temperature Range .... −65°C to +175°C
Storage Temperature Range .... −65°C to +200°C

MECHANICAL SPECIFICATIONS

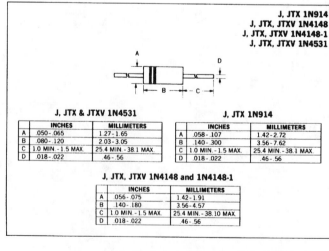

J, JTX 1N914
J, JTX, JTXV 1N4148
J, JTX, JTXV 1N4148-1
J, JTX, JTXV 1N4531

J, JTX & JTXV 1N4531

	INCHES	MILLIMETERS
A	.050-.065	1.27-1.65
B	.080-.120	2.03-3.05
C	1.0 MIN.-1.5 MAX.	25.4 MIN.-38.1 MAX.
D	.018-.022	.46-.56

J, JTX 1N914

	INCHES	MILLIMETERS
A	.058-.107	1.42-2.72
B	.140-.300	3.56-7.62
C	1.0 MIN.-1.5 MAX.	25.4 MIN.-38.1 MAX.
D	.018-.022	.46-.56

J, JTX, JTXV 1N4148 and 1N4148-1

	INCHES	MILLIMETERS
A	.056-.075	1.42-1.91
B	.140-.180	3.56-4.57
C	1.0 MIN.-1.5 MAX.	25.4 MIN.-38.10 MAX.
D	.018-.022	.46-.56

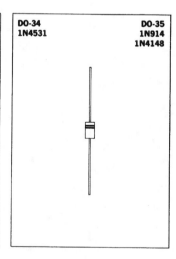

DO-34
1N4531

DO-35
1N914
1N4148

Figure A2.1 Vendor's data sheet for diode 1N4148. (Courtesy of Unitrode Semiconductor Products, Watertown MA.)

1N914; J, JTX 1N914
J, JTX, JTXV 1N4148-1N4148-1
1N4531; J, JTX, JTXV 1N4531

ELECTRICAL SPECIFICATIONS (at 25°C unless noted)

Reverse Current @ 25°C	Reverse Current @ 25°C	Peak Reverse Current @ 25°C	Reverse Current @ 150°C	Reverse Current @ 150°C
25nAdc @ $V_R = 20$Vdc	0.5μAdc @ $V_R = 75$Vdc	100μA (pk) @ $V_R = 100$V (pk)	50μAdc @ $V_R = 20$Vdc	100μAdc @ $V_R = 75$Vdc

Forward Voltage	Foward Recovery Voltage	Forward Recovery Time	Reverse Recovery Time	Capacitance
1.0Vdc @ $I_F = 10$mAdc	5.0V (pk) @ $I_F = 50$mAdc	20ns @ $I_F = 50$mAdc	5ns @ $I_F = I_R = 10$mA $R_L = 100$ ohms	4.0 pF @ $V_R = 0$V, f = 1 MHz $v_{sig} = 50$mV (pk-pk) 2.8 pF @ $V_R = 1.5$V, f = 1 MHz $v_{sig} = 50$mV (pk-pk)

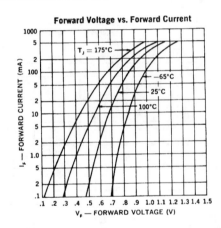

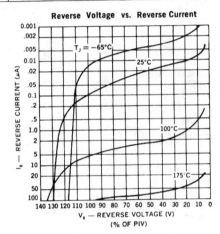

Figure A2.1 *(Continued)*

MAXIMUM RATINGS

Rating	Symbol	Value	Unit
Collector-Emitter Voltage	V_{CEO}	40	Vdc
Collector-Base Voltge	V_{CBO}	60	Vdc
Emitter-Base Voltage	V_{EBO}	6.0	Vdc
Collector Current — Continuous	I_C	200	mAdc
Total Device Dissipation @ T_A = 25°C Derate above 25°C	P_D	625 5.0	mW mW/°C
*Total Device Dissipation @ T_C = 25°C Derate above 25°C	P_D	1.5 12	Watts mW/°C
Operating and Storage Junction Temperature Range	T_J, T_{stg}	−55 to +150	°C

*THERMAL CHARACTERISTICS

Characteristic	Symbol	Max	Unit
Thermal Resistance, Junction to Ambient	$R_{\theta JA}$	200	°C/W
Thermal Resistance, Junction to Case	$R_{\theta JC}$	83.3	°C/W

*Indicates Data in addition to JEDEC Requirements.

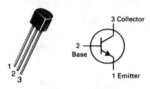

2N3903
2N3904★

CASE 29-04, STYLE 1
TO-92 (TO-226AA)

GENERAL PURPOSE
TRANSISTORS

NPN SILICON

★This is a Motorola
designated preferred device.

ELECTRICAL CHARACTERISTICS (T_A = 25°C unless otherwise noted.)

Characteristic		Symbol	Min	Max	Unit
OFF CHARACTERISTICS					
Collector-Emitter Breakdown Voltage(1) (I_C = 1.0 mAdc, I_B = 0)		$V_{(BR)CEO}$	40	—	Vdc
Collector-Base Breakdown Voltage (I_C = 10 μAdc, I_E = 0)		$V_{(BR)CBO}$	60	—	Vdc
Emitter-Base Breakdown Voltage (I_E = 10 μAdc, I_C = 0)		$V_{(BR)EBO}$	6.0	—	Vdc
Base Cutoff Current (V_{CE} = 30 Vdc, V_{EB} = 3.0 Vdc)		I_{BL}	—	50	nAdc
Collector Cutoff Current (V_{CE} = 30 Vdc, V_{EB} = 3.0 Vdc)		I_{CEX}	—	50	nAdc
ON CHARACTERISTICS					
DC Current Gain(1) (I_C = 0.1 mAdc, V_{CE} = 1.0 Vdc)	2N3903 2N3904	h_{FE}	20 40	— —	—
(I_C = 1.0 mAdc, V_{CE} = 1.0 Vdc)	2N3903 2N3904		35 70	— —	
(I_C = 10 mAdc, V_{CE} = 1.0 Vdc)	2N3903 2N3904		50 100	150 300	
(I_C = 50 mAdc, V_{CE} = 1.0 Vdc)	2N3903 2N3904		30 60	— —	
(I_C = 100 mAdc, V_{CE} = 1.0 Vdc)	2N3903 2N3904		15 30	— —	
Collector-Emitter Saturation Voltage(1) (I_C = 10 mAdc, I_B = 1.0 mAdc) (I_C = 50 mAdc, I_B = 5.0 mAdc)		$V_{CE(sat)}$	— —	0.2 0.3	Vdc
Base-Emitter Saturation Voltage(1) (I_C = 10 mAdc, I_B = 1.0 mAdc) (I_C = 50 mAdc, I_B = 5.0 mAdc)		$V_{BE(sat)}$	0.65 —	0.85 0.95	Vdc
SMALL-SIGNAL CHARACTERISTICS					
Current-Gain — Bandwidth Product (I_C = 10 mAdc, V_{CE} = 20 Vdc, f = 100 MHz)	2N3903 2N3904	f_T	250 300	— —	MHz

Rev 2

Figure A2.2   Vendor's data sheet for NPN transistor 2N3904. (Copyright of Motorola,
used by permission.)

2N3903 2N3904

ELECTRICAL CHARACTERISTICS (continued) (T_A = 25°C unless otherwise noted.)

Characteristic		Symbol	Min	Max	Unit
Output Capacitance (V_{CB} = 5.0 Vdc, I_E = 0, f = 1.0 MHz)		C_{obo}	—	4.0	pF
Input Capacitance (V_{EB} = 0.5 Vdc, I_C = 0, f = 1.0 MHz)		C_{ibo}	—	8.0	pF
Input Impedance (I_C = 1.0 mAdc, V_{CE} = 10 Vdc, f = 1.0 kHz)	2N3903 2N3904	h_{ie}	1.0 1.0	8.0 10	k ohms
Voltage Feedback Ratio (I_C = 1.0 mAdc, V_{CE} = 10 Vdc, f = 1.0 kHz)	2N3903 2N3904	h_{re}	0.1 0.5	5.0 8.0	X 10^{-4}
Small-Signal Current Gain (I_C = 1.0 mAdc, V_{CE} = 10 Vdc, f = 1.0 kHz)	2N3903 2N3904	h_{fe}	50 100	200 400	—
Output Admittance (I_C = 1.0 mAdc, V_{CE} = 10 Vdc, f = 1.0 kHz)		h_{oe}	1.0	40	μmhos
Noise Figure (I_C = 100 μAdc, V_{CE} = 5.0 Vdc, R_S = 1.0 k ohms, f = 1.0 kHz)	2N3903 2N3904	NF	— —	6.0 5.0	dB

SWITCHING CHARACTERISTICS

		Symbol	Min	Max	Unit
Delay Time	(V_{CC} = 3.0 Vdc, V_{BE} = 0.5 Vdc, I_C = 10 mAdc, I_{B1} = 1.0 mAdc)	t_d	—	35	ns
Rise Time		t_r	—	35	ns
Storage Time	(V_{CC} = 3.0 Vdc, I_C = 10 mAdc, I_{B1} = I_{B2} = 1.0 mAdc) 2N3903 2N3904	t_s	— —	175 200	ns
Fall Time		t_f	—	50	ns

(1) Pulse Test: Pulse Width $\leq$ 300 μs, Duty Cycle $\leq$ 2.0%.

FIGURE 1 – DELAY AND RISE TIME EQUIVALENT TEST CIRCUIT

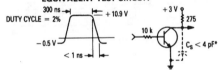

FIGURE 2 – STORAGE AND FALL TIME EQUIVALENT TEST CIRCUIT

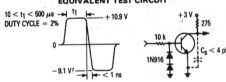

*Total shunt capacitance of test jig and connectors

TYPICAL TRANSIENT CHARACTERISTICS
— T_J = 25°C - - - T_J = 125°C

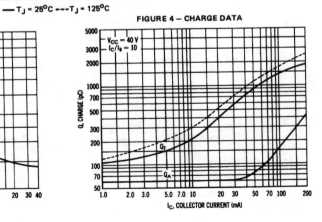

FIGURE 3 – CAPACITANCE

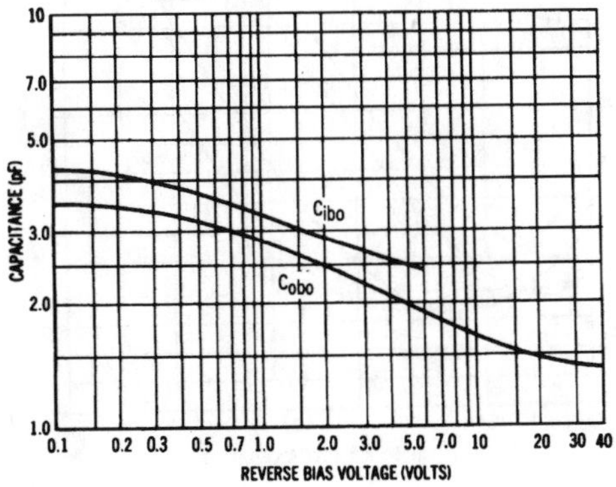

FIGURE 4 – CHARGE DATA

Figure A2.2 (*Continued*)

2N3903 2N3904

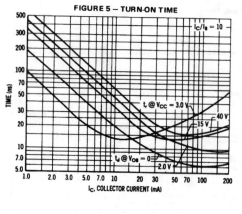

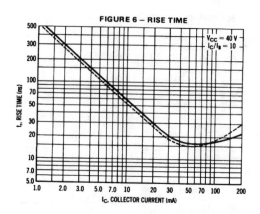

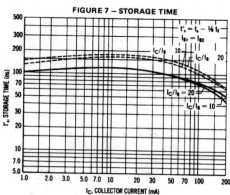

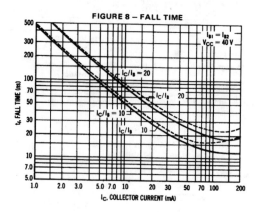

TYPICAL AUDIO SMALL-SIGNAL CHARACTERISTICS
NOISE FIGURE VARIATIONS
V_{CE} = 5.0 Vdc, T_A = 25°C,
Bandwidth = 1.0 Hz

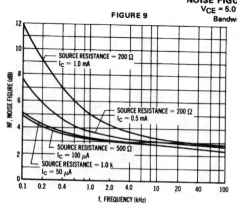

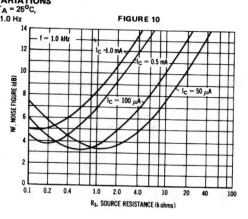

Figure A2.2   (*Continued*)

2N3903 2N3904

h PARAMETERS

(V$_{CE}$ = 10 Vdc, f = 1.0 kHz, T$_A$ = 25°C)

FIGURE 11 – CURRENT GAIN

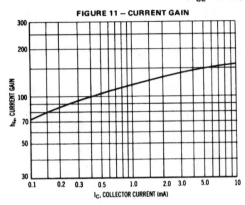

FIGURE 12 – OUTPUT ADMITTANCE

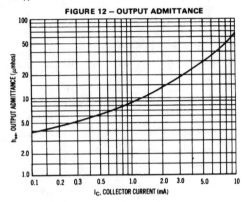

FIGURE 13 – INPUT IMPEDANCE

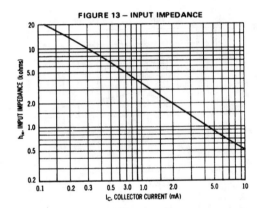

FIGURE 14 – VOLTAGE FEEDBACK RATIO

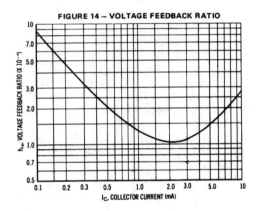

TYPICAL STATIC CHARACTERISTICS

FIGURE 15 – DC CURRENT GAIN

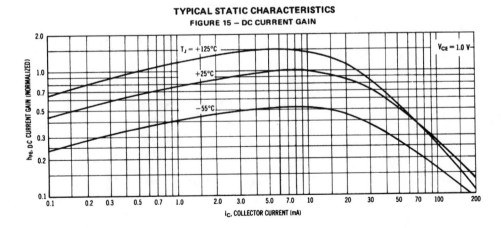

Figure A2.2 *(Continued)*

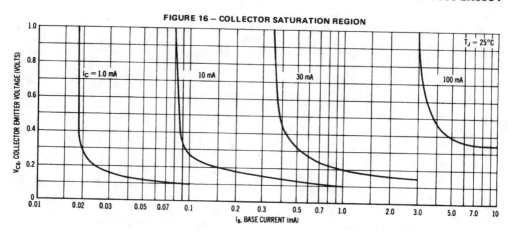

FIGURE 16 – COLLECTOR SATURATION REGION

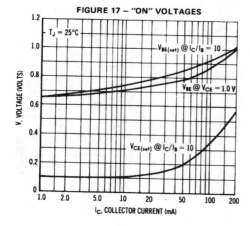

FIGURE 17 – "ON" VOLTAGES

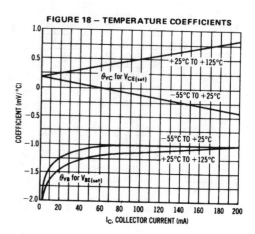

FIGURE 18 – TEMPERATURE COEFFICIENTS

Figure A2.2 (*Continued*)

MOTOROLA
SEMICONDUCTOR ▬▬▬▬
TECHNICAL DATA

LM139,A
LM239,A, LM2901,
LM339,A, MC3302

Quad Single Supply Comparators

These comparators are designed for use in level detection, low-level sensing and memory applications in consumer automotive and industrial electronic applications.

- Single or Split Supply Operation
- Low Input Bias Current: 25 nA (Typ)
- Low Input Offset Current: ±5.0 nA (Typ)
- Low Input Offset Voltage: ±1.0 mV (Typ) LM139A Series
- Input Common Mode Voltage Range to Gnd
- Low Output Saturation Voltage: 130 mV (Typ) @ 4.0 mA
- TTL and CMOS Compatible
- ESD Clamps on the Inputs Increase Reliability without Affecting Device Operation

QUAD COMPARATORS

SILICON MONOLITHIC
INTEGRATED CIRCUIT

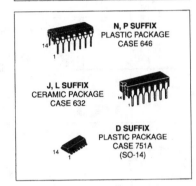

N, P SUFFIX
PLASTIC PACKAGE
CASE 646

J, L SUFFIX
CERAMIC PACKAGE
CASE 632

D SUFFIX
PLASTIC PACKAGE
CASE 751A
(SO-14)

MAXIMUM RATINGS

Rating	Symbol	Value	Unit
Power Supply Voltage LM139, A/LM239, A/LM339A/LM2901 MC3302	V_{CC}	+36 or ±18 +30 or ±15	Vdc
Input Differential Voltage Range LM139, A/LM239, A/LM339, A/LM2901 MC3302	V_{IDR}	36 30	Vdc
Input Common Mode Voltage Range	V_{ICMR}	−0.3 to V_{CC}	Vdc
Output Short Circuit to Ground (Note 1)	I_{SC}	Continuous	
Input Current (V_{in} < − 0.3 Vdc) (Note 2)	I_{in}	50	mA
Power Dissipation @ T_A = 25°C Ceramic Plastic Package Derate above 25°C	P_D	1.0 8.0	W mW/°C
Junction Temperature Ceramic & Metal Package Plastic Package	T_J	175 150	°C
Operating Ambient Temperature Range LM139, A LM239, A MC3302 LM2901 LM339, A	T_A	−55 to +125 −25 to +85 −40 to +85 −40 to +105 0 to +70	°C
Storage Temperature Range	T_{stg}	−65 to +150	°C

PIN CONNECTIONS

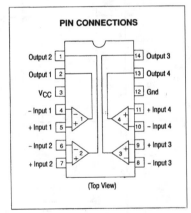

Output 2 [1] — [14] Output 3
Output 1 [2] — [13] Output 4
V_{CC} [3] — [12] Gnd
− Input 1 [4] — [11] + Input 4
+ Input 1 [5] — [10] − Input 4
− Input 2 [6] — [9] + Input 3
+ Input 2 [7] — [8] − Input 3

(Top View)

Figure 1. Circuit Schematic

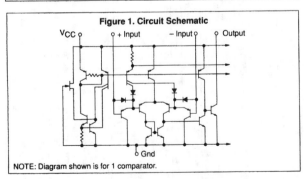

V_{CC} ○   ○ + Input   − Input ○   ○ Output

○ Gnd

NOTE: Diagram shown is for 1 comparator.

ORDERING INFORMATION

Device	Temperature Range	Package
LM139J, AJ	−55° to +125°C	Ceramic DIP
LM239D, AD LM239J, AJ LM239N, AN	−25° to +85°C	SO-14 Ceramic DIP Plastic DIP
LM339D, AD LM339J, AJ LM339N, AN	0° to +70°C	SO-14 Ceramic DIP Plastic DIP
LM2901D LM2901N	−40° to +105°C	SO-14 Plastic DIP
MC3302L MC3302P	−40° to +85°C	Ceramic DIP Plastic DIP

Figure A2.3   Vendor's data sheet for Quad Comparator LM139. (Copyright of Motorola, used by permission.)

LM139,A, LM239,A, LM339,A, MC3302

ELECTRICAL CHARACTERISTICS (V_{CC} = +5.0 Vdc, T_A = +25°C, unless otherwise noted)

Characteristics	Symbol	LM139A			LM239A/339A			LM139			LM239/339			LM2901			MC3302			Unit
		Min	Typ	Max	Min	Typ	Max	Min	Typ	Max	Min	Typ	Max	Min	Typ	Max	Min	Typ	Max	
Input Offset Voltage (Note 4)	V_{IO}	—	±1.0	±2.0	—	±1.0	±2.0	—	±2.0	±5.0	—	±2.0	±5.0	—	±2.0	±7.0	—	±3.0	±20	mVdc
Input Bias Current (Notes 4, 5) (Output in Linear Range)	I_{IB}	—	25	100	—	25	250	—	25	100	—	25	250	—	25	250	—	25	500	nA
Input Offset Current (Note 4)	I_{IO}	—	±3.0	±25	—	±5.0	±50	—	±3.0	±25	—	±5.0	±50	—	±5.0	±50	—	±3.0	±100	nA
Input Common Mode Voltage Range	V_{ICMR}	0	—	V_{CC} -1.5	0	—	V_{CC} -1.5	0	—	V_{CC} -1.5	0	—	V_{CC} -1.5	0	—	V_{CC} -1.5	0	—	V_{CC} -1.5	V
Supply Current R_L = ∞ (For All Comparators)	I_{CC}	—	0.8	2.0	—	0.8	2.0	—	0.8	2.0	—	0.8	2.0	—	0.8	2.0	—	0.8	2.0	mA
R_L = ∞, V_{CC} = 30 Vdc		—	1.0	2.5	—	1.0	2.5	—	1.0	2.5	—	1.0	2.5	—	1.0	2.5	—	1.0	2.5	
Voltage Gain R_L ≥ 15 kΩ, V_{CC} = 15 Vdc	A_{VOL}	50	200	—	50	200	—	50	200	—	25	200	—	25	100	—	2	30	—	V/mV
Large Signal Response Time V_I = TTL Logic Swing, V_{ref} = 1.4 Vdc, V_{RL} = 5.0 Vdc, R_L = 5.1 kΩ	—	—	300	—	—	300	—	—	300	—	—	300	—	—	300	—	—	300	—	ns
Response Time (Note 6) V_{RL} = 5.0 Vdc, R_L = 5.1 kΩ	—	—	1.3	—	—	1.3	—	—	1.3	—	—	1.3	—	—	1.3	—	—	1.3	—	µs
Output Sink Current V_I (−) ≥ +1.0 Vdc, V_I(+) = 0, V_O ≤ 1.5 Vdc	I_{sink}	6.0	16	—	6.0	16	—	6.0	16	—	6.0	16	—	6.0	16	—	6.0	16	—	mA
Saturation Voltage V_I(−) ≥ +1.0 Vdc, V_I(+) = 0, I_{sink} ≤ 4.0 mA	V_{sat}	—	130	400	—	130	400	—	130	400	—	130	400	—	130	400	—	130	500	mV
Output Leakage Current V_I(+) ≥ +1.0 Vdc, V_I(−) = 0, V_O = +5.0 Vdc	I_{OL}	—	0.1	—	—	0.1	—	—	0.1	—	—	0.1	—	—	0.1	—	—	0.1	—	nA

PERFORMANCE CHARACTERISTICS (V_{CC} = +5.0 Vdc, T_A = T_{low} to T_{high} [Note 3])

Characteristics	Symbol	LM139A			LM239A/339A			LM139			LM239/339			LM2901			MC3302			Unit
		Min	Typ	Max	Min	Typ	Max	Min	Typ	Max	Min	Typ	Max	Min	Typ	Max	Min	Typ	Max	
Input Offset Voltage (Note 4)	V_{IO}	—	—	±4.0	—	—	±4.0	—	—	±9.0	—	—	±9.0	—	—	±15	—	—	±40	mVdc
Input Bias Current (Notes 4, 5) (Output in Linear Range)	I_{IB}	—	—	300	—	—	400	—	—	300	—	—	400	—	—	500	—	—	1000	nA
Input Offset Current (Note 4)	I_{IO}	—	—	±100	—	—	±150	—	—	±100	—	—	±150	—	—	±200	—	—	±300	nA
Input Common Mode Voltage Range	V_{ICMR}	0	—	V_{CC} -2.0	0	—	V_{CC} -2.0	0	—	V_{CC} -2.0	0	—	V_{CC} -2.0	0	—	V_{CC} -2.0	0	—	V_{CC} -2.0	V
Saturation Voltage V_I(−) ≥ +1.0 Vdc, V_I(+) = 0, I_{sink} ≤ 4.0 mA	V_{sat}	—	—	700	—	—	700	—	—	700	—	—	700	—	—	700	—	—	700	mV
Output Leakage Current V_I(+) ≥ +1.0 Vdc, V_I(−) = 0, V_O = 30 Vdc	I_{OL}	—	—	1.0	—	—	1.0	—	—	1.0	—	—	1.0	—	—	1.0	—	—	1.0	µA
Differential Input Voltage All V_I ≥ 0 Vdc	V_{ID}	—	—	V_{CC}	—	—	V_{CC}	—	—	V_{CC}	—	—	V_{CC}	—	—	V_{CC}	—	—	V_{CC}	Vdc

NOTES:

1. The maximum output current may be as high as 20 mA, independent of the magnitude of V_{CC}. Output short circuits to V_{CC} can cause excessive heating and eventual destruction.

2. This magnitude of input current will only occur if the leads are driven more negative than ground or the negative supply voltage. This is due to the input PNP collectorbase (junction becoming forward biased, acting as an input clamp diode. There is also a lateral PNP parasitic transistor action which can cause the output voltage of the comparators to go to the V_{CC} voltage level (or ground if overdrive is large) during the time that an input is driven negative. This will not destroy the device when limited to the max rating and normal output states will recover when the inputs become ≥ ground or negative supply.

3. (LM139/139A) T_{low} = -55°C, T_{high} = +125°C
   (LM239/239A) T_{low} = -25°C, T_{high} = +85°C
   (LM339/339A) T_{low} = 0°C, T_{high} = +70°C
   (MC3302) T_{low} = -40°C, T_{high} = +85°C
   (LM2901) T_{low} = -40°C, T_{high} = +105°C

4. At the output switch point, V_O = 1.4 Vdc, R_S ≤ 100 Ω 5.0 Vdc ≤ V_{CC} ≤ 30 Vdc, with the inputs over the full common mode range (0 Vdc to V_{CC} -1.5 Vdc).

5. The bias current flows out of the inputs due to the PNP input stage. This current is virtually constant, independent of the output state.

6. The response time specified is for a 100 mV input step with 5.0 mV overdrive. For larger signals, 300 ns is typical.

Figure A2.3 (*Continued*)

LM139,A, LM239,A, LM339,A, LM2901, MC3302

Typical Characteristics
(V$_{CC}$ = 1.5 Vdc, T$_A$ = +25°C (each comparator) unless otherwise noted.)

Figure 4. Normalized Input Offset Voltage

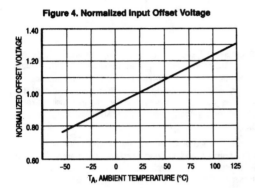

Figure 5. Input Bias Current

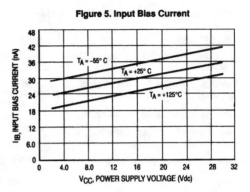

Figure 6. Output Sink Current versus
Output Saturation Voltage

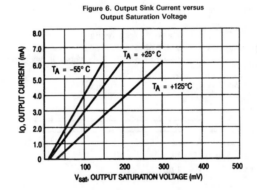

Figure A2.3 (*Continued*)

UC1825
UC2825
UC3825

High Speed PWM Controller

FEATURES

* Compatible with Voltage or Current Mode Topologies

* Practical Operation Switching Frequencies to 1MHz

* 50ns Propagation Delay to Output

* High Current Dual Totem Pole Outputs (1.5A Peak)

* Wide Bandwidth Error Amplifier

* Fully Latched Logic with Double Pulse Suppression

* Pulse-by-Pulse Current Limiting

* Soft Start / Max. Duty Cycle Control

* Under-Voltage Lockout with Hysteresis

* Low Start Up Current (1.1mA)

* Trimmed Bandgap Reference (5.1V ±1%)

DESCRIPTION

The UC1825 family of PWM control ICs is optimized for high frequency switched mode power supply applications. Particular care was given to minimizing propagation delays through the comparators and logic circuitry while maximizing bandwidth and slew rate of the error amplifier. This controller is designed for use in either current-mode or voltage mode systems with the capability for input voltage feed-forward.

Protection circuitry includes a current limit comparator with a 1V threshold, a TTL compatible shutdown port, and a soft start pin which will double as a maximum duty cycle clamp. The logic is fully latched to provide jitter free operation and prohibit multiple pulses at an output. An under-voltage lockout section with 800mV of hysteresis assures low start up current. During under-voltage lockout, the outputs are high impedance.

These devices feature totem pole outputs designed to source and sink high peak currents from capacitive loads, such as the gate of a power MOSFET. The on state is designed as a high level.

BLOCK DIAGRAM

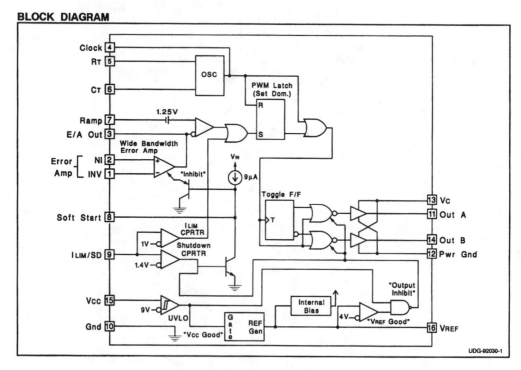

UDG-92030-1

Figure A2.4 Vendor's data sheet for PWM controller UC2825. (Courtesy of Unitrode Semiconductor Products, Watertown MA.)

ABSOLUTE MAXIMUM RATINGS (Note 1)

Supply Voltage (Pins 13, 15) 30V
Output Current, Source or Sink (Pins 11, 14)
DC. 0.5A
Pulse (0.5ms) 2.0A
Analog Inputs
(Pins 1, 2, 7) .... -0.3V to 7V
(Pin 8, 9) .... -0.3V to 6V
Clock Output Current (Pin 4) .... -5mA
Error Amplifier Output Current (Pin 3) 5mA
Soft Start Sink Current (Pin 8) 20mA
Oscillator Charging Current (Pin 5) .... -5mA
Power Dissipation 1W
Storage Temperature Range .... -65°C to +150°C
Lead Temperature (Soldering, 10 seconds) .... 300°C

Note 1: All voltages are with respect to GND (Pin 10); all currents are positive into, negative out of part; pin numbers refer to DIL-16 package.

Note 3: Consult Unitrode Integrated Circuit Databook for thermal limitations and considerations of package.

SOIC-16 (Top View)
DW Package

INV 1 — 16 VREF 5.1V
NI 2 — 15 Vcc
E/A Out 3 — 14 Out B
Clock 4 — 13 Vc
RT 5 — 12 Pwr Gnd
CT 6 — 11 Out A
Ramp 7 — 10 Gnd
Soft Start 8 — 9 ILIM/SD

CONNECTION DIAGRAMS   **UC3825**

DIL-16 (Top View)
J Or N Package

INV 1 — 16 VREF 5.1V
NI 2 — 15 Vcc
E/A Out 3 — 14 Out B
Clock 4 — 13 Vc
RT 5 — 12 Pwr Gnd
CT 6 — 11 Out A
Ramp 7 — 10 Gnd
Soft Start 8 — 9 ILIM/SD

PLCC-20 & LCC-20
(Top View)
Q & L Packages

PACKAGE PIN FUNCTION	
FUNCTION	**PIN**
N/C	1
INV	2
NI	3
E/A Out	4
Clock	5
N/C	6
RT	7
CT	8
Ramp	9
Soft Start	10
N/C	11
ILIM/SD	12
Gnd	13
Out A	14
Pwr Gnd	15
N/C	16
Vc	17
Out B	18
Vcc	19
VREF 5.1V	20

ELECTRICAL CHARACTERISTICS: Unless otherwise stated, these specifications apply for , RT = 3.65k, CT = 1nF, Vcc = 15V, -55°C<TA<125°C for the UC1825, -40°C<TA<85°C for the UC2825, and 0°C<TA<70°C for the UC3825, TA=TJ.

PARAMETERS	TEST CONDITIONS	UC1825 UC2825			UC3825			
		MIN	TYP	MAX	MIN	TYP	MAX	UNITS
Reference Section								
Output Voltage	TJ = 25°C, Io = 1mA	5.05	5.10	5.15	5.00	5.10	5.20	V
Line Regulation	10V < Vcc < 30V		2	20		2	20	mV
Load Regulation	1mA < Io < 10mA		5	20		5	20	mV
Temperature Stability*	TMIN < TA < TMAX		0.2	0.4		0.2	0.4	mV/°C
Total Output Variation*	Line, Load, Temperature	5.00		5.20	4.95		5.25	V
Output Noise Voltage*	10Hz < f < 10kHz		50			50		µV
Long Term Stability*	TJ = 125°C, 1000hrs.		5	25		5	25	mV
Short Circuit Current	VREF = 0V	-15	-50	-100	-15	-50	-100	mA
Oscillator Section								
Initial Accuracy*	TJ = 25°C	360	400	440	360	400	440	kHz
Voltage Stability*	10V < Vcc < 30V		0.2	2		0.2	2	%
Temperature Stability*	TMIN < TA < TMAX		5			5		%
Total Variation*	Line, Temperature	340		460	340		460	kHz

Figure A2.4 *(Continued)*

ELECTRICAL CHARACTERISTICS (cont.) Unless otherwise stated,these specifications apply for , RT = 3.65k, CT = 1nF, Vcc = 15V, -55°C<TA<125°C for the UC1825, -40°C<TA<85°C for the UC2825, and 0°C<TA<70°C for the UC3825, TA=TJ.

PARAMETERS	TEST CONDITIONS	UC1825 UC2825			UC3825			
		MIN	TYP	MAX	MIN	TYP	MAX	UNITS
Oscillator Section (cont)								
Clock Out High		3.9	4.5		3.9	4.5		V
Clock Out Low			2.3	2.9		2.3	2.9	V
Ramp Peak*		2.6	2.8	3.0	2.6	2.8	3.0	V
Ramp Valley*		0.7	1.0	1.25	0.7	1.0	1.25	V
Ramp Valley to Peak*		1.6	1.8	2.0	1.6	1.8	2.0	V
Error Amplifier Section								
Input Offset Voltage				10			15	mV
Input Bias Current			0.6	3		0.6	3	μA
Input Offset Current			0.1	1		0.1	1	μA
Open Loop Gain	1V < Vo < 4V	60	95		60	95		dB
CMRR	1.5V < VCM < 5.5V	75	95		75	95		dB
PSRR	10V < Vcc < 30V	85	110		85	110		dB
Output Sink Current	VPIN 3 = 1V	1	2.5		1	2.5		mA
Output Source Current	VPIN 3 = 4V	-0.5	-1.3		-0.5	-1.3		mA
Output High Voltage	IPIN 3 = -0.5mA	4.0	4.7	5.0	4.0	4.7	5.0	V
Output Low Voltage	IPIN 3 = 1mA	0	0.5	1.0	0	0.5	1.0	V
Unity Gain Bandwidth*		3	5.5		3	5.5		MHz
Slew Rate*		6	12		6	12		V/μs
PWM Comparator Section								
Pin 7 Bias Current	VPIN 7 = 0V		-1	-5		-1	-5	μA
Duty Cycle Range		0		80	0		85	%
Pin 3 Zero DC Threshold	VPIN 7 = 0V	1.1	1.25		1.1	1.25		V
Delay to Output*			50	80		50	80	ns
Soft Start Section								
Charge Current	VPIN 8 = 0.5V	3	9	20	3	9	20	μA
Discharge Current	VPIN 8 = 1V	1			1			mA
Current Limit / Shutdown Section								
Pin 9 Bias Current	0 < VPIN 9 < 4V			15			10	μA
Current Limit Threshold		0.9	1.0	1.1	0.9	1.0	1.1	V
Shutdown Threshold		1.25	1.40	1.55	1.25	1.40	1.55	V
Delay to Output			50	80		50	80	ns
Output Section								
Output Low Level	IOUT = 20mA		0.25	0.40		0.25	0.40	V
	IOUT = 200mA		1.2	2.2		1.2	2.2	V
Output High Level	IOUT = -20mA	13.0	13.5		13.0	13.5		V
	IOUT = -200mA	12.0	13.0		12.0	13.0		V
Collector Leakage	Vc = 30V		100	500		10	500	μA
Rise/Fall Time*	CL = 1nF		30	60		30	60	ns
Under-Voltage Lockout Section								
Start Threshold		8.8	9.2	9.6	8.8	9.2	9.6	V
UVLO Hysteresis		0.4	0.8	1.2	0.4	0.8	1.2	V
Supply Current Section								
Start Up Current	Vcc = 8V		1.1	2.5		1.1	2.5	mA
ICC	VPIN 1, VPIN 7, VPIN 9 = 0V; VPIN 2 = 1V		22	33		22	33	mA

This parameter not 100% tested in production but guaranteed by design.

Figure A2.4   *(Continued)*

Printed Circuit Board Layout Considerations

High speed circuits demand careful attention to layout and component placement. To assure proper performance of the UC1825 follow these rules: 1) Use a ground plane. 2) Damp or clamp parasitic inductive kick energy from the gate of driven MOSFETs. Do not allow the output pins to ring below ground. A series gate resistor or a shunt 1 Amp Schottky diode at the output pin will serve this purpose. 3) Bypass Vcc, Vc, and VREF. Use 0.1µF monolithic ceramic capacitors with low equivalent series inductance. Allow less than 1 cm of total lead length for each capacitor between the bypassed pin and the ground plane. 4) Treat the timing capacitor, CT, like a bypass capacitor.

Error Amplifier Circuit

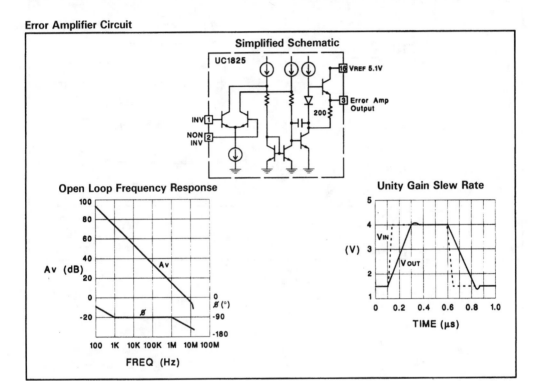

PWM Applications

Figure A2.4   (*Continued*)

Oscillator Circuit

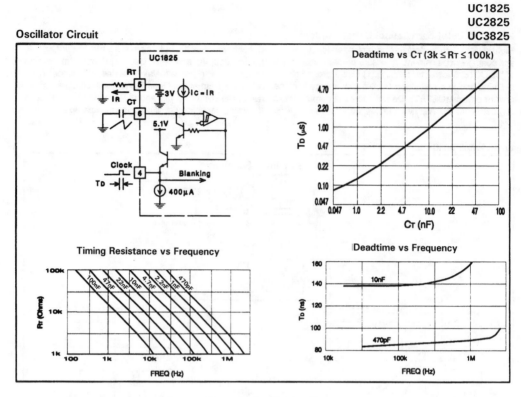

Figure A2.4   (*Continued*)

Output Section

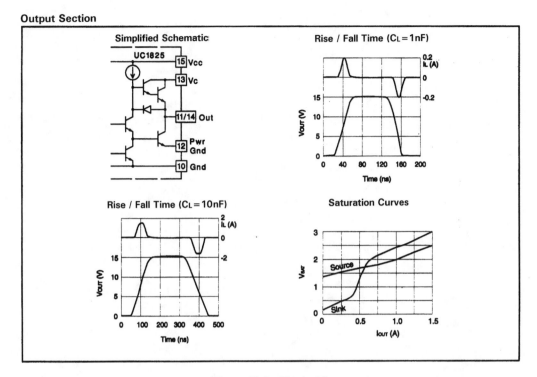

Figure A2.4   (*Continued*)

Index

A

AC Mains, 3
  Frequencies, 3
  Voltage, 3
Acronyms. *See* Appendix
Air Core. *See* Core Materials
Air Gaps. *See* Magnetics
Aliasing, 66
Ampere's Law, 72
Average Current-Mode. *See* Current-Mode

B

Ballast, Fluorescent Lighting, 12
Baluns. *See* Filters
Bandwidth
  Large Signal vs. Small Signal, 7, 135
  Limitations, 142
Batteries
  "C", 11
  as Loads, 10
  as Sources, 4
  Charging, 11
  Defined, 4
  Frequency Characteristics, 4
  I-V Characteristics, 5
  Self-Discharge, 5
  Trickle Charge, 11
Beads. *See* Filters
Bipolar Transistor, Power, 20

Baker Clamp, 49
  Beta, 49
  Emitter-Base Zenering, 49
  Leakage, 49
  Pulse Current, 48
  Temperature, 49
Bode Plots. *See Also* Loop
  Don't Make Sense. *See* Loop,
    Non-Minimum Phase System
  Technique, 67
Boost. *See* Topologies
Bootstrap Winding. *See* Startup
Buck. *See* Topologies
Buck-Boost. *See* Topologies

C

Calculators
  Significant Digits, 59
Capacitors, 43
  Aging, 45
  Aluminum Electrolytic, 43
  Ceramic, 44
  dV/dt, 45
  Electrolytic, 43
  ESR, 44, 191
  Life, 190
  Limitations, 216
  Minimum Value, 44, 142
  Selection Guide, 43

Series Connection, 46
Tantalum Electrolytic, 43
Temperature Effects, 190
Tolerance, 44
Types, 43
Values, 44, 140
Voltage Limitations, 45
X. *See* EMI
Y. *See* EMI
Comparators
  Hysteresis, 57, 174
  Offsets, 57
  Oscillating, 174
  Output Saturation Voltage, 58
Compensation. *See* Loop
Complex Numbers, 122
Component
  Life, 190
Compound Converters, 35
  When to Use Them, 36
Conditional Stability. *See* Loops
Continuous Conduction, 20
  Buck, 23
  EMI, 206
  Flyback, 27
  Synchronous Rectification, 21
Control Theory. *See* Loop
Converters. *See Also* Topologies
  as Loads for Other Converters, 13. *See Also*
    Stability, Multiple Converters
  Compound. *See* Compound Converters
  Continuous vs. Discontinuous, 20, 206
  Current-Mode, 22
  Duty Cycle Limits, 18
  Efficiency. *See* Efficiency
  High-Speed Requirements, 7
  Isolation, 19
  Low-Noise, 8
  Modules, 180, 191
  Number of Outputs, 19
  Paralleling, 2, 171
  Quasi-Resonant. *See* Soft-Switching
    Converters
  Resonant. *See* Resonant Converters
  Soft-Switching. *See* Soft-Switching
    Converters
  Step-Down, 18
  Step-Up, 18
  Synchronous Rectification, 20
  Voltage-Mode, 22
Core Materials, 80, 88
  Air, 81

Curie Temperature, 82
Ferrite, 81
High Perm, 89
Losses, 82
Molyperm, 81
MPP, 81
Powdered Iron, 81
Saturation, 80
Selecting, 88
Steel Laminations, 81
Current Fed Push-Pull. *See* Topologies
Current Limiting, 170
Current-Mode, 22, 138, 149
  Average, 152
  Limitations, 150
  Slope Compensation, 150
    Necessity Of, 152
  Stability Requirement, 153
  Subharmonic Oscillation, 151

D

dB, 121
DC Inductor. *See* Magnetics
Decibels, 121
Differential Amplifiers, 175, 176
  Error Estimate, 177
Diodes, 47
  Forward Voltage, 111
  Germanium, 47
  MOSFET body, 48
  MOSFETs as, 47
  Noise, 205, 206
  Paralleling, 47
  Reverse Recovery, 47
  Reverse Recovery Time, 48
  Schottky, 46
    High Voltage, 47
Discontinuous Conduction, 20
  Buck, 23
  EMI, 206
  Flyback, 27
DMMs. *See* Meters
Duty Cycle
  Limits, 18, 134
DVMs. *See* Meters

E

Efficiency, 179
  Definition, 179
  Good, 180

Improvement, 189
Measurement, 63
Modules, 180
Power Stage, 179
Electromagnetic Interference. *See* EMI
Electronic Loads
Minimum Input Voltage, 66
Stability, 65
EMI
"X" Caps, 214
"Y" Caps, 214, 216
Buck, 19
Common Mode, 201, 202
Separating from Normal Mode, 203
Conducted, 200
Current Monitoring, 175
Definitions, 199
Differential Mode. *See* Normal Mode
Diodes, 48
Effects of Topology, 19
FCC, 203
Filters. *See* Filters
Ground vs. Return, 202
Layout. *See* Layout
LISN, 203
Military vs. Commercial, 202
MIL-STD-461, 203
Modules, 180
Noise Estimation, 218
Normal Mode, 201, 202
Separating from Common Mode, 203
Origins
Capacitive Coupling, 205
Switching Waveforms, 204
Radiated, 200
Fixes, 200
Resonant Converters, 205
Shields, 200
Material, 201
Soft-Switching Converters, 205
Spectrum, 124
VDE, 203
Error Amplifier. *See* Loop Compensation
ESR, 44, 191

F

Faraday's Law, 72
FCC. *See* EMI
Feedback, 168. *See Also* Loop
Feedthroughs. *See* Filters

Ferrite Cores. *See* Core Materials
Filter Pins, 201. *See Also* Filters
Filters
"X" Caps. *See* EMI
"Y" Caps. *See* EMI
Component Limitations, 216
Converter Stability, 222
High Frequency, 217
Beads, 217
Feedthroughs, 218
Filter Pins, 218
Low Frequency, 212
Baluns, 215, 216
Commercial vs. Military, 213
Common Mode, 214
LC, Mathematics, 123, 125
Limitations, 217
Normal Mode, 213, 216
Values, 214, 215
Middlebrook's Criterion, 222
Optimization, 219
Finite Element Analysis, 197
Fluorescent Tubes, 12
Flyback. *See* Topologies
Flyback Transformer. *See* Transformers
Forward. *See* Topologies

G

Gain Margin. *See* Loop
Grounds. *See* Layout

H

Heatsinks, 196
High-Current Resistors, 42

I

ICs
Temperature, 191
IGBT, 20
Impedance
Input, 155
Output, 158
Inductance
Leakage. *See* Leakage Inductance
Magnetizing. *See* Magnetizing Inductance
Inductors. *See Also* Magnetics
Common Mode. *See* Filters, Low
Frequency, Baluns
Limitations, 216
Input Impedance. *See* Impedance

Instrumentation Amplifiers. *See* Differential
    Amplifiers
  Use as Isolator, 169
Isolation
  Achievable Regulation, 173
  Requirements, 19
  Techniques, 168

J

JFETs, 50

K

K-Factor. *See* Loop

L

Lab supplies, 2
Layout
  Component Placement, 212
  Current Sense Transformer, 210
  EMI, 217
  Feedback Lines, 211
  Gate Drivers, 209
  Ground Islands, 209
  Ground Loops, 208
  Signal Ground vs. Power Ground, 207
  Single Point Ground, 208
  Star Ground, 208
Leakage Inductance, 79
  in a Forward, 30
LEDs, 178
LISN, 203
Logarithms, 121
Loop
  Bandwidth Limitations, 142
  Bode Plots, 129
    Stability, 130
  Compensation, 138, 152
  Conditional Stability, 134
  Control Theory, 128
  Feedback. *See* Feedback
  Gain Margin, 133
  Measurement
    Closed Loop, 143, 145
    Current Loop, 152
    How To, 146
    If Non-Inverting Pin Isn't Available, 149
    Mixer Method, 144
    Open Loop, 136, 147
    Transformer Method, 144
  Multiple Converter Stability, 159
  Non-Minimum Phase Systems, 153

Phase Boost, 140
Phase Margin, 129, 130
  How Much?, 132
  Worst Case Analysis, 227
Right Half Plane Zero, 133, 153
Stability
  How To, 135
  Small Signal vs. Large Signal, 134
Stable, 132
Unstable, 126, 131

M

Magnetics. *See Also* Transformers
  Air Gaps, 97
    Making your Own, 102
    Minimum, 101
    Selecting, 100
  Ampere's Law, 72
  Analogy with Electronics, 75
  Core Loss, 104
    Dependence on Switching Frequency,
      106
  Core Materials. *See* Core Materials
  Core Selection, 84, 97, 98
  Core Utilization, 33
  Faraday's Law, 72
  Fill Factor, 90
  Flux Density Calculation, 84
  Flux Density Formulae, 110
  Inductance, 73
  Inductor Design, 83
  Isolation, 116
  Layering, 117
  Length per Turn, 92
  Manufacturability, 115
  Number of Windings, 117
  Optimum Design, 83
  Permeability, 73, 74
  Potting, 117
  Power Loss, 92, 94
  Skin Depth, 108
    Insulation Thickness, 109
  Specifications, 118
  Temperature Rise, 94
  Units, 74
  Winding Area, 90
  Wire
    Insulation, 90
    Loss, 107
    Resistance, 92
    Selection, 90

Magnetizing Inductance, 80, 114
Measurements. *See* Loop, etc., *or*
    Meters
Metastability. *See* Loop, Conditional Stability
Meters
  Accuracy vs. Precision, 61
  Averaging, 61
  Bandwidth, 62
  Cross-Calibration, 63
  Efficiency Measurement, 63
  Filtering, 62
  MOSFET Measurement, 65
  Probe Placement, 63
  Resistance, 64
  RMS, 62
Middlebrook's Criterion. *See* Filters
MIL-HDBK-217, 192
Modules
  Efficiency, 180
  Power Rating, 191
  Thermal, 191
Molyperm Cores. *See* Core Materials
Monitoring
  Current, 175
    Compensating Inductance, 177
  Fail Signal, 178
  Failure, 178
  LEDs, 178
  Negative Voltages, 173
  Voltage, 172
MOSFETs, 20
  as Rectifiers, 47
  Bidirectional Conduction, 50
  Body Diode, 48
  Capacitive Coupling, 206
  Conduction Losses, 51
  Gate Charge, 51
  Gate Resistors, 52
  Gate Voltage
  Maximum, 52
  Logic-Level, 51
  Losses, 51, 181
  Measurement, 65
  N-Channel vs. P-Channel, 50
  Noise, 205, 206
  Rds,on vs. Temperature, 182
  Switching Losses, 51
  Temperature Calculation, 51, 195
  Thermal Runaway, 191
  vs. JFETs, 50
MOVs, 216
MPP Cores. *See* Core Materials

MTBF, 191, 192. *See Also* Stress Analysis
  Improving, 194

N

Negative Input Impedance. *See* Impedance
Network Analyzer, 67
  Gate Waveforms, 69
  Nyquist Plots, 69
  Problems, 130
  Step by Step Instructions, 67
  Using, 136
Noise. *See Also* EMI
  Estimation, 218
  Filter, 10
  Line, 2
Non-Minimum Phase Systems. *See* Loop
Nyquist Plots, 69, 154

O

Opamps
  Errors, Minimizing, 54
  Gain Limitations, 54
  Gain-Bandwidth, 56
  Input Bias Current, 54
  Input Offset Current, 53
  Input Offset Voltage, 53
  Phase Shift, 56, 145
  Slew Rate, 56, 134
Open Loop. *See* Loop
Optocouplers
  Use as Isolator, 169
Oscilloscopes
  Aliasing, 66
  Safety, 14
Output Impedance. *See* Impedance
Overcurrent, 167

P

Permeability. *See* Magnetics
PFM, 190
Phase Boost. *See* Loop
Phase Margin. *See* Loop
Poles
  at the Origin, 145
  Defined, 123
Powdered Iron Cores. *See* Core Materials
Power Good, 172
Preload, 30, 179
Push-Pull. *See* Topologies

PWMs
  Problems, 137

R

Reactance, 75
Reference Voltages, 173
Regulation, 173
Reliability. *See* Worst Case Analysis
Reluctance, 75
Remanence, 75
Resistors
  Carbon Comp, 38
  Maximum Value, 38, 142
  Power Rating, 39
  Pulse Power, 40
  Ratios, Selecting, 39
  Rheostat, 40
  Selection Guide, 38
  Shunts, 42
  Temperature Coefficient, 39
  Tolerance, 39
  Trace, Using as, 43, 207
  Types, 38
  Values, 38
  Voltage Rating, 39
  Wire-Wound, 38
    Non-Inductive, 38, 42
Resonant Converters, 33
  EMI, 205
  Why Not To Use Them, 34
Rheostats, 40
RHPZ. *See* Loop, Right Half Plane Zero
Right Half Plane Zero. *See* Loop

S

Safety, 13
  Lab, 15
  Oscilloscope, 14
Saturation. *See* Core Materials
Schottky Diodes. *See* Diodes
Sequencing, 168
Shoot-Through, 21
Short
  Hard vs. Soft, 170
Shunts, 42
  Compensating Inductance, 177
  Using, 64, 175
Simulations, 161, 227
  Monte Carlo, 228
  Sensitivity Analysis, 228
Skin Depth. *See* Magnetics
Slow Start. *See* Soft Start

Soft Start, 167
  Circuit, 168
Soft-Switching Converters, 33
  EMI, 205
  Why You Should Use Them, 34
Solar Cells, 6
  Stability of Converter Running From, 6
  Transfer Function, 128
Stability. *See Also* Loop
  EMI Filter. *See* Filters
  Making a Converter Oscillate, 2
  Multiple Converter, 159
  System, 155
Startup, 165
  Bootstrap Winding, 165
  Circuits, 166
  Problems, 165, 168
  Worst Case Analysis, 226
Steel Laminations. *See* Core Materials
Stress Analysis, 236
  Purpose, 226
Subharmonic Oscillation. *See* Current-Mode
Supplies, 2
  New vs. Old, 2
Susceptibility. *See* EMI
Swinging Choke, 30
Switch Selection, 20
Switching Frequency, 171, 189
  Maximum, 171
Synchronization, 171
  Limits, 172
Synchronous Rectification, 21
  Shoot-Through, 21, 48, 218
System Stability. *See* Stability

T

Telephones, 11
  Model, 11
Thermal, 190
  Component Life, 190
  Electrical Analogy, 195
  Finite Element Analysis, 197
  Heatsinks, 196
  ICs, 191
  Modules, 191
Topologies
  Boost, 26
  Buck, 22
    Continuous Conduction, 23
    Discontinuous Conduction, 23
    Gate Drive, 23
    Limitations, 23

Buck-Boost, 28
  Limitations, 29
Compound Converters. *See* Compound
  Converters
Flyback
  Capacitor Limitations, 27
  Continuous Conduction, 27
  Discontinuous Conduction, 27
  Efficiency Calculation, 181
  Gain Margin, 133
  Isolated, 25
  Non-Isolated, 25
  Number of Outputs, 28
  Power Limits, 27
  Right-Half Plane Zero. *See* Loop
Forward, 29
  Leakage Inductance, 30
  Minimum Load, 30
  Use as Isolator, 169
Importance of Selection of, 17
Push-Pull, 31
  Current Fed, 32
  Deadtime, 32
  Voltage-Fed, 31
Quasi-Resonant. *See* Soft-Switching
  Converters
Resonant. *See* Resonant Converters
Selection Checklist, 22
Soft-Switching. *See* Soft-Switching
  Converters
Toroids, 78
  Fill Factor, 90
  Winding Limits, 116
Trace
  Using as a Resistor, 43, 207
Transfer Functions
  Closed Loop, 126
  Composition Law, 126
  Defined, 126
  Nonlinear Systems, 128
Transformers. *See* Also Magnetics
  Coupling, 78
  Current, 113
  Placement, 210
  Flyback, 77, 95
    Fundamental Equation, 96

Forward, 110
Fundamentals, 77
Ideal, 76
Non-Idealities, 78
Optimum Design, 83
Toroids, 78
Turns Ratio Limit, 18
Winding, 76
Transforms, 124
  Fourier, 124
  Laplace, 124
Transients, 200, 216
Type I, II & III Amplifiers, 139

V

VDE. *See* EMI
Voltage Fed Push Pull. *See* Topologies
Voltage References, 173
Voltage-Mode, 22

W

Wire
  Gauge Ratio, 116
  Insulation, 117
  Maximum Size, 115
  Minimum Size, 114, 115
  Selection. *See* Magnetics
Worst Case Analysis
  How To, 225
  Purpose, 225
  Table Evaluation Techniques, 230
  vs. RMS, 227

X

X Caps. *See* EMI

Y

Y Caps. *See* EMI

Z

Zeroes
  Defined, 123

About the Author

Ron Lenk received his first patent, for SCUBA gear utilizing electrolysis of water, while in high school. He graduated from M.I.T. in 1980 with a degree in physics, and did graduate work in theoretical physics at Boston University.

He began his career in power electronics designing electronic ballasts for fluorescent lighting. After several years of this, he worked at a military contractor designing conventional low-power converters for avionics.

Mr. Lenk's next position was "a real love affair" as principal engineer at Space Systems/Loral. He helped design the power system for the International Space Station, for which he holds the key patents, as well as other satellite power converters. This was the time in which he devised the idea of average-current-mode control of converters. He also spent several years doing simulations of the Space Station power system using SABER; the simulations involved as many as 5000 components, and revealed a previously unrecognized potential system instability despite the stability of the individual converters comprising the system. He also did experimental and theoretical work on solar cell characterization and ionospheric plasma interactions with spacecraft power systems.

Mr. Lenk spent two years in telecom power and now heads the applications department at Fairchild Semiconductor's power IC division. Mr. Lenk holds numerous patents and publishes regularly on the subject of digital control of power supplies, in which he is recognized as one of the world's experts. He is on the advisory board of PCIM magazine, the leading magazine for power designers, and is currently the recording secretary for the Santa Clara Valley chapter of the IEEE Power Electronics Society (PELS).

Mr. Lenk has spent several years writing software, including a fully automated Windows system for design of magnetics. He is also chief software engineer for *X-Plain!* software from Optimized Engineering. His hobbies include a life-long fascination with exact solutions of classical general relativity.